Vauxhall
Astra
Owners
Workshop
Manual

Peter G Strasman

Models covered
All Vauxhall Astra Hatchback, Saloon and Estate models,
including GTE
1196 cc, 1297 cc, 1598 cc & 1796 cc petrol engines

Covers major features of the Bedford Astra Van
Does not cover Diesel engine variants

(635-9S8)

ABCDE
FGHIJ
KLMNO
PQRST

Haynes Publishing Group
Sparkford Nr Yeovil
Somerset BA22 7JJ England

Haynes Publications, Inc
861 Lawrence Drive
Newbury Park
California 91320 USA

Acknowledgements

Thanks are due to the Champion Sparking Plug Company Limited who supplied the illustrations showing spark plug conditions, to Holt Lloyd Limited who supplied the illustrations showing bodywork repair, and to Duckhams Oils who provided lubrication data.

Thanks are also due to Vauxhall Motors Limited for the supply of technical information and certain illustrations and to all the staff at Sparkford who assisted in the production of this manual.

Printed by J. H. Haynes & Co. Ltd, Sparkford, Nr Yeovil, Somerset BA22 7JJ, England

ISBN 1 85010 199 X

British Library Cataloguing in Publication Data
Strasman, Peter G.
Vauxhall Astra '80 to '84 owners workshop manual
—(Owners Workshop Manual)
1. Vauxhall Astra automobile
1. Title   II. Series
629.28'722   TL215.V3
ISBN 1-85010-199-X

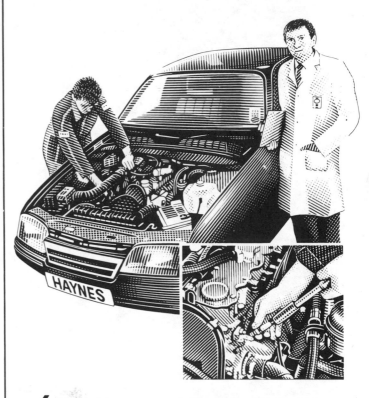

Contents

Vauxhall Astra E 2-door Saloon

Vauxhall Astra L Estate

About this manual

Its aim

The aim of this manual is to help you get the best from your car. It can do so in several ways. It can help you decide what work must be done (even should you choose to get it done by a garage), provide information on routine maintenance and servicing, and give a logical course of action and diagnosis when random faults occur. However, it is hoped that you will use the manual by tackling the work yourself. On simpler jobs it may even be quicker than booking the car into a garage and going there twice to leave and collect it. Perhaps most important, a lot of money can be saved by avoiding the costs the garage must charge to cover its labour and overheads.

The manual has drawings and descriptions to show the function of the various components so that their layout can be understood. Then the tasks are described and photographed in a step-by-step sequence so that even a novice can do the work.

Its arrangement

The manual is divided into thirteen Chapters, each covering a logical sub-division of the vehicle. The Chapters are each divided into Sections, numbered with single figures, eg 5; and the Sections into paragraphs (or sub-sections), with decimal numbers following on from the Section they are in, eg 5.1. 5.2 etc.

It is freely illustrated, especially in those parts where there is a detailed sequence of operations to be carried out. There are two forms of illustration: figures and photographs. The figures are numbered in sequence with decimal numbers, according to their position in the Chapter – Fig. 6.4 is the fourth drawing/illustration in Chapter 6. Photographs carry the same number (either individually or in related groups) as the Section or sub-section to which they relate.

There is an alphabetical index at the back of the manual as well as a contents list at the front. Each Chapter is also preceded by its own individual contents list.

References to the 'left' or 'right' of the vehicle are in the sense of a person in the driver's seat facing forwards.

Unless otherwise stated, nuts and bolts are removed by turning anti-clockwise, and tightened by turning clockwise.

Vehicle manufacturers continually make changes to specifications and recommendations, and these, when notified, are incorporated into our manuals at the earliest opportunity.

Whilst every care is taken to ensure that the information in this manual is correct, no liability can be accepted by the authors or publishers for loss, damage or injury caused by any errors in, or omissions from, the information given.

Introduction to the Vauxhall Astra

The Vauxhall Astra was introduced to the UK market early in 1980, initially being offered in 5-door Hatchback or Estate form with a 1297 cc ohc engine. The transverse engine drove the front wheels via a 4-speed all-synchro gearbox. Before the end of the year these models were also available in 3-door form, and 2-door and 4-door Saloons, powered by an ohv engine of 1196 cc, were introduced. The smaller engine was a well-proven unit used in earlier GM vehicles.

No major changes were made to the range until 1982, when the pushrod engine became available in other body styles besides the Saloon. At the other end of the scale, a 1598 cc ohc engine (as used in the Cavalier) was introduced. Later in the same year automatic transmission became an option on certain models. A diesel-powered version (not covered in this book) was launched and the Saloon body style was discontinued. A 5-speed gearbox appeared first on the SR Hatchback, later to become available on a wider range of models. The ultimate performance derivative at the time of writing is the GTE Hatchback, powered by a fuel-injected 1796 cc ohc engine. Once again, this is a close relative of the same size Cavalier engine.

Various trim levels are available, up to a very high standard. Mechanical units are reliable and for the most part easy to work on. In the overcrowded field of middle-sized front wheel drive cars, the Astra makes a favourable impression.

Buying spare parts and vehicle identification numbers

Buying spare parts

Spare parts are available from many sources, for example: Vauxhall garages, other garages and accessory shops, and motor factors. Our advice regarding spare part sources is as follows:

Officially appointed Vauxhall garages – This is the best source of parts which are peculiar to your vehicle and are otherwise not generally available (eg complete cylinder heads, internal gearbox components, badges, interior trim etc). It is also the only place at which you should buy parts if your vehicle is still under warranty: non-Vauxhall components may invalidate the warranty. To be sure of obtaining the correct parts it will always be necessary to give the storeman your vehicle's engine and chassis number, and if possible, to take the 'old' part along for positive identification. Remember that many parts are available on a factory exchange scheme – any parts returned should always be clean! It obviously makes good sense to go straight to the specialists on your vehicle for this type of part for they are best equipped to supply you.

Other garages and accessory shops – These are often very good places to buy materials and components needed for the maintenance of your vehicle (eg spark plugs, bulbs, drivebelts, oils and greases, touch-up paint, filler paste, etc). They also sell general accessories, usually have convenient opening hours, charge lower prices and can often be found not far from home.

Motor factors – Good factors will stock all of the more important components which wear out relatively quickly (eg clutch components, pistons, valves, exhaust systems, brake cylinders/pipes/hoses/seals/shoes and pads etc). Motor factors will often provide new or reconditioned components on a part exchange basis – this can save a considerable amount of money.

Vehicle identification numbers

The Vehicle Identification Number is located inside the engine compartment on top of the front end panel. The plate is marked with the vehicle chassis and designation number and the colour code. Also shown is the maximum gross weight for the car.

The engine number is stamped on a flat machined on the engine cylinder block (photo).

The chassis number is stamped on the body floor panel between the driver's seat (RHD) or passenger seat (LHD) at the door sill (photo).

Engine number (ohc)

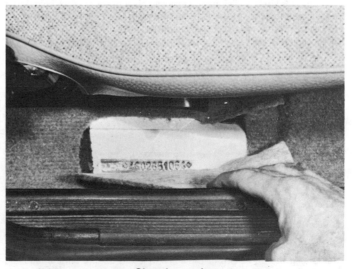

Chassis number

Tools and working facilities

Introduction

A selection of good tools is a fundamental requirement for anyone contemplating the maintenance and repair of a motor vehicle. For the owner who does not possess any, their purchase will prove a considerable expense, offsetting some of the savings made by doing-it-yourself. However, provided that the tools purchased meet the relevant national safety standards and are of good quality, they will last for many years and prove an extremely worthwhile investment.

To help the average owner to decide which tools are needed to carry out the various tasks detailed in this manual, we have compiled three lists of tools under the following headings: *Maintenance and minor repair, Repair and overhaul,* and *Special.* The newcomer to practical mechanics should start off with the *Maintenance and minor repair* tool kit and confine himself to the simpler jobs around the vehicle. Then, as his confidence and experience grow, he can undertake more difficult tasks, buying extra tools as, and when, they are needed. In this way, a *Maintenance and minor repair* tool kit can be built-up into a *Repair and overhaul* tool kit over a considerable period of time without any major cash outlays. The experienced do-it-yourselfer will have a tool kit good enough for most repair and overhaul procedures and will add tools from the *Special* category when he feels the expense is justified by the amount of use these tools will be put to.

It is obviously not possible to cover the subject of tools fully here. For those who wish to learn more about tools and their use there is a book entitled *How to Choose and Use Car Tools* available from the publishers of this manual.

Maintenance and minor repair tool kit

The tools given in this list should be considered as a minimum requirement if routine maintenance, servicing and minor repair operations are to be undertaken. We recommend the purchase of combination spanners (ring one end, open-ended the other); although more expensive than open-ended ones, they do give the advantages of both types of spanner.

Combination spanners - 10,11,12,13,14,15,16,17,18,19 mm
Adjustable spanner - 9 inch
Spark plug spanner (with rubber insert)
Spark plug gap adjustment tool
Set of feeler gauges
Screwdriver - 4 in long x $\frac{1}{4}$ in dia (flat blade)
Screwdriver - 4 in long x $\frac{1}{4}$ in dia (cross blade)
Combination pliers - 6 inch
Hacksaw, junior
Tyre pump
Tyre pressure gauge
Oil can
Fine emery cloth (1 sheet)
Wire brush (small)
Funnel (medium size)

Repair and overhaul tool kit

These tools are virtually essential for anyone undertaking any major repairs to a motor vehicle, and are additional to those given in the *Maintenance and minor repair* list. Included in this list is a comprehensive set of sockets. Although these are expensive they will be found invaluable as they are so versatile - particularly if various drives are included in the set. We recommend the $\frac{1}{2}$ in square-drive type, as this can be used with most proprietary torque spanners. If you cannot afford a socket set, even bought piecemeal, then inexpensive tubular box wrenches are a useful alternative.

The tools in this list will occasionally need to be supplemented by tools from the *Special* list.

Splined bolt tools (see Chapter 1 — ohv only)
Sockets (or box spanners) to cover range in previous list
Reversible ratchet drive (for use with sockets)
Extension piece, 10 inch (for use with sockets)
Universal joint (for use with sockets)
Torque wrench (for use with sockets)
Mole wrench - 8 inch
Ball pein hammer
Soft-faced hammer, plastic or rubber
Screwdriver - 6 in long x $\frac{5}{16}$ in dia (flat blade)
Screwdriver - 2 in long x $\frac{5}{16}$ in square (flat blade)
Screwdriver - 1$\frac{1}{2}$ in long x $\frac{1}{4}$ in dia (cross blade)
Screwdriver - 3 in long x $\frac{1}{8}$ in dia (electricians)
Pliers - electricians side cutters
Pliers - needle nosed
Pliers - circlip (internal and external)
Cold chisel - $\frac{1}{2}$ inch
Scriber
Scraper
Centre punch
Pin punch
Hacksaw
Valve grinding tool
Steel rule/straight-edge
Allen keys
Selection of files
Wire brush (large)
Axle-stands
Jack (strong scissor or hydraulic type)

Special tools

The tools in this list are those which are not used regularly, are expensive to buy, or which need to be used in accordance with their manufacturers' instructions. Unless relatively difficult mechanical jobs are undertaken frequently, it will not be economic to buy many of these tools. Where this is the case, you could consider clubbing together with friends (or joining a motorists' club) to make a joint purchase, or borrowing the tools against a deposit from a local garage or tool hire specialist.

The following list contains only those tools and instruments freely available to the public, and not those special tools produced by the vehicle manufacturer specifically for its dealer network. You will find occasional references to these manufacturers' special tools in the text of this manual. Generally, an alternative method of doing the job without the vehicle manufacturers' special tool is given. However, sometimes, there is no alternative to using them. Where this is the case and the relevant tool cannot be bought or borrowed you will have to entrust the work to a franchised garage.

> Valve spring compressor
> Piston ring compressor
> Balljoint separator
> Universal hub/bearing puller
> Impact screwdriver
> Micrometer and/or vernier gauge
> Dial gauge
> Stroboscopic timing light
> Dwell angle meter/tachometer
> Universal electrical multi-meter
> Cylinder compression gauge
> Lifting tackle
> Trolley jack
> Light with extension lead

Buying tools

For practically all tools, a tool factor is the best source since he will have a very comprehensive range compared with the average garage or accessory shop. Having said that, accessory shops often offer excellent quality tools at discount prices, so it pays to shop around.

There are plenty of good tools around at reasonable prices, but always aim to purchase items which meet the relevant national safety standards. If in doubt, ask the proprietor or manager of the shop for advice before making a purchase.

Care and maintenance of tools

Having purchased a reasonable tool kit, it is necessary to keep the tools in a clean serviceable condition. After use, always wipe off any dirt, grease and metal particles using a clean, dry cloth, before putting the tools away. Never leave them lying around after they have been used. A simple tool rack on the garage or workshop wall, for items such as screwdrivers and pliers is a good idea. Store all normal spanners and sockets in a metal box. Any measuring instruments, gauges, meters, etc, must be carefully stored where they cannot be damaged or become rusty.

Take a little care when tools are used. Hammer heads inevitably become marked and screwdrivers lose the keen edge on their blades from time to time. A little timely attention with emery cloth or a file will soon restore items like this to a good serviceable finish.

Working facilities

Not to be forgotten when discussing tools, is the workshop itself. If anything more than routine maintenance is to be carried out, some form of suitable working area becomes essential.

It is appreciated that many an owner mechanic is forced by circumstances to remove an engine or similar item, without the benefit of a garage or workshop. Having done this, any repairs should always be done under the cover of a roof.

Wherever possible, any dismantling should be done on a clean flat workbench or table at a suitable working height.

Any workbench needs a vice: one with a jaw opening of 4 in (100 mm) is suitable for most jobs. As mentioned previously, some clean dry storage space is also required for tools, as well as the lubricants, cleaning fluids, touch-up paints and so on which become necessary.

Another item which may be required, and which has a much more general usage, is an electric drill with a chuck capacity of at least $\frac{5}{16}$ in (8 mm). This, together with a good range of twist drills, is virtually essential for fitting accessories such as wing mirrors and reversing lights.

Last, but not least, always keep a supply of old newspapers and clean, lint-free rags available, and try to keep any working area as clean as possible.

Spanner jaw gap comparison table

Jaw gap (in)	Spanner size
0.250	$\frac{1}{4}$ in AF
0.276	7 mm
0.313	$\frac{5}{16}$ in AF
0.315	8 mm
0.344	$\frac{11}{32}$ in AF; $\frac{1}{8}$ in Whitworth
0.354	9 mm
0.375	$\frac{3}{8}$ in AF
0.394	10 mm
0.433	11 mm
0.438	$\frac{7}{16}$ in AF
0.445	$\frac{3}{16}$ in Whitworth; $\frac{1}{4}$ in BSF
0.472	12 mm
0.500	$\frac{1}{2}$ in AF
0.512	13 mm
0.525	$\frac{1}{4}$ in Whitworth; $\frac{5}{16}$ in BSF
0.551	14 mm
0.563	$\frac{9}{16}$ in AF
0.591	15 mm
0.600	$\frac{5}{16}$ in Whitworth; $\frac{3}{8}$ in BSF
0.625	$\frac{5}{8}$ in AF
0.630	16 mm
0.669	17 mm
0.686	$\frac{11}{16}$ in AF
0.709	18 mm
0.710	$\frac{3}{8}$ in Whitworth; $\frac{7}{16}$ in BSF
0.748	19 mm
0.750	$\frac{3}{4}$ in AF
0.813	$\frac{13}{16}$ in AF
0.820	$\frac{7}{16}$ in Whitworth; $\frac{1}{2}$ in BSF
0.866	22 mm
0.875	$\frac{7}{8}$ in AF
0.920	$\frac{1}{2}$ in Whitworth; $\frac{9}{16}$ in BSF
0.938	$\frac{15}{16}$ in AF
0.945	24 mm
1.000	1 in AF
1.010	$\frac{9}{16}$ in Whitworth; $\frac{5}{8}$ in BSF
1.024	26 mm
1.063	$1\frac{1}{16}$ in AF; 27 mm
1.100	$\frac{5}{8}$ in Whitworth; $\frac{11}{16}$ in BSF
1.125	$1\frac{1}{8}$ in AF
1.181	30 mm
1.200	$\frac{11}{16}$ in Whitworth; $\frac{3}{4}$ in BSF
1.250	$1\frac{1}{4}$ in AF
1.260	32 mm
1.300	$\frac{3}{4}$ in Whitworth; $\frac{7}{8}$ in BSF
1.313	$1\frac{5}{16}$ in AF
1.390	$\frac{13}{16}$ in Whitworth; $\frac{15}{16}$ in BSF
1.417	36 mm
1.438	$1\frac{7}{16}$ in AF
1.480	$\frac{7}{8}$ in Whitworth; 1 in BSF
1.500	$1\frac{1}{2}$ in AF
1.575	40 mm; $\frac{15}{16}$ in Whitworth
1.614	41 mm
1.625	$1\frac{5}{8}$ in AF
1.670	1 in Whitworth; $1\frac{1}{8}$ in BSF
1.688	$1\frac{11}{16}$ in AF
1.811	46 mm
1.813	$1\frac{13}{16}$ in AF
1.860	$1\frac{1}{8}$ in Whitworth; $1\frac{1}{4}$ in BSF
1.875	$1\frac{7}{8}$ in AF
1.969	50 mm
2.000	2 in AF
2.050	$1\frac{1}{4}$ in Whitworth; $1\frac{3}{8}$ in BSF
2.165	55 mm
2.362	60 mm

Jacking and towing

Use the jack supplied with the car only for wheel changing during roadside emergencies (photo).

Whenever underbody repairs are being carried out, use a hydraulic, screw or trolley jack placed under the body side or crossmembers. Always supplement the jacks with axle stands.

Do not attempt to raise the vehicle by placing the jack under the rear axle tube, the engine sump pan or the transmission casing.

To remove a roadwheel, first prise out the centre trim (photo). The plastic bolt covers will automatically be withdrawn from the roadwheel bolts. Slacken the bolts slightly, raise the vehicle and fully unscrew the bolts (photo). Remove the roadwheel. When refitting, push on the plastic bolt head covers after the centre trim has been refitted (photo).

Towing hooks are welded to the front and the rear of the vehicle and should only be used in an emergency, as their designed function is as lash-down hooks for use during transportation.

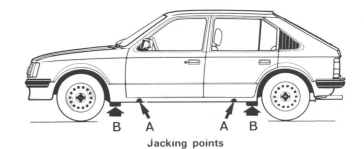

Jacking points

A   Sill jacking points (wheel changing)
B   Workshop jacking points

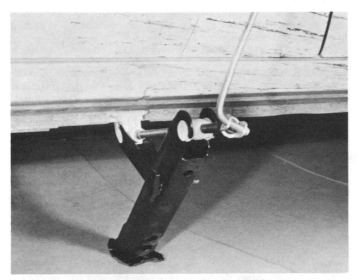

Using the tool kit emergency jack

Prising out hub trim plate

Unscrewing wheel bolt

Fitting wheel bolt head cover

Safety first!

Professional motor mechanics are trained in safe working procedures. However enthusiastic you may be about getting on with the job in hand, do take the time to ensure that your safety is not put at risk. A moment's lack of attention can result in an accident, as can failure to observe certain elementary precautions.

There will always be new ways of having accidents, and the following points do not pretend to be a comprehensive list of all dangers; they are intended rather to make you aware of the risks and to encourage a safety-conscious approach to all work you carry out on your vehicle.

Essential DOs and DON'Ts

DON'T rely on a single jack when working underneath the vehicle. Always use reliable additional means of support, such as axle stands, securely placed under a part of the vehicle that you know will not give way.

DON'T attempt to loosen or tighten high-torque nuts (e.g. wheel hub nuts) while the vehicle is on a jack; it may be pulled off.

DON'T start the engine without first ascertaining that the transmission is in neutral (or 'Park' where applicable) and the parking brake applied.

DON'T suddenly remove the filler cap from a hot cooling system – cover it with a cloth and release the pressure gradually first, or you may get scalded by escaping coolant.

DON'T attempt to drain oil until you are sure it has cooled sufficiently to avoid scalding you.

DON'T grasp any part of the engine, exhaust or catalytic converter without first ascertaining that it is sufficiently cool to avoid burning you.

DON'T allow brake fluid or antifreeze to contact vehicle paintwork.

DON'T syphon toxic liquids such as fuel, brake fluid or antifreeze by mouth, or allow them to remain on your skin.

DON'T inhale dust – it may be injurious to health (see *Asbestos* below).

DON'T allow any spilt oil or grease to remain on the floor – wipe it up straight away, before someone slips on it.

DON'T use ill-fitting spanners or other tools which may slip and cause injury.

DON'T attempt to lift a heavy component which may be beyond your capability – get assistance.

DON'T rush to finish a job, or take unverified short cuts.

DON'T allow children or animals in or around an unattended vehicle.

DO wear eye protection when using power tools such as drill, sander, bench grinder etc, and when working under the vehicle.

DO use a barrier cream on your hands prior to undertaking dirty jobs – it will protect your skin from infection as well as making the dirt easier to remove afterwards; but make sure your hands aren't left slippery. Note that long-term contact with used engine oil can be a health hazard.

DO keep loose clothing (cuffs, tie etc) and long hair well out of the way of moving mechanical parts.

DO remove rings, wristwatch etc, before working on the vehicle – especially the electrical system.

DO ensure that any lifting tackle used has a safe working load rating adequate for the job.

DO keep your work area tidy – it is only too easy to fall over articles left lying around.

DO get someone to check periodically that all is well, when working alone on the vehicle.

DO carry out work in a logical sequence and check that everything is correctly assembled and tightened afterwards.

DO remember that your vehicle's safety affects that of yourself and others. If in doubt on any point, get specialist advice.

IF, in spite of following these precautions, you are unfortunate enough to injure yourself, seek medical attention as soon as possible.

Asbestos

Certain friction, insulating, sealing, and other products – such as brake linings, brake bands, clutch linings, torque converters, gaskets, etc – contain asbestos. *Extreme care must be taken to avoid inhalation of dust from such products since it is hazardous to health.* If in doubt, assume that they *do* contain asbestos.

Fire

Remember at all times that petrol (gasoline) is highly flammable. Never smoke, or have any kind of naked flame around, when working on the vehicle. But the risk does not end there – a spark caused by an electrical short-circuit, by two metal surfaces contacting each other, by careless use of tools, or even by static electricity built up in your body under certain conditions, can ignite petrol vapour, which in a confined space is highly explosive.

Always disconnect the battery earth (ground) terminal before working on any part of the fuel or electrical system, and never risk spilling fuel on to a hot engine or exhaust.

It is recommended that a fire extinguisher of a type suitable for fuel and electrical fires is kept handy in the garage or workplace at all times. Never try to extinguish a fuel or electrical fire with water.

Note: *Any reference to a 'torch' appearing in this manual should always be taken to mean a hand-held battery-operated electric lamp or flashlight. It does NOT mean a welding/gas torch or blowlamp.*

Fumes

Certain fumes are highly toxic and can quickly cause unconsciousness and even death if inhaled to any extent. Petrol (gasoline) vapour comes into this category, as do the vapours from certain solvents such as trichloroethylene. Any draining or pouring of such volatile fluids should be done in a well ventilated area.

When using cleaning fluids and solvents, read the instructions carefully. Never use materials from unmarked containers – they may give off poisonous vapours.

Never run the engine of a motor vehicle in an enclosed space such as a garage. Exhaust fumes contain carbon monoxide which is extremely poisonous; if you need to run the engine, always do so in the open air or at least have the rear of the vehicle outside the workplace.

If you are fortunate enough to have the use of an inspection pit, never drain or pour petrol, and never run the engine, while the vehicle is standing over it; the fumes, being heavier than air, will concentrate in the pit with possibly lethal results.

The battery

Never cause a spark, or allow a naked light, near the vehicle's battery. It will normally be giving off a certain amount of hydrogen gas, which is highly explosive.

Always disconnect the battery earth (ground) terminal before working on the fuel or electrical systems.

If possible, loosen the filler plugs or cover when charging the battery from an external source. Do not charge at an excessive rate or the battery may burst.

Take care when topping up and when carrying the battery. The acid electrolyte, even when diluted, is very corrosive and should not be allowed to contact the eyes or skin.

If you ever need to prepare electrolyte yourself, always add the acid slowly to the water, and never the other way round. Protect against splashes by wearing rubber gloves and goggles.

When jump starting a car using a booster battery, for negative earth (ground) vehicles, connect the jump leads in the following sequence: First connect one jump lead between the positive (+) terminals of the two batteries. Then connect the other jump lead first to the negative (–) terminal of the booster battery, and then to a good earthing (ground) point on the vehicle to be started, at least 18 in (45 cm) from the battery if possible. Ensure that hands and jump leads are clear of any moving parts, and that the two vehicles do not touch. Disconnect the leads in the reverse order.

Mains electricity and electrical equipment

When using an electric power tool, inspection light etc, always ensure that the appliance is correctly connected to its plug and that, where necessary, it is properly earthed (grounded). Do not use such appliances in damp conditions and, again, beware of creating a spark or applying excessive heat in the vicinity of fuel or fuel vapour. Also ensure that the appliances meet the relevant national safety standards.

Ignition HT voltage

A severe electric shock can result from touching certain parts of the ignition system, such as the HT leads, when the engine is running or being cranked, particularly if components are damp or the insulation is defective. Where an electronic ignition system is fitted, the HT voltage is much higher and could prove fatal.

Routine maintenance

For modifications, and information applicable to later models, see Supplement at end of manual

The Routine Maintenance instructions listed are basically those recommended by the vehicle manufacturer. They are sometimes supplemented by additional maintenance tasks proven to be necessary.

The following maintenance instructions should always be used in conjunction with the servicing schedule detailed in the owner's handbook or maintenance booklet supplied with the each new car, as the servicing requirement may be altered by the manufacturer in the course of time.

Where the vehicle is used under severe operating conditions (extremes of heat or cold, dusty conditions, or mainly stop-start driving), more frequent oil changes may be desirable. If in doubt consult your dealer.

Weekly or before a long journey

Check engine oil level (photo)
Check operation of all lights, flashers, wipers and horn
Check battery electrolyte level (photo)
Check coolant level (photo)
Check washer fluid level(s) (photos), adding a screen wash such as Turtle Wax High Tech Screen Wash
Check tyre pressures (cold), not forgetting the spare (photo)
Check brake fluid level (photo)

Checking engine oil level

Topping up the battery

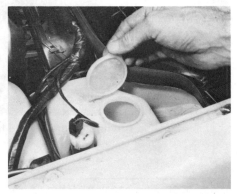
Washer fluid reservoir (windscreen)

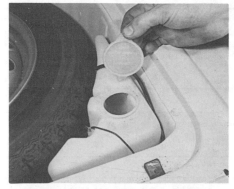
Washer fluid reservoir (rear window)

Checking a tyre pressure

Topping up engine oil level

Topping up coolant level

Removing engine oil drain plug

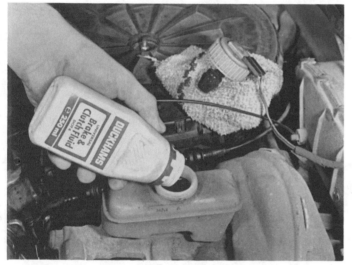

Topping up brake fluid level

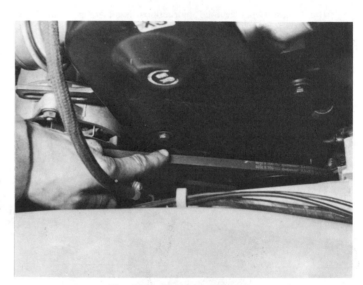

Checking the drivebelt tension

Every 6000 miles (10 000 km) or six months, whichever comes first

Renew engine oil and filter (photos)
Clean or renew distributor contact breaker (early models)
Clean and re-gap spark plugs
Lubricate controls, hinges and locks
Adjust rear brakes (if applicable) and check lining wear
Inspect tyres for damage and wear
Check front disc pads for wear
Check and adjust valve clearances (ohv)
Check dwell angle
Check ignition timing
Check carburettor adjustment
Check front wheel alignment
Check steering and suspension for wear and gaiters and bellows for damage
Check transmission oil level
Check drivebelt tension and condition (photo)
Check brake hydraulic hoses and pipes for damage or corrosion

Check brake pressure proportioning valve adjustment (Estate only). Refer to Chapter 9, Section 15, paragraphs 8 to 11

Every 12 000 miles (20 000 km) or twelve months, whichever comes first

Renew air filter
Renew spark plugs
Check exhaust system for corrosion and security of mountings
Check rear hub bearing adjustment
Renew fuel filter

Annually

Renew coolant antifreeze mixture
Renew brake hydraulic fluid by bleeding

Every 50 000 miles (80 000 km)

Renew timing belt (ohc)

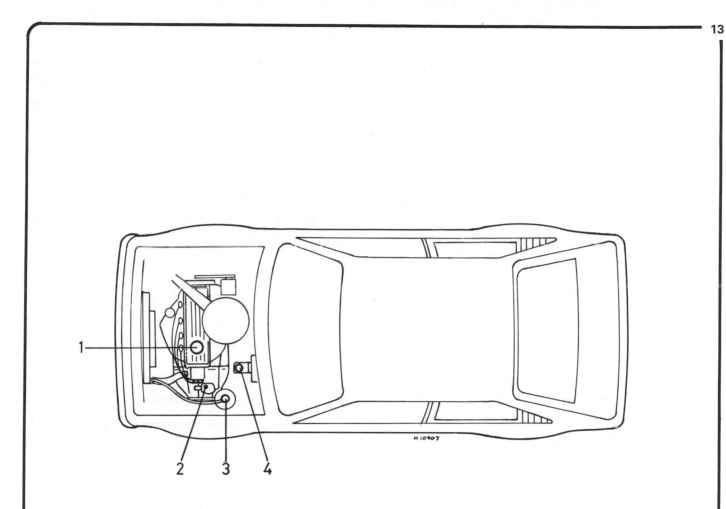

Recommended lubricants and fluids

Component or system	Lubricant type/specification	Duckhams recommendation
1 Engine	Multigrade engine oil, viscosity range SAE 10W/40 to 20W/50, to API SF/CC or better	Duckhams QXR, Hypergrade, or 10W/40 Motor Oil
2 Manual transmission*		
4-speed	Gear oil, viscosity SAE 80, to API GL3 or GL4	Duckhams Hypoid 80
5-speed (not GTE)	Gear oil, viscosity SAE 80, to API GL3 or GL4	Duckhams Hypoid 75W/90S
5-speed (GTE)	Special transmission oil, GM part No 90 188 629	Duckhams Hypoid 75W/90S
Automatic transmission	Dexron II type ATF	Duckhams D-Matic
3 Cooling system	Antifreeze to B53151 or 6580	Duckhams Universal Antifreeze and Summer Coolant
4 Brake hydraulic system	Hydraulic fluid to SAE J1703	Duckhams Universal Brake and Clutch Fluid

Fault diagnosis

Introduction

The car owner who does his or her own maintenance according to the recommended schedules should not have to use this section of the manual very often. Modern component reliability is such that, provided those items subject to wear or deterioration are inspected or renewed at the specified intervals, sudden failure is comparatively rare. Faults do not usually just happen as a result of sudden failure, but develop over a period of time. Major mechanical failures in particular are usually preceded by characteristic symptoms over hundreds or even thousands of miles. Those components which do occasionally fail without warning are often small and easily carried in the car.

With any fault finding, the first step is to decide where to begin investigations. Sometimes this is obvious, but on other occasions a little detective work will be necessary. The owner who makes half a dozen haphazard adjustments or replacements may be successful in curing a fault (or its symptoms), but he will be none the wiser if the fault recurs and he may well have spend more time and money than was necessary. A calm and logical approach will be found to be more satisfactory in the long run. Always take into account any warning signs or abnormalities that may have been noticed in the period preceding the fault – power loss, high or low gauge readings, unusual noises or smells, etc – and remember that failure of components such as fuses or spark plugs may only be pointers to some underlying fault.

The pages which follow here are intended to help in cases of failure to start or breakdown on the road. There is also a Fault Diagnosis Section at the end of each Chapter which could be consulted if the preliminary checks prove unfruitful. Whatever the fault, certain basic principles apply. These are as follows:

Verify the fault. This is simply a matter of being sure that you know what the symptoms are before starting work. This is particularly important if you are investigating a fault for someone else who may not have described it very accurately.

Don't overlook the obvious. For example, if the car won't start, is there petrol in the tank? (Don't take anyone else's word on this particular point, and don't trust the fuel gauge either!). If an electrical fault is indicated, look for loose or broken wires before digging out the test gear.

Cure the disease, not the symptom. Substituting a flat battery with a fully charged one will get you off the hard shoulder, but if the underlying cause is not attended to, the new battery will go the same way. Similarly, changing oil-fouled spark plugs for a new set will get you moving again, but remember that the reason for the fouling (if it wasn't simply an incorrect grade of plug) will have to be established and corrected.

Don't take anything for granted. Particularly, don't forget that a 'new' component may itself be defective (especially if it's been rattling round in the boot for months), and don't leave components out of a fault diagnosis sequence just because they are new or recently fitted. When you do finally diagnose a difficult fault, you'll probably realise that all the evidence was there from the start.

Electrical faults

Electrical faults can be more puzzling than straightforward mechanical failures, but they are no less susceptible to logical analysis if the basic principles of operation are understood. Car electrical wiring exists in extremely unfavourable conditions – heat, vibration and chemical attack – and the first things to look for are loose or corroded connections and broken or chafed wires, especially where the wires

Carrying a few spares may save a long walk

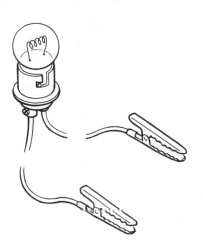

A simple test lamp is useful for tracing electrical faults

pass through holes in the bodywork or are subject to vibration.

All metal-bodies cars in current production have one pole of the battery 'earthed', ie connected to the car bodywork, and in nearly all modern cars it is the negative (–) terminal. The various electrical components – motors, bulb holders etc – are also connected to earth, either by means of a lead or directly by their mountings. Electric current flows through the component and then back to the battery via the car bodywork. If the component mounting is loose or corroded, or if a good path back to the battery is not available, the circuit will be incomplete and malfunction will result. The engine and/or gearbox are also earthed by means of flexible metal straps to the body or subframe; if these straps are loose or missing, starter motor, generator and ignition trouble may result.

Assuming the earth return to be satisfactory, electrical faults will be due either to component malfunction or to defects in the current supply. Individual components are dealt with in Chapter 10. If supply wires are broken or cracked internally this results in an open-circuit, and the easiest way to check for this is to bypass the suspect wire temporarily with a length of wire having a crocodile clip or suitable connector at each end. Alternatively, a 12V test lamp can be used to verify the presence of supply voltage at various points along the wire and the break can be thus isolated.

If a bare portion of a live wire touches the car bodywork or other earthed metal part the electricity will take the low-resistance path thus formed back to the battery: this is known as a short-circuit. Hopefully a short-circuit will blow a fuse, but otherwise it may cause burning of the insulation (and possible further short-circuits) or even a fire. This is why it is inadvisable to bypass persistently blowing fuses with silver foil or wire.

Spares and tool kit

Most cars are only supplied with sufficient tools for wheel changing; the *Maintenance and minor repair* tool kit detailed in *Tools and working facilities*, with the addition of a hammer, is probably sufficient for those repairs that most motorists would consider attempting at the roadside. In addition a few items which can be fitted without too much trouble in the event of a breakdown should be carried. Experience and available space will modify the list below, but the following may save having to call on professional assistance:

Spark plugs, clean and correctly gapped
HT lead and plug cap – long enough to reach the plug furthest from the distributor
Distributor rotor, condenser and contact breaker points
Drivebelt – emergency type may suffice
Spare fuses
Set of principal light bulbs
Tin of radiator sealer and hose bandage
Exhaust bandage

Roll of insulating tape
Length of soft iron wire
Length of electrical flex
Torch or inspection lamp (can double as test lamp)
Battery jump leads
Tow-rope
Ignition water dispersant aerosol
Litre of engine oil
Sealed can of hydraulic fluid
Emergency windscreen
Tyre valve core

If spare fuel is carried, a can designed for the purpose should be used to minimise the risks of leakage and collision damage. A first aid kit and a warning triangle, whilst not at present compulsory in the UK, are obviously sensible items to carry in addition to the above.

When touring abroad it may be advisable to carry additional spares which, even if you cannot fit them yourself, could save having to wait while parts are obtained. The items below may be worth considering:

Clutch and throttle cables
Cylinder head gasket
Alternator brushes
Fuel pump repair kit

Engine will not start

Engine fails to turn when starter operated
    Flat battery (recharge, use jump leads, or push start)
    Battery terminals loose or corroded
    Battery earth to body defective
    Engine earth strap loose or broken
    Starter motor (or solenoid) wiring loose or broken
    Ignition/starter switch faulty
    Major mechanical failure (seizure) or long disuse (piston rings rusted to bores)
    Starter or solenoid internal fault (see Chapter 10)

Starter motor turns engine slowly
    Partially discharged battery (recharge, use jump leads, or push start)
    Battery terminals loose or corroded
    Battery earth to body defective
    Engine earth strap loose
    Starter motor (or solenoid) wiring loose
    Starter motor internal fault (see Chapter 10)

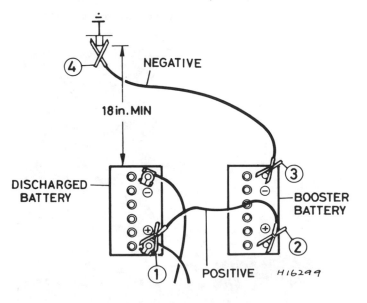

Jump start lead connections for negative earth – connect leads in order shown

Starter motor spins without turning engine
Flat battery
Flywheel gear teeth damaged or worn
Starter motor mounting bolts loose

Engine turns normally but fails to start
Damp or dirty HT leads and distributor cap (crank engine and check for spark) – try moisture dispersant such as Holts Wet Start
Dirty or incorrectly gapped contact breaker points
No fuel in tank (check for delivery at carburettor) (photo)
Excessive choke (hot engine) or insufficient choke (cold engine)
Fouled or incorrectly gapped spark plugs (remove, clean and regap)
Other ignition system fault (see Chapter 4)
Other fuel system fault (See Chapter 3)
Poor compression (see Chapter 1)
Major mechanical failure (eg camshaft drive)

Engine fires but will not run
Insufficient choke (cold engine)
Air leaks at carburettor or inlet manifold
Fuel starvation (see Chapter 3)
Ignition fault (see Chapter4)

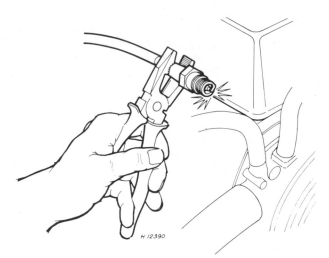

Crank engine and check for spark. Note use of insulated tool

Checking fuel delivery. Disconnect ignition and then crank engine

Engine cuts out and will not restart

Engine cuts out suddenly – ignition fault
Loose or disconnected LT wires
Wet HT leads or distributor cap (after traversing water splash)
Coil or condenser failure (check for spark)
Other ignition fault (see Chapter 4)

Engine misfires before cutting out – fuel fault
Fuel tank empty
Fuel pump defective or filter blocked (check for delivery)
Fuel tank filler vent blocked (suction will be evident on releasing cap)
Carburettor needle valve sticking
Carburettor jets blocked (fuel contaminated)
Other fuel system fault (see Chapter 3)

Engine cuts out – other causes
Serious overheating
Major mechanical failure (eg camshaft drive)

Engine overheats

Ignition (no-charge) warning light illuminated
Slack or broken drivebelt (ohv only) – retension or renew (Chapter 2)

Ignition warning light not illuminated
Coolant loss due to internal or external leakage (see Chapter 2)
Thermostat defective
Low oil level
Brakes binding
Radiator clogged externally or internally
Electric cooling fan not operating correctly
Engine waterways clogged
Ignition timing incorrect or automatic advance malfunctioning
Mixture too weak
Note: *Do not add cold water to an overheated engine or damage may result*

Low engine oil pressure

Warning light illuminated with engine running
Oil level low or incorrect grade
Defective sender unit
Wire to sender unit earthed
Engine overheating
Oil filter clogged or bypass valve defective
Oil pressure relief valve defective
Oil pick-up strainer clogged
Oil pump worn or mountings loose
Worn main or big-end bearings
Note: *Low oil pressure in a high-mileage engine at tickover is not necessarily a cause for concern. Sudden pressure loss at speed is far more significant. In any event, check the gauge or warning light sender before condemning the engine.*

Engine noises

Pre-ignition (pinking) on acceleration
Incorrect grade of fuel
Ignition timing incorrect
Distributor faulty or worn
Worn or maladjusted carburettor
Excessive carbon build-up in engine

Whistling or wheezing noises
Leaking vacuum hose
Leaking carburettor or manifold gasket

General dimensions, weights and capacities

Dimensions

	Saloon/Hatchback	Estate
Overall length (without bumper guards)	3998 mm (157.4 in)	4206 mm (165.6 in)
Overall length (with bumper guards)	4031 mm (158.7 in)	4240 mm (166.9 in)
Overall width (except SR)	1636 mm (64.4 in)	1636 mm (64.4 in)
Overall width (with SR equipment)	1656 mm (65.2 in)	
Front track (except 1.6)	1400 mm (55.1 in)	1400 mm (55.1 in)
Front track (1.6)	1406 mm (55.4 in)	1406 mm (55.4 in)
Rear track	1406 mm (55.4 in)	1406 mm (55.4 in)
Wheelbase	2520 mm (99.2 in)	2520 mm (99.2 in)

Kerb weights*

	Saloon/Hatchback	Estate
1.2, 2/3-door	865 kg (1907 lb)	—
1.2, 4/5-door	885 kg (1951 lb)	—
1.3, 2/3-door	875 kg (1929 lb)	895 kg (1973 lb)
1.3, 4/5-door	895 kg (1973 lb)	915 kg (2017 lb)
1.6, 3-door	920 kg (2028 lb)	945 kg (2083 lb)
1.6, 5-door	940 kg (2072 lb)	965 kg (2127 lb)
1.8	980 kg (2161 lb)	—

Weights are approximate and will vary with trim level. For automatic transmission add 25 kg (55 lb)

Trailer weights (maximum)

Unbraked trailer:

1.2	400 kg (882 lb)
1.3 (manual and automatic)	400 kg (882 lb)
1.6 and 1.8	450 kg (992 lb)

Braked trailer:

	Saloon/Hatchback	Estate
1.2	650 kg (1430 lb)	600 kg (1323 lb)
1.3:		
Manual	950 kg (2094 lb)	900 kg (1984 lb)
Automatic	700 kg (1543 lb)	700 kg (1543 lb)
1.6 and 1.8	1000 kg (2204 lb)	—

Roof rack load (maximum)

All models	80 kg (176 lb)

Capacities (approx)

Fuel tank:

Saloon/Hatchback	41.8 litres (9.2 gallons)
Estate	50.0 litres (11.0 gallons)

Cooling system:

1.2	5.9 litres (10.4 pints)
1.3 (manual transmission)	6.3 litres (11.1 pints)
1.3 (automatic transmission)	7.1 litres (12.5 pints)
1.6 (manual transmission)	7.8 litres (13.7 pints)
1.6 (automatic transmission)	7.6 litres (13.4 pints)
1.8	7.6 litres (13.4 pints)

Engine oil (with filter change):

1.2	2.75 litres (4.8 pints)
1.3 up to chassis No C2 549 985	2.75 litres (4.8 pints)
1.3, later models	3.00 litres (5.3 pints)
1.6 and 1.8	3.25 litres (5.7 pints)

Manual transmission:

1.2 and 1.3	1.7 litres (3.0 pints)
1.6 (4-speed)	2.0 litres (3.5 pints)
1.6 and 1.8 (5-speed)	2.1 litres (3.7 pints)
Automatic transmission (drain and refill)	6.3 litres (11.1 pints)

Chapter 1 Engine

For modifications, and information applicable to later models, see Supplement at end of manual

Contents

Specifications

Part A: OHV engine
General

Type	Four-cylinder, in-line, ohv
Designation	12 (low compression), 12S (high compression)
Bore	79.0 mm (3.11 in)
Stroke	61.0 mm (2.40 in)
Displacement	1196 cc (73.0 cu in)
Compression ratio	7.8 : 1 (12 engine), 9.0 : 1 (12S engine)
Firing order	1 - 3 - 4 - 2
Location of No 1 cylinder	At timing cover end
Output (DIN)	53 bhp at 5400 rpm (12), 57 bhp at 5800 rpm (12S)
Torque (DIN)	58 lbf ft at 3600 rpm (12), 61 lbf ft at 3400 rpm (12S)

Cylinder block (crankcase)

Type	Cast iron – cylinders cast integrally with upper half of crankcase
Maximum cylinder ovality	0.013 mm (0.00051 in)
Maximum cylinder taper	0.013 mm (0.00051 in)
Standard production bore available in 16 grades	78.95 to 79.10 mm (3.108 to 3.114 in)
Oversize bore size (nominal 0.5 mm)	79.47 to 79.50 mm (3.129 to 3.130 in)

Crankshaft

Endfloat	0.09 to 0.20 mm (0.0035 to 0.0078 in)
No of main bearings	3

Main bearing diameter – standard:

No 1 journal	53.997 to 54.010 mm (2.1259 to 2.1264 in)
Nos 2 and 3 journals	54.007 to 54.020 mm (2.1263 to 2.1268 in)

Main bearing play:

Bearing 1	0.020 to 0.046 mm (0.00078 to 0.0018 in)
Bearing 2	0.010 to 0.036 mm (0.00039 to 0.0014 in)
Bearing 3	0.00 to 0.0315 mm (0.0 to 0.00124 in)
Main bearing journals – undersize diameters available	0.25 and 0.50 mm (0.0098 and 0.0197 in)
Big-end journal diameter (standard)	44.971 to 44.987 mm (1.770 to 1.771 in)
Big-end journal – undersize diameters available	0.25 and 0.50 mm (0.0098 and 0.0197 in)
Big-end clearance	0.015 to 0.059 mm (0.0005 to 0.002 in)
Maximum ovality	0.006 mm (0.0002 in)
Maximum taper	0.01 mm (0.00039 in)

Camshaft

Endfloat	0.2 to 0.3 mm (0.0078 to 0.0118 in)
Camshaft drive	Single row chain
Number of bearings	3

Bearing journal diameters – standard:

No 1 journal	40.960 to 40.975 mm (1.612 to 1.613 in)
No 2 journal	40.460 to 40.475 mm (1.592 to 1.593 in)
No 3 journal	39.960 to 39.975 mm (1.573 to 1.574 in)

Maximum undersize diameters:

No 1 journal	40.460 to 40.475 mm (1.592 to 1.593 in)
No 2 journal	39.960 to 39.975 mm (1.573 to 1.574 in)
No 3 journal	39.460 to 39.475 mm (1.553 to 1.554 in)

Pistons and rings

Piston type	Recessed head
Number of rings	2 compression and 1 oil control
Piston diameter	78.93 to 79.07 mm (3.1075 to 3.1130 in)
Piston clearance in bore	0.01 to 0.03 mm (0.0004 to 0.0011 in)
Oversize pistons	+ 0.5 mm (0.020 in)
Gudgeon pin location	Interference fit in connecting rod

Piston ring/groove clearance:

Top compression	0.060 to 0.087 mm (0.0024 to 0.0034 in)
Second compression	0.033 to 0.063 mm (0.0013 to 0.0025 in)

Ring end gap:

Compression rings	0.30 to 0.45 mm (0.012 to 0.018 in)
Oil control ring	0.25 to 0.40 mm (0.010 to 0.016 in)

Cylinder head

Material	Cast iron
Maximum permissible distortion of sealing face	0.015 mm (0.0006 in) over 150 mm (5.9 in) or 0.05 mm (0.0019 in) over total surface area

Valve seat width:

Inlet	1.25 to 1.50 mm (0.0492 to 0.0590 in)
Exhaust	1.60 to 1.85 mm (0.0629 to 0.0728 in)

Valves

Valve clearances – hot:

Inlet	0.15 mm (0.006 in)
Exhaust	0.25 mm (0.010 in)

Valve timing:

Inlet opens btdc	46°
Inlet closes abdc	90°
Exhaust opens bbdc	70°
Exhaust closes atdc	30°
Valve seat angle	44°
Inlet valve head diameter	32 mm (1.260 in)
Exhaust valve head diameter	27 mm (1.063 in)
Valve stem diameter	7.00 to 7.010 mm (0.275 to 0.276 in)
Oversizes available	0.075 mm (0.0029 in), 0.150 mm (0.0059 in), 0.250 mm (0.0098 in)

Valve overall length:

Inlet	99.3 mm (3.901 in)
Exhaust	101.1 mm (3.980 in)

Maximum permissible valve stem clearance:

Inlet	0.015 to 0.045 mm (0.0006 to 0.0018 in)
Exhaust	0.035 to 0.065 mm (0.0014 to 0.0026 in)

Valve guide internal diameter:

Standard	7.025 to 7.045 mm (0.2766 to 0.2774 in)
Oversizes	0.075 mm (0.0029 in), 0.150 mm (0.0059 in), 0.250 mm (0.0098 in)

Valve springs:
    Length at load of 15 kg (33.0 lb) .... 32.5 mm (1.280 in)
    Length at load of 45 kg (99.1 lb) .... 23.0 mm (0.906 in)

Lubrication system
Oil capacity:
    With filter change .... 2.75 litres (4.8 pints) approx
Oil type/specification .... Multigrade engine oil viscosity range SAE 10W/40 to 20W/50, to API SF/CC or better (Duckhams QXR, Hypergrade, or 10W/40 Motor Oil)
Oil filter .... Champion C103
Oil pump:
    Permissible tooth surface play .... 0.1 to 0.2 mm (0.0039 to 0.0079 in)
    Gear endfloat .... 0.04 to 0.1 mm (0.0015 to 0.0039 in)
Oil pressure at idle .... Not lower than 0.3 bar (4.4 lbf/in^2)

Torque wrench settings (ohv engine)

	Nm	lbf ft
Cylinder head bolts (cold):		
Stage 1	25	18
Stage 2	Through 60°	
Stage 3	Through 60°	
Stage 4	Through 60°	
Main bearing cap bolts	62	45
Big-end cap bolts	27	20
Flywheel bolts	35	26
Oil pump mounting bolts	20	15
Sump pan bolts	5	4
Camshaft sprocket bolt	40	30
Crankshaft pulley bolt	40	30
Manifold bolts and nuts	23	17
Carburettor mounting nuts	18	13
Spark plugs	40	30
Engine front mounting bracket-to-crankcase	20	15
Engine flexible mounting bolt	40	30
Oil drain plug	45	33

Part B: OHC engine
General
Type .... Four-cylinder, in-line, ohc
Designation .... 13 (low compression), 13S (high compression)
Bore .... 75.0 mm (2.95 in)
Stroke .... 73.4 mm (2.89 in)
Displacement .... 1297 cc (79.1 cu in)
Compression ratio .... 8.2: 1 (13), 9.2: 1 (13 S)
Firing order .... 1 - 3 - 4 - 2
Location of No 1 cylinder .... At timing cover end
Output (DIN):
    13 .... 44 kW (60 bhp) at 5800 rpm
    13S .... 55 kW (75 bhp) at 5800 rpm
Torque (DIN):
    13 .... 94 Nm (69 lbf ft) at 3400 to 3800 rpm
    13S .... 101 Nm (75 lbf ft) at 3800 to 4600 rpm

Cylinder block (crankcase)
Type .... Cast iron, cylinders cast integrally with upper half of crankcase
Maximum cylinder ovality .... 0.013 mm (0.00051 in)
Maximum cylinder taper .... 0.013 mm (0.00051 in)
Standard production bore available in 16 grades .... 74.95 to 75.10 mm (2.95 to 2.96 in)
Oversize bore size (nominal 0.5 mm) .... 75.47 to 75.50 mm (2.9712 to 2.9724 in)

Crankshaft
Number of main bearings 5
Endfloat .... 0.08 to 0.18 mm (0.003 to 0.007 in)
Main bearing diameter .... 54.972 to 54.985 mm (2.1642 to 2.1647 in)
Undersizes available .... 0.25 and 0.50 mm (0.0098 and 0.0197 in)
Main bearing running clearance .... 0.025 to 0.051 mm (0.00098 to 0.00200 in)
Big-end crankpin diameter .... 42.971 to 42.987 mm (1.6918 to 1.6924 in)
Undersizes available .... 0.25 and 0.50 mm (0.0098 and 0.0197 in)
Big-end bearing running clearance .... 0.02 to 0.06 mm (0.0008 to 0.0024 in)

Camshaft
Endfloat .... 0.04 to 0.16 mm (0.0016 to 0.0063 in)
Cam lift:
    13 .... 5.54 mm (0.2181 in)
    13S .... 6.00 mm (0.2362 in)

Bearing journal diameter:
- No 1 .... 39.435 to 39.450 mm (1.5526 to 1.5531 in)
- No 2 .... 39.685 to 39.700 mm (1.5624 to 1.5630 in)
- No 3 .... 39.935 to 39.950 mm (1.5722 to 1.5728 in)
- No 4 .... 40.125 to 40.200 mm (1.5797 to 1.5827 in)
- No 5 .... 40.435 to 40.450 mm (1.5919 to 1.5925 in)

Bearing bore in camshaft housing:
- No 1 .... 39.500 to 39.525 mm (1.5551 to 1.5561 in)
- No 2 .... 39.750 to 39.775 mm (1.5650 to 1.5659 in)
- No 3 .... 40.000 to 40.025 mm (1.5748 to 1.5758 in)
- No 4 .... 40.250 to 40.275 mm (1.5846 to 1.5856 in)
- No 5 .... 40.525 to 40.550 mm (1.5955 to 1.5964 in)

Camshaft belt tension (using special tool KM 420) .... 1 to 2

Pistons and rings

Piston type	Recessed head
Number of rings	2 compression and 1 oil control
Piston clearance in bore	0.02 mm (0.0008 in)
Oversize pistons	+ 0.5 mm (0.020 in)
Gudgeon pin location	Interference fit in connecting rod

Piston ring/groove clearance:
- Top compression .... 0.060 to 0.087 mm (0.0024 to 0.0034 in)
- Second compression .... 0.033 to 0.063 mm (0.0013 to 0.0025 in)

Ring end gap:
- Compression rings .... 0.30 to 0.45 mm (0.012 to 0.018 in)
- Oil control ring .... 0.38 to 1.40 mm (0.015 to 0.055 in)

Cylinder head

Material	Aluminium alloy
Maximum permissible distortion of sealing face	0.015 mm (0.0006 in) over 150 mm (5.9 in), or 0.05 mm (0.0019 in) over total length

Valve seat width:
- Inlet valves .... 1.3 to 1.4 mm (0.0512 to 0.1312 in)
- Exhaust valves .... 1.7 to 1.8 mm (0.0669 to 0.0709 in)

Valves

Valve clearance adjustment .... Automatic, by hydraulic lifters

	13	13S
Valve timing:		
Inlet opens btdc	24°	24°
Inlet closes abdc	73°	78°
Exhaust opens bbdc	66°	68°
Exhaust closes atdc	30°	36°
Valve seat angle	44°	44°

Inlet valve head diameter	33 mm (1.299 in)
Exhaust valve head diameter	33 mm (1.299 in)
Valve stem diameter	7.0 mm (0.2756 in)
Oversizes available	0.075 mm (0.0030 in), 0.150 mm (0.0059 in), 0.250 mm (0.0098 in)

Valve overall length:
- Inlet .... 104.6 mm (4.118 in)
- Exhaust .... 104.6 mm (4.118 in)

Maximum valve stem clearance:
- Inlet .... 0.020 to 0.045 mm (0.0008 to 0.0018 in)
- Exhaust .... 0.040 to 0.065 mm (0.0016 to 0.0026 in)

Valve guide installed height .... 81.23 to 81.25 mm (3.198 to 3.199 in)

Lubrication system

Oil capacity (with filter change):
- Up to chassis No C2 549 985 .... 2.75 litres (4.8 pints) approx
- Later models .... 3.00 litres (5.3 pints) approx

Oil filter	Champion C103

Oil pump:
- Tooth play (gear-to-gear) .... 0.1 to 0.2 mm (0.004 to 0.008 in)
- Clearance (outer gear-to-housing) .... 0.08 to 0.15 mm (0.0031 to 0.0059 in)

Oil type/specification	Multigrade engine oil, viscosity range SAE 10W/40 to 20W/50, to API SF/CC or better (Duckhams QXR, Hypergrade, or 10W/40 Motor Oil
Oil pressure at idle	Not lower than 0.3 bar (4.4 lbf/in^2)

Torque wrench settings (ohc engine)

	Nm	lbf ft
Cylinder head bolts:		
Stage 1 (cold)	25	18
Stage 2 (cold)	Through 60°	
Stage 3 (cold)	Through 60°	
Stage 4 (cold)	Through 30°	
Stage 5 (hot)	Through 30° to 50°	
Main bearing cap bolts	80	59
Big-end cap bolts	25	18

	Nm	lbf ft
Flywheel bolts	60	44
Oil pump bolts	6	4
Pressure regulator valve	30	22
Coolant pump bolts	8	6
Alternator bracket bolts	40	29
Oil pan screws	5	4
Camshaft sprocket bolt	45	33
Crankshaft pulley bolt	55	40
Starter motor bolts	25	18
Manifold nuts	20	15
Carburettor nuts	20	15
Spark plugs	20	15
Engine front stabiliser bracket bolts at crankcase	50	37
Engine front stabiliser at damper pad	40	29
Oil pressure switch	30	22
Coolant temperature sensor	10	7
Oil drain plug	45	33

PART A : OHV ENGINE

For modifications, and information applicable to later models, see Supplement at end of manual

1 Description

The 1196 cc engine is of four-cylinder overhead valve type. It has been in use in previous ranges of rear wheel drive vehicles for a considerable time.

This slightly modified unit is now coupled to a transmission and fitted transversely to drive the front wheels through open driveshafts.

The engine is oversquare with four cylinders in-line, the overhead valves being operated via rocker arms, short pushrods and tappets. The camshaft is mounted high in the cylinder block and is chain-driven from the crankshaft sprocket. An automatic chain tensioner is fitted. The crankshaft is mounted on three main bearings and the centre main bearing shell is flanged. Various thicknesses of flange are available so that the correct crankshaft endfloat can be achieved. The pistons have a solid cutaway skirt and have three rings, two compression and one oil control. The gudgeon pin floats in the pistons and is an interference fit in the connecting rod.

The centrifugal coolant pump is belt-driven from a crankshaft pulley wheel. The distributor is mounted at the left-hand side of the engine and is advanced by centrifugal and vacuum means. There is no vernier control for the static ignition setting. The oil pump is of the gear type and is driven from the camshaft skew gear.

Certain engine bolts will require the use of special splined wrenches to unscrew their socket heads. The bolts concerned are fitted haphazardly and include those for the flywheel, thermostat housing and oil pump.

2 Operations possible without removing engine

The following operations may be carried out without having to remove the engine from the vehicle:

(a) *Adjustment of valve clearances*
(b) *Removal and refitting of cylinder head*
(c) *Removal and refitting of sump*
(d) *Removal and refitting of oil pump*
(e) *Removal and refitting of timing cover and chain*
(f) *Removal and refitting of pistons/connecting rods*
(g) *Removal and refitting of flywheel*
(h) *Removal of crankshaft rear oil seal*
(j) *Removal and refitting of ancillaries (coolant pump, fuel pump, manifolds, distributor, carburettor – refer to appropriate Chapters)*
(k) *Removal and refitting of mountings and brackets*

3 Valve clearances – adjustment

1 This should be carried out with the engine at normal operating temperature. If it is being done after overhaul when the engine is cold, repeat the adjustment after a few hundred miles have been covered

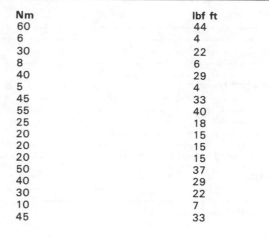

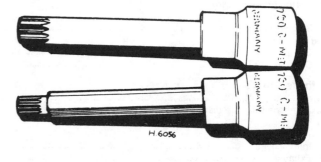

Fig. 1.1 Special splined socket wrenches (Sec 1)

when the engine is hot.

2 Turn the crankshaft by means of the pulley bolt until No 1 piston is at tdc on the firing stroke (the spark plug can be removed and a finger placed over the plug hole to detect the compression being generated). The ignition timing marks should be in alignment (refer to Chapter 4). Adjust in the following sequence:

Cylinder	Valves to adjust
1	1 (EX), 2 (IN)
2	3 (IN)
3	5 (EX)
Turn the crankshaft through one complete turn, then:	
4	7 (IN), 8 (EX)
3	6 (IN)
2	4 (EX)

3 Counting from the timing cover end of the engine, the sequence of valves is as follows:

1	Exhaust
2	Intake
3	Intake
4	Exhaust
5	Exhaust
6	Intake
7	Intake
8	Exhaust

4 As each clearance is being checked, slide the appropriate feeler blade between the end of the valve stem and the rocker. Adjust the clearance by turning the nut until the feeler blade is a stiff sliding fit (photo).

4 Cylinder head – removal and refitting

1 Make sure that the engine is cold before commencing operations, to avoid any chance of the head distorting.
2 Disconnect the battery negative lead.

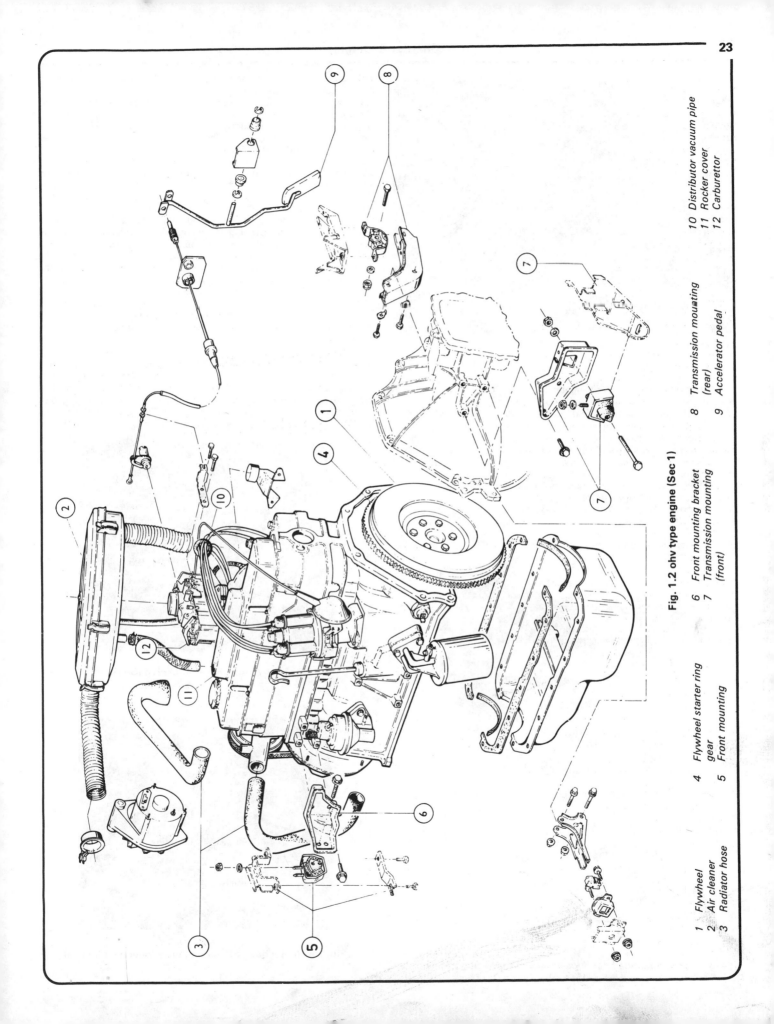

Fig. 1.2 ohv type engine (Sec 1)

1 Flywheel
2 Air cleaner
3 Radiator hose
4 Flywheel starter ring gear
5 Front mounting
6 Front mounting bracket
7 Transmission mounting (front)
8 Transmission mounting (rear)
9 Accelerator pedal
10 Distributor vacuum pipe
11 Rocker cover
12 Carburettor

3.4 Checking a valve clearance

3   Remove the air cleaner (Chapter 3).
4   Disconnect the exhaust pipe support bracket.
5   Unbolt the exhaust manifold from the cylinder head and tie it to one side of the engine compartment.
6   Unscrew the cylinder block drain plug and drain the coolant, retaining it for further use if required. Refit the drain plug.
7   Disconnect the control cables and electrical leads from the carburettor.
8   Unbolt and remove the carburettor from the intake manifold.
9   Unbolt and remove the intake manifold.
10   Disconnect the coolant and heater hoses from the thermostat housing and the coolant pump, also from the connector on the cylinder head.
11   Release the alternator adjuster link and mounting bolts, push the

alternator in towards the engine and slip the drivebelt from the pulleys.
12   Remove the rocker cover.
13   Unscrew the rocker arm nuts until the arms can be swivelled and the pushrods withdrawn. Do not allow the pushrods to slip out of your fingers when partially withdrawn or they may drop into the crankcase.
14   Unscrew the cylinder head bolts, working from the centre ones towards each end of the head (Fig. 1.5).
15   Lift the head from the block. If it is stuck, tap it gently with a plastic-faced hammer, or use a club hammer and a block of hardwood as an insulator.
16   Refer to Sections 23 and 24, for details of dismantling and decarbonising the cylinder head.
17   Clean the cylinder head and cylinder block surfaces, removing old gasket and carbon by scraping and a wire brush, preferably fitted in an electric drill. Take care to cover the coolant passages and other openings with masking tape or rag to prevent dirt and carbon falling in. Mop out oil from the bolt holes; hydraulic pressure could crack the block when the bolts are screwed in if oil is left in the holes.
18   When all is clean, screw two guide pins into the cylinder block. These can be made from two old cylinder head bolts by cutting off their heads and sawing a screwdriver slot in their ends.
19   Locate a new gasket over the guide pins so that the word 'OBEN' is uppermost (photos).
20   Lower the cylinder head carefully into position. Screw in the bolts finger tight, remove the guide pins and screw in the two remaining bolts (photo).
21   Tighten the cylinder head bolts in the order shown to the first stage specified torque. Now tighten the bolts in three further stages by turning them through 60° on each occasion. The handle of the wrench knuckle bar should provide sufficient indication of the required angle

Fig. 1.4 Cylinder block drain plug (Sec 4)

Fig. 1.3 Exhaust pipe support bracket (Sec 4)

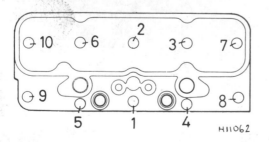

H11062

Fig. 1.5 Cylinder head bolt loosening and tightening sequence (Sec 4)

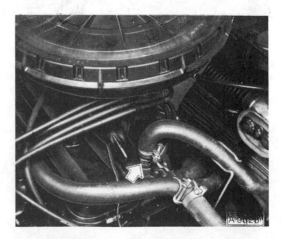

Fig. 1.6 Heater hose connection to cylinder head (Sec 4)

4.19A Cylinder head gasket and temporary guide studs

4.19B Cylinder head gasket top face marking

4.20 Lowering cylinder head into position

4.22 Installing a pushrod

4.24 Installing the exhaust manifold

5.6 Applying sealant to the sump gasket joints

as it is moved through a sixth of a turn. No further retightening will be required.

22 Refit the pushrods, making quite sure that each one is safely located in its cam follower before releasing your grip on it (photo).

23 Reposition the rocker arms over the ends of the pushrods and then adjust the valves clearances as described in Section 3.

24 Using a new gasket, bolt the exhaust manifold to the cylinder head. Tighten to the specified torque (photo).

25 Using a new gasket, bolt the intake manifold to the cylinder head. Tighten to the specified torque.

26 Using a new gasket, refit the rocker cover.

27 Refit the carburettor and the air cleaner and reconnect all the disconnected hoses, controls and wires.

28 Fit the alternator drivebelt and adjust (refer to Chapter 2).

29 Release the clip which secures the heater hose to its cylinder head adaptor and then fill the cooling system through the expansion tank. As soon as coolant is seen escaping from the loose cylinder hose, retighten the clip and fill the tank to the indicated level.

5 Sump – removal and refitting

1 Drain the engine oil, refit the drain plug and tighten securely.

2 Unbolt the engine support from the flywheel bellhousing and cylinder block.

3 Unbolt and remove the sump.

4 Thoroughly clean the mating flanges of the cylinder block and sump.

5 Before refitting, a thick bead of sealant should be squeezed onto the block flange and at the joints of the rear main bearing cap and the front main bearing cap.

6 Locate the cork gasket strips in position on the cylinder block surfaces and the bearing caps. Apply more sealant at the gasket joints (photo).

7 Offer up the sump and bolt it into position, tightening the bolts to the specified torque.

8 Refit the engine support.

9 Fill the engine with oil.

Fig. 1.7 Crankcase sealant application points (Sec 5)

6 Oil pump – removal and refitting

1 Remove the sump as described in the preceding Section.

2 Using a special splined tooth wrench, unscrew the oil pump mounting bolts (photo).

3 Withdraw the oil pump carefully downwards (photo).

4 Refitting is a reversal of removal. Tighten the oil pump mounting bolts to the specified torque.

7 Timing cover and chain – removal and refitting

1 Remove the alternator drivebelt.

6.2 Oil pump, showing socket-headed mounting bolts

6.3 Removing the oil pump

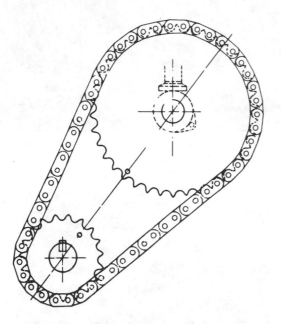

Fig. 1.8 Sprocket timing marks in alignment (Sec 7)

Fig. 1.9 Dished washer on front of crankshaft sprocket (Sec 7)

2   Remove the flywheel housing lower cover and jam the flywheel starter ring gear with a suitable tool.

3   Unscrew and remove the crankshaft pulley bolt and pull off the pulley.

4   Unscrew the timing cover bolts and remove the cover. Turn the crankshaft until the timing marks are in alignment and closest together (Fig. 1.8).

5   Clean away the gasket, not allowing pieces to fall inside the timing chain case.

6   Take the dished washer from the face of the crankshaft sprocket.

7   Unbolt and remove the chain tensioner.

8   Mark the front face of the timing chain if it is to be re-used, so that it can be refitted to run in its original direction of travel.

9   Pass a bar through one of the holes in the camshaft sprocket and unscrew and remove the sprocket bolts.

10 Pull off the sprocket complete with chain.

11 Renew the timing cover oil seal, using a piece of tubing as a removal and refitting tool. Fill the seal lips with grease and make sure that the seal is installed as shown in Fig. 1.10 (photo).

12 Commence reassembly by engaging the chain around the crankshaft sprocket.

13 Engage the camshaft sprocket within the loop of the chain so that it can be fitted to the camshaft and will have its timing mark in

alignment with the one on the crankshaft sprocket. Adjust the camshaft sprocket as necessary within the chain loop to achieve this. Hold the sprocket still and screw in and tighten the bolt with its washer (photo).

14 Refit the chain tensioner.

15 Locate the dished washer on the crankshaft sprocket.

16 Stick a new timing cover gasket onto the face of the cylinder block using a little grease and then fit the timing cover.

17 Insert the bolts only finger tight.

18 Push the crankshaft pulley into position so that it acts as a centralising tool to slightly displace the timing cover as necessary to provide perfect alignment (photo).

19 Pull off the pulley without disturbing the timing cover. Tighten the timing cover bolts evenly.

20 Fit the crankshaft pulley, screw in its bolt and tighten to the specified torque, again preventing the crankshaft from rotating by jamming the flywheel starter ring gear.

21 Refit the flywheel housing lower cover.

22 Fit and tighten the alternator drivebelt.

8   Pistons/connecting rods – removal and refitting

1   Remove the cylinfer head, the sump and the oil pump as described in earlier Sections.

2   The connecting rod big-end caps and rods may not be marked numerically for location when new and therefore they must be inspected for identification marks before dismantling. If no marks are evident, punch, scribe or file identification marks on the caps and rods

7.11 Timing cover oil seal

7.13 Method of tightening camshaft sprocket bolt

7.18 Fitting the crankshaft pulley

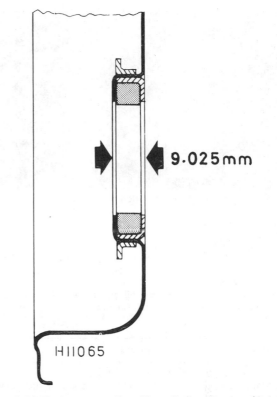

9·025mm

H11065

Fig. 1.10 Timing cover oil seal installation diagram (Sec 7)

starting with No 1 at the timing cover end. Mark them all on the same side to avoid confusion during reassembly. If they have already been marked then this will not of course be necessary.

3   Undo and remove the big-end cap retaining bolts and keep them in order for correct refitting.

4   Detach the big-end bearing caps. If they are stuck, lightly tap them free using a soft-faced mallet.

5   To remove the bearing shells for inspection and/or renewal, press the bearing end opposite the groove in both connecting rod and bearing cap and the shells will slide out. Again keep the shells in order of removal.

6   The piston and rod assemblies are removed through the top of each cylinder bore, being pushed upwards from underneath using a wooden hammer handle which is pushed against the connecting rod. Rotate the crankshaft accordingly to gain suitable access to each rod assembly. Note that if there is a pronounced wear ridge at the top of the cylinder bore, there is a risk of piston and ring damage unless the ridge is first removed using a suitable ridge reaming tool.

7   The pistons should not be separated from their connecting rods unless they or the gudgeon pins are to be renewed. The gudgeon pin is a press fit and special tools are required for removing and installation. This task should therefore be entrusted to your local agent or automotive machine shop.

8   If for any reason the pistons are separated from their rods, mark them numerically on the same side as the rod markings to ensure correct refitting.

9   Commence reassembly by laying the piston/connecting rod assemblies out in their correct order, complete with bearing shells, ready for refitting into their respective bores in the cylinder block. Remember that the connecting rods have been numbered to indicate to which cylinder they are to be fitted.

10   Clean the cylinder bores with a clean non-fluffy rag.

11   Apply some upper cylinder lubricant to the piston rings and then wrap the piston ring compressor around the first assembly to be fitted (photo).

12   Insert the connecting rod and piston into the top of the cylinder block and gently tap the piston through the ring compressor into the cylinder bore with a wooden or soft-headed mallet. Guide the big-end of the connecting rod near to its position on the crankshaft. Fit the bearing shells, cap and bolts (photos).

13   Repeat the sequence described for the remaining three

8.11 Piston ring compressor in position

8.12A Fitting a big-end cap with bearing shell

8.12B Tightening a big-end cap bolt

piston/connecting rod assemblies.
14 Check that the pistons and connecting rods have been fitted the correct way round in the cylinder block, the connecting rod/cap marking will indicate this.
15 Refit the cylinder head, the oil pump and the sump, all as described in earlier Sections of this Chapter.

9 Flywheel – removal and refitting

1 Refer to Chapter 5 and remove the clutch.
2 Mark the position of the flywheel in relation to the crankshaft mounting flange or pulley.
3 Remove the clutch release bearing and guide sleeve, again referring to Chapter 5.
4 Jam the flywheel starter ring gear and using the special splined tool, unscrew and remove the flywheel fixing bolts.
5 Remove the flywheel.
6 Refit by reversing the removal operations and tighten the bolts to the specified torque.

10 Crankshaft rear oil seal – renewal

1 Remove the clutch (Chapter 5).
2 Remove the flywheel as described in the preceding Section.
3 The oil seal can now be extracted using a suitably hooked tool or a small extractor with outward-facing claws, but take care not to damage the surface of the crankshaft flange or the pilot bearing.
4 Grease the lips of the new seal and insert it squarely. As there is very little space to tap the seal into position, it is better to use a bolt with a thick nut and a suitable piece of tubing inserted between the outer face of the seal and the clutch release bearing guide. If the nut is then unscrewed to effectively increase the length of the bolt, the seal will be pressed into its seat.
5 Refit the flywheel and clutch by reversing the removal operations.

11 Engine mountings and brackets – renewal

1 Provided the engine/transmission is adequately supported on jacks or a hoist, the individual mountings and their brackets may be unbolted and removed for renewal of their flexible components which will age and deform over a period of time (photos).

12 Engine – methods of removal

1 It is possible to remove the engine on its own or to remove it complete with gearbox and final drive.
2 It is much easier to remove the engine independently and this should be done if overhaul of the transmission is not required at the same time.
3 Both methods are described in the following Sections.

13 Engine – removal without transmission

1 Open the bonnet and prop it fully open, then disconnect the battery and raise and support the front of the vehicle.
2 Remove the air cleaner and the air ducting.
3 Drain the coolant (Chapter 2).
4 Disconnect the heater hoses from the coolant pump and cylinder head.
5 Disconnect the fuel hoses from the fuel pump.
6 Disconnect the control cables from the carburettor, also the fuel cut-off solenoid lead, the HT lead from the coil and the LT leads. Disconnect the leads from the temperature sender and oil pressure switch.
7 Remove the alternator and its drivebelt (Chapter 10).
8 Unscrew and remove the upper bolts from the flywheel housing.
9 Unbolt the engine support from the lower part of the flywheel housing.
10 Disconnect the electrical leads from the starter motor.
11 Unbolt the exhaust pipe from the manifold.
12 Disconnect the exhaust pipe clamp at the rear of the transmission mounting.
13 Withdraw the clutch splined shaft as described in Section 5 of Chapter 5.
14 Attach a hoist and slings to the engine and take its weight. Disconnect the engine front stabiliser from the cylinder block.
15 Separate the engine from the flywheel housing until the engine can be swivelled and lifted from the engine compartment. Take care not to damage the radiator as the engine is swivelled.

14 Engine – removal with transmission

1 This is very similar to the procedure described in Section 44 for the ohc engine.
2 Carry out the operations described in paragraphs 1 to 7 of Section 13.
3 Disconnect the leads from the starter motor.
4 Unbolt the exhaust downpipe from the manifold and disconnect the exhaust pipe clamp at the rear of the transmission mounting.
5 Refer to Section 44 and carry out the operations described in paragraphs 3 to 14 inclusive.

15 Engine dismantling – general

1 It is best to mount the engine on a dismantling stand, but if this is not available, stand the engine on a strong bench at a comfortable working height. Failing this, it will have to be stripped down on the floor.
2 During the dismantling process, the greatest care should be taken to keep the exposed parts free from dirt. As an aid to achieving this thoroughly clean down the outside of the engine, first removing all traces of oil and congealed dirt.
3 A good grease solvent will make the job much easier, for, after the solvent has been applied and allowed to stand for a time, a vigorous

11.1A Engine right-hand mounting to frame

11.1B Tightening a right-hand engine mounting bolt

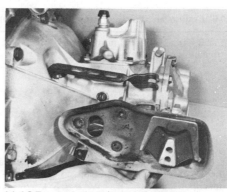

11.1C Transmission left-hand mounting

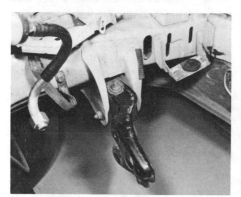

11.1D Transmission left-hand mounting to frame

11.1E Engine front stabiliser

11.1F Engine rear mounting

Fig. 1.11 Flywheel housing upper bolts (Sec 13)

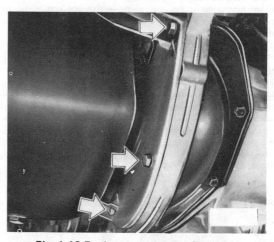

Fig. 1.12 Engine support bolts (Sec 13)

jet of water will wash off the solvent and grease with it. If the dirt is thick and deeply embedded, work the solvent into it with a strong stiff brush.

4   Finally, wipe down the exterior of the engine with a rag and only then, when it is quite clean, should the dismantling process begins. As the engine is stripped, clean each part in a bath of paraffin or petrol.

5   Never immerse parts with oilways in paraffin (eg crankshaft and camshaft). To clean these parts, wipe down carefully with a petrol-dampened rag. Oilways can be cleaned out with wire. If an air line is available, all parts can be blown dry and the oilways blown through as an added precaution.

6   Re-use of old gaskets is false economy. To avoid the possibility of trouble after the engine has been reassembled **always** use new gaskets throughout.

7   Do not throw away the old gaskets, for sometimes it happens that

an immediate replacement cannot be found and the old gasket is then very useful as a template. Hang up the gaskets as they are removed.

8   To strip the engine, it is best to work from the top down. When the stage is reached where the crankshaft must be removed, the engine can be turned on its side and all other work carried out with it in this position.

9   Wherever possible, refit nuts, bolts and washers finger tight from wherever they were removed. This helps to avoid loss and muddle. If they cannot be fitted then arrange them in a sequence that ensures correct reassembly.

10   Before dismantling begins it is important that special tools are obtained otherwise certain work cannot be carried out. The special socket adaptors for removing the cylinder head bolts and for the manifold, flywheel, and oil pump bolts, also a valve grinding tool and valve spring compressor, will be required.

16 Engine ancillary components – removal

1 Before basic engine dismantling begins it is necessary to remove ancillary components as follows:

    (a) *Alternator*
    (b) *Fuel pump*
    (c) *Thermostat*
    (d) *Inlet manifold and carburettor*
    (e) *Exhaust manifold*
    (f) *Distributor*
    (g) *Coolant pump*

2 Presuming the engine to be out of the car and on a bench, and that the items mentioned are still on the engine, follow the procedures described below.

3 Alternator: slacken the alternator retaining nuts and bolts; move the unit towards the cylinder block and then remove the drivebelt. Remove the nuts and bolts retaining the alternator to the mounting bracket and then lift the unit away. Remove the mounting bracket and store it with the alternator.

4 Fuel pump: two bolts secure the fuel pump to the engine block. Once the two have been removed, the pump together with the gasket and spacer can be removed. Remove the fuel line to the carburettor.

5 Thermostat: this item is located in the upper hose outlet from the water pump. Prise free the retaining ring and extract the thermostat from the housing.

6 Inlet/exhaust manifolds and carburettor: first remove the carburettor from the inlet manifold (and it must be done to gain access to a manifold retaining bolt within the inlet tract) (photo). Unscrew and remove the two retaining nuts, and lift the carburettor clear; note the rubber O-ring seal in the stepped flange of the manifold.

7 To remove the inlet and exhaust manifolds, you will need to use the special tool to unscrew the special bolts. (Note retaining bolt within the inlet manifold).

8 Distributor: before removing the distributor turn the engine to bring No 1 piston to tdc on the firing stroke and check the distributor timing as described in Chapter 4. Unscrew the retaining bolt and remove the distributor and flange clamp.

9 Coolant pump: unscrew and remove the coolant pump retaining bolts and remove the pump assembly. To unscrew all the bolts it will be necessary to first remove the pulley.

10 The engine is now ready for further dismantling of the sub-assemblies as required.

17 Engine – complete dismantling

1 With the engine removed from the vehicle and clean, dismantle by following the operations described in Sections 4 to 9 in that order.

16.6 Using special tool to install intake manifold centre bolt

2 Invert the engine. The three main bearing caps are all different so note their locations.

3 Unscrew the retaining bolts and remove the main bearing caps.

4 Lift the crankshaft from the crankcase.

5 If the bearing shells are to be used again, keep them identified in respect of their original cap or crankcase recess.

6 The camshaft and cam followers (tappets) are now the last components to be removed.

7 Again have the engine inverted to prevent the cam followers falling out when the camshaft is withdrawn.

8 Unbolt the camshaft retaining plate and withdraw the camshaft (photo).

9 Remove the cam followers and keep them in their originally fitted sequence. If difficulty is experienced in withdrawing the cam followers, a valve grinding suction tool will be useful.

18 Oil filter and bypass valves – removal and refitting

1 The engine oil filter on all models is located low down on the left-hand side of the cylinder block. It is therefore best removed from underneath.

2 It should normally only be necessary to renew the filter cartridge at the specified service intervals but if the vehicle is used in hot, dusty or other adverse conditions, it should be renewed at more frequent intervals.

3 Working from underneath, the filter should unscrew under hand pressure, providing that both the filter body and your hands are free from oil and grease. It often occurs that the filter has been over-tightened when fitted and is therefore reluctant to unscrew. This being the case you will need to use a strap wrench, or failing this, punch a hole through the filter on each side and insert a long-handled screwdriver through it to get extra leverage to initially break the seal grip. Be prepared for oil spillage if this last method is adopted.

4 Discard the oil filter on removal and wipe clean the mating surface of the block mounting flange.

5 A new sealing ring will be supplied with the new filter and this must be lubricated with clean engine oil before fitting.

6 Screw the new filter into position so that it is hand tightened only.

7 When the engine is started up again, check around the filter seal for signs of leakage.

Oil filter bypass valve

8 To inspect or renew the oil filter bypass valve, remove the filter element as given above.

9 Using a suitable drift, tap and tilt the valve retaining sleeve from its bore, but take care not to damage the filter body sealing face.

10 Wash out the bore with petrol and wipe dry.

11 Insert the replacement spring and ball (Fig. 1.14) and tap a new retaining sleeve into position, with the concave side downwards.

12 Fit the new oil filter element into position to complete.

17.8 Camshaft retaining plate

Fig. 1.13 Unscrewing the oil filter (Sec 18)

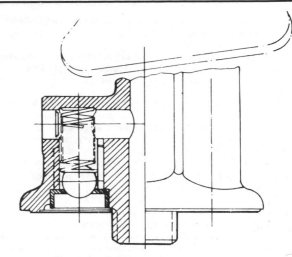

Fig. 1.14 Oil filter bypass valve (Sec 18)

19 Engine lubrication system – general description

The engine lubrication system is quite conventional (Fig. 1.15). A gear type oil pump draws oil up from the sump, via the suction pipe and strainer, and pumps the oil under pressure into the cartridge oil filter. From the oil filter the oil flows into galleries drilled in the engine block to feed the main bearings on the crankshaft and the moving components of the cylinder head. Oil is bled from the main bearing journals in the crankshaft to supply the big-end bearings.

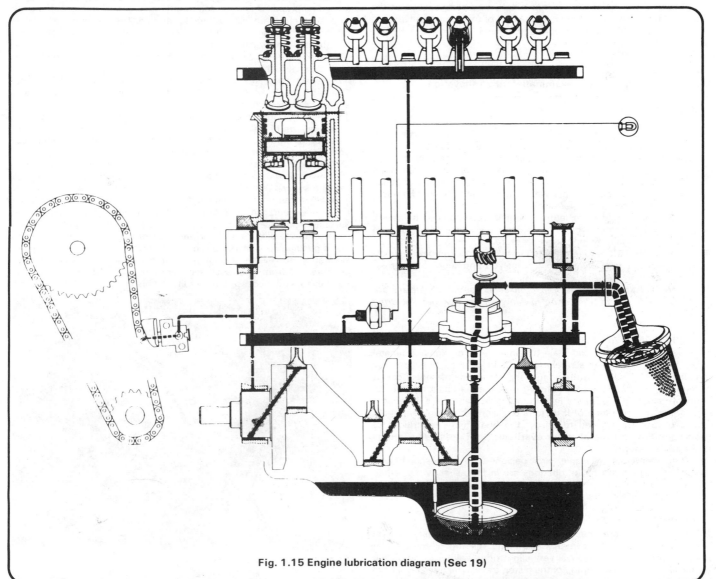

Fig. 1.15 Engine lubrication diagram (Sec 19)

Therefore, the bearings which receive pressure lubrication are the main crankshaft bearings, the big-end bearings, the camshaft bearings, and the rocker arms.

The remaining moving parts receive oil by splash or drip feed and these include the timing chain and associated items, the distributor and fuel pump drive, the tappets, the valve stems and to a certain extent the pistons.

The lubrication system incorporates two safeguards. The first is a pressure operated ball valve situated in the gallery between the oil pump and oil filter. This is in effect a filter bypass valve and allows oil to pass directly into the engine block gallery, downstream of the filter, when the filter is clogged up and resists the flow of oil.

The second system is an oil pressure relief valve, located in the oil pump casing, which controls the oil pressure to the specified maximum (see Section 22).

20 Engine examination and renovation – general

1   With the engine stripped and all parts thoroughly cleaned, every component should be examined for wear. The items listed in the Sections following should receive particular attention and where necessary be renewed or renovated.
2   So many measurements of engine components require accuracies down to tenths of a thousandth of an inch. It is advisable therefore to either check your micrometer against a standard gauge occasionally to ensure that the instrument zero is set corectly.
3   If in doubt as to whether or not a particular component must be renewed, take into account not only the cost of the component, but the time and effort which will be required to renew it if it subsequently fails at an early date.

21 Engine components – examination and renovation

Crankshaft

1   Examine the crankpin and main journal surfaces for signs of scoring or scratches, and check the ovality and taper of the crankpins and main journals. If the bearing surface dimensions do not fall within the tolerance ranges given in the Specifications at the beginning of this Chapter, the crankpins and/or main journals will have to be reground.
2   Big-end and crankpin wear is accompanied by distinct metallic knocking, particularly noticeable when the engine is pulling from low revs, and some loss of oil pressure.
3   Main bearing and main journal wear is accompanied by severe engine vibration rumble – getting progressively worse as engine revs increase – and again by loss of oil pressure.
4   If the crankshaft requires regrinding take it to an engine reconditioning specialist, who will machine it for you and supply the correct undersize bearing shells.
5   **Note:** *On some engines, the crankshaft journal diameters are machined undersize in production to allow for greater manufacturing tolerances.*

Big-end and main bearing shells

6   Inspect the big-end and main bearing shells for signs of general wear, scoring, pitting and scratches. The bearings should be matt grey in colour. With lead-indium bearings, should a trace of copper colour be noticed, the bearings are badly worn as the lead bearing material has worn away to expose the indium underlay. Renew the bearings if they are in this condition or if there is any signs of scoring or pitting. **You are strongly advised to renew the bearings – regardless of their condition at time of major overhaul. Refitting used bearings is a false economy.**
7   The undersizes available are designed to correspond with crankshaft regrind sizes. The bearings are in fact, slightly more than the stated undersize as running clearances have been allowed for during their manufacture.

Cylinder bores

8   The cylinder bores must be examined for taper, ovality, scoring and scratches. Start by carefully examining the top of the cylinder bores. If they are at all worn a very slight ridge will be found on the thrust side. This marks the top of the piston travel. The owner will have a good indication of the bore wear prior to dismantling the engine, or

removing the cylinder head. Excessive oil consumption accompanied by blue smoke from the exhaust is a sure sign of worn cylinder bores and piston rings.
9   Measure the bore diameter across the block and just below any ridge. This can be done with an internal micrometer or a dial gauge. Compare this with the diameter of the bottom of the bore, which is not subject to wear. If no measuring instruments are available, use a piston from which the rings have been removed and measure the gap between it and the cylinder wall with a feeler gauge.
10 Refer to the Specifications. If the cylinder wear exceeds the permitted tolerances then the cylinders will need reboring. If the wear is marginal and within the tolerances given, new special piston rings can be fitted to offset the wear.
11 If the cylinders have already been bored out to their maximum it may be possible to have liners fitted. This situation will not often be encountered.

Connecting rods

12 Examine the mating faces of the big-end caps to see if they have ever been filed in a mistaken attempt to take up wear. If so, the offending rods must be renewed.
13 Check the alignment of the rods visually, and if all is not well, take the rods to your local agent for checking on a special jig.

Pistons and piston rings

14 If the pistons and/or rings are to be re-used, remove the rings from the pistons. Three strips of tin or 0.015 in (0.38 mm) feeler gauges should be prepared and the top ring then sprung open just sufficiently to allow them to be slipped behind the ring. The ring can then be slid off the piston upwards without scoring or scratching the piston lands.
15 Repeat the process for the second and third rings.
16 Mark the rings or keep them in order so they may be refitted in their original location.
17 Inspect the pistons to ensure that they are suitable for re-use. Check for cracks, damage to the piston ring grooves and lands, and scores or signs of picking-up on the piston walls.
18 Clean the ring grooves using a piece of old piston ring ground to a suitable width and scrape the deposits out of the grooves, taking care not to remove any metal or score the piston lands (photo). Protect your fingers – piston rings are sharp!
19 Check the rings in their respective bores. Press the ring down to the unworn lower section of the bore (use a piston to do this, and keep the ring square in the bore). Measure the ring end gap and check that it is within the tolerance allowed (see Specifications). Also check the ring's side clearance in its groove. If these measurements exceed the specified tolerances the rings will have to be renewed, and if the ring grooves in the pistons are worn new pistons may be needed.
20 If genuine spares are used new pistons and rings are not supplied separately; however if the pistons are in good condition, new rings can be obtained from specialist suppliers who will also undertake any machining work necessary to modify the pistons to suit the new rings.

21.18 Cleaning a piston ring groove

21 If new rings (or pistons and rings) are to be fitted to an existing bore the top ring must be stepped to clear the wear ridge at the top of the bore, or the bore must be de-ridged.

22 Check the clearance and end gap of any new rings as described in paragraph 19. If a ring is slightly tight in its groove it may be rubbed down using an oilstone or a sheet of carborundum paper laid on a sheet of glass. If the end gap is inadequate the ring can be carefully ground until the specified clearance is achieved.

23 If new pistons are to be installed they will be selected from the grades available (see Specifications), after measuring the bores as described in paragraph 9. Normally the appropriate oversize pistons are supplied by the repairer when the block is rebored.

24 Removing and refitting pistons on the connecting rod is a job for your dealer or specialist repairer. Press equipment and a means of accurately heating the connecting rod will be required for removal and insertion of the gudgeon pin.

Camshaft and bearings

25 With the camshaft removed, examine the bearings for signs of obvious wear and pitting. If there are signs, then the three bearings will need renewal. This is not a common requirement and to have to do so is indicative of severe engine neglect at some time. As special tools are necessary to do this work properly, it is recommended that is is done by your dealer. Check that the bearings are located properly so that the oilways from the bearing housings are not obstructed.

26 The camshaft itself should show no marks on either the bearing journals or the profiles. If it does, it should be renewed.

27 Examine the skew gear for signs of wear or damage. If this is badly worn it will mean renewing the camshaft.

28 The thrust plate (which also acts as the locating plate) should not be ridged or worn in any way. If it is, renew it.

Timing chain, sprockets and tensioner

29 Examine the teeth of both sprockets for wear. Each tooth is the shape of an inverted V and if the driving (or driven) side is concave in shape, the tooth is worn and the sprocket should be renewed. The chain should also be renewed if the sprocket teeth are worn. It is sensible practice to renew the chain anyway.

30 Inspect the chain tensioner, which is automatic in operation. The most important item to check is the shoe which wears against the chain. If it is obviously worn, scratched or damaged in any way, then it must be renewed. Check the grooved piston and spring for signs of wear and renew the unit if generally worn or defective, or when a new chain is being fitted.

Valve rocker arms, pushrods and cam followers

31 Each rocker arm has three wearing surfaces, namely the pushrod recess, the valve stem contact, and the centre pivot recess. If any of these surfaces appears severely grooved or worn the arm should be renewed. If only the valve stem contact area is worn it is possible to clean it up with a fine file.

32 If the rocker ball is pitted, or has flats worn in it, this should also be renewed.

33 The nut on the rocker stud is a self-locking type. If it has been removed or adjusted many times, the self-locking ring may have become ineffective and the nut may be slack enough to turn involuntarily and alter the tappet clearance.

34 The rocker studs should be examined to ensure that the threads are undamaged and that the oil delivery hole in the side of the stud at the base of the thread is clear. Place a straight edge along the top of all the studs to ensure that none is standing higher than the rest. If any are, it means that they have pulled out of the head some distance. They should be removed and replaced with an oversize stud. As this involves reaming out the stud hole to an exact size to provide an interference fit for the replacement stud, you should seek professional advice and assistance to ensure that the new oversize stud is securely fitted at the correct angle.

35 Any pushrods which are bent should be renewed. On no account attempt to straighten them. They are easily checked by rolling over a perfectly flat surface such as a sheet of glass. The radial run-out should not exceed 0.007 in (0.2 mm).

36 Examine the bearing surfaces of the cam followers (tappets) which lie on the camshaft. Any indentation in these surfaces or any cracks indicate serious wear and the tappets should be renewed. Thoroughly clean them out, removing all traces of sludge. It is most unlikely that the sides of the tappets will prove worn but, if they are a very loose fit in their bores and can readily be rocked, they should be exchanged for new ones. It is very unusual to find any wear in the tappets, and any wear present is likely to occur only at very high mileages, or in cases of neglect. If the tappets are worn, examine the camshaft carefully as well.

Flywheel

37 If the teeth on the flywheel starter ring are badly worn, or if some are missing, then it will be necessary to remove the ring and fit a new one.

38 Either split the ring with a cold chisel after making a cut with a hacksaw blade between two teeth, or use a soft-headed hammer (not steel) to knock the ring off, striking it evenly and alternately, at equally spaced points. Take great care not to damage the flywheel during this process, and protect your eyes from flying fragments.

39 Clean and polish with emery cloth four evenly spaced areas on the outside face of the new starter ring.

40 Heat the ring evenly with a flame until the polished portions turn dark blue. Alternatively heat the ring in a bath of oil to a temperature of 350°C. (If a naked flame is used take careful fire precautions.) Hold the ring at this temperature for five minutes and then quickly fit it to the flywheel so the chamfered portion of the teeth faces the gearbox side of the flywheel. Wipe all oil off the ring before fitting it.

41 The ring should be tapped gently down onto its register and left to cool naturally when the contraction of the metal on cooling will ensure that it is a secure and permanent fit. Great care must be taken not to overheat the ring, indicated by it turning light metallic blue, as if this happens the temper of the ring will be lost.

42 If the driven plate contact surface of the flywheel is scored or on close inspection shows evidence of small hair cracks, caused by overheating, it may be possible to have the flywheel surface ground provided the overall thickness of the flywheel is not reduced too much. Consult your specialist engine repairer and if it is not possible, renew the flywheel complete.

43 If the needle bearing in the centre of the crankshaft flange is worn, fill it with grease and tap in a close-fitting rod. Hydraulic pressure will remove it. Tap the new bearing into position and apply a little grease.

22 Oil pump – overhaul

1 The oil pump must be carefully inspected for any signs of damage and/or excessive wear. The pump must be clean and dry when checking.

2 Commence by checking for slackness in the spindle bushes.

3 Check the two gears (impellers) and the inside of the pump body for wear using a feeler gauge. Measure:

(a) The gear backlash with the feeler gauge blade inserted between the sides of the gearteeth in mesh. This must be within 0.004 to 0.007 in (0.10 to 0.20 mm)

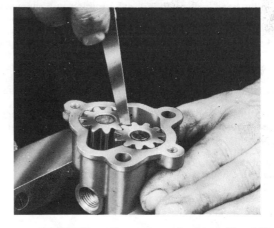

Fig. 1.16 Checking oil pump gear backlash (Sec 22)

22.3 Checking oil pump gear endfloat

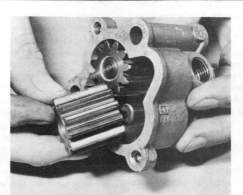

22.5 Reassembling the oil pump

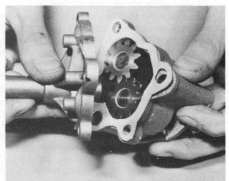

22.6 Reassembling the oil pump body sections

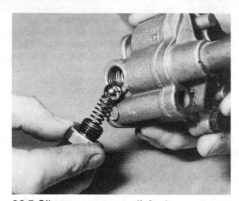

22.7 Oil pump pressure relief valve

23.12 Rocker arm stud showing oil hole

(b)   Check the gear endfloat by placing a straight-edge across the top of the pump chamber and measuring the clearance between the gears and the straight-edge (photo). The clearance should be within 0.001 to 0.004 in (0.04 to 0.10 mm)

4   Renew the pump if the above mentioned tolerances are exceeded.
5   When reassembling the pump (or fitting a new one), it must be well lubricated with clean engine oil (photo).
6   Always use a new gasket as shown (photo).
7   Ensure that the seating faces are clean and insert the pressure release ball, spring and nut, and tighten the retaining cap (photo).

23 Cylinder head – dismantling, examination and renovation

1   Unscrew the rocker arm retaining/adjustment nuts and withdraw the rocker arms from the studs. Keep them in order as they are removed.
2   To remove the valves the springs will have to be compressed to allow the split collets to be released from the groove in the upper section of the valve stems. A valve spring compressor will therefore be necessary.
3   Locate the compressor to enable the forked end of the arm to be positioned over the valve spring collar whilst the screw part of the clamp is situated squarely on the face of the valve.
4   Screw up the clamp to compress the spring and release the pressure of the collar acting on the collets. If the collar sticks, support the head and clamp frame and give the end of the clamp a light tap with a hammer to help release it.
5   Extract the two collets and then release the tension of the clamp. Remove the clamp, withdraw the collar and spring and extract the valve.
6   As they are released and removed, keep the valves in order so that if they are to be refitted they will be replaced in their original positions in the cylinder head. A piece of stiff card with eight holes punched in it is a sure method of keeping the valves in order.

7   Examine the head of the valves for pitting and burning, especially the heads of the exhaust valves. The valve seatings should be examined at the same time. If the pitting on valve and seat is very slight, the marks can be removed by grinding the seats and valves together with coarse, and then fine, valve grinding paste.
8   Where bad pitting has occurred to the valve seats it will be necessary to recut them and fit new valves. This latter job should be entrusted to the local agent or engineering works. In practice it is very seldom that the seats are so badly worn. Normally it is the valve that is too badly worn for refitting, and the owner can easily purchase a new set of valves and match them to the seats by valve grinding.
9   Valve grinding is carried out as follows. Smear a trace of coarse carborundum paste on the seat face and apply a suction grinder tool to the valve head. With a semi-rotary motion, grind the valve head to its seat, lifting the valve occasionally to redistribute the grinding paste. When a dull matt even surface is produced on both the valve seat and the valve, wipe off the paste and repeat the process with fine carborundum paste, lifting and turning the valve to redistribute the paste as before. A light spring placed under the valve head will greatly ease this operation. When a smooth unbroken ring of light grey matt finish is produced, on both valve and valve seat faces, the grinding operation is complete.
10 Scrape away all carbon from the valve head and the valve stem. Carefully clean away every trace of grinding compound, take great care to leave none in the ports or in the valve guides. Clean the valves and valve seats with a paraffin soaked rag, then with a clean rag, and finally, if an air line is available, blow the valves, valve guides and valve ports clean.
11 Check that all valve springs are intact. If any one is broken, all should be renewed. Check the free height of the springs against new ones. If some springs are not within specification, replace them all. Springs suffer from fatigue and it is a good idea to renew them even if they look serviceable.
12 Check that the oil supply holes in the rocker arm studs are clear (photo).
13 The cylinder head can be checked for warping either by placing it on a piece of plate glass or using a straight-edge and feeler blades.

Slight distortion may be corrected by having the head machined to remove metal from the mating face.

14 The renewal of worn valve guides and seats should be left to your dealer.

24 Cylinder head and pistons – decarbonising

1   This can be carried out with the engine either in or out of the car. With the cylinder head removed, carefully use a wire brush and blunt scraper to clean all traces of carbon deposits from the combustion spaces and the ports. The valve head stems and valve guides should also be freed from any carbon deposits. Wash the combustion spaces and ports down with petrol and scrape the cylinder head surface free of any foreign matter with the side of a steel rule, or a similar article.

2   If the engine is installed in the car, clean the pistons and the top of the cylinder bores. If the pistons are still in the block, then it is essential that great care is taken to ensure that no carbon gets into the cylinder bores as this could scratch the cylinder walls or cause damage to the piston and rings. To ensure this does not happen, first turn the crankshaft so that two of the pistons are at the top of their bores. Stuff rag into the other two bores or seal them off with paper and masking tape. The waterways should also be covered with small pieces of masking tape to prevent particles of carbon entering the cooling system and damaging the water pump.

3   Press a little grease into the gap between the cylinder walls and the two pistons which are to be worked on. With a blunt scraper carefully scrape away the carbon from the piston crown, taking great care not to scratch the aluminium. Also scrape away the carbon from the surrounding lip of the cylinder wall. When all carbon has been removed, scrape away the grease which will now be contaminated with carbon particles, taking care not to press any into the bores. To assist prevention of carbon build-up the piston crown can be polished with a metal polish. Remove the rags or masking tape from the other two cylinders and turn the crankshaft so that the two pistons which were at the bottom are now at the top. Place rag or masking tape in the cylinders which have been decarbonised and proceed as just described. Decarbonising is now complete.

25 Engine reassembly – general

1   To ensure maximum life with minimum trouble from a rebuilt engine, not only must everything be correctly assembled, but everything must be spotlessly clean, all the oilways must be clear, locking washers and spring washers must always be fitted where indicated and all bearing and other working surfaces must be thoroughly lubricated during assembly.

2   Before assembly begins renew any bolts or studs, the threads of which are in any way damaged, and whenever possible use new spring washers.

3   Apart from your normal tools, a supply of clean rag, an oil can filled with engine oil (an empty plastic detergent bottle thoroughly cleaned and washed out, will do just as well), a new supply of assorted spring washers, a set of new gaskets, and a torque wrench, should be collected together.

26 Engine – complete reassembly

Crankshaft and main bearings

1   Ensure that the crankcase and crankshaft are thoroughly clean and that all oilways are clear. If possible blow the drillings out with compressed air, and then inject clean engine oil through them to ensure they are clear.

2   Avoid using old bearing shells; wipe the shell seats in the crankcase clean and then fit the upper halves of the main bearing shells into their seats (photo).

3   Note that there is a tab on the back of each bearing which engages with a groove in the shell seating (in both crankcase and bearing cap).

4   Wipe away all traces of protective grease on the new shells.

5   The central bearing shell also takes up the crankshaft endfloat (photo). Note that the half-shells fitted to the cylinder block all have oil duct holes, while only the centre main bearing cap half-shell has an oil duct hole.

6   When the shells are fully located in the crankcase and bearing caps, lubricate them with clean engine oil.

7   Carefully install the crankshaft into position in the crankcase and to ensure correct seating lightly tap the crankshaft webs as shown (photos).

8   Lubricate the crankshaft main bearing journals and then refit the centre main bearing cap. Tighten the retaining bolts to the specified torque wrench setting (photo).

9   Locate the new oil seal onto the rear end of the crankshaft and apply sealant to the block mating flange (photo).

10 Fit the rear main bearing cap and tighten the retaining bolts to the specified torque.

11 Fit the front main bearing cap but before fitting the retaining bolts, smear them with sealant, and then tighten to the specified torque wrench setting (photos). Check that the bearing cap is exactly flush with the end face of the crankcase as it is tightened.

12 Now rotate the crankshaft and check that it turns freely, and shows no signs of binding or tight spots. Check that the crankshaft endfloat is within the limits specified using a feeler gauge as shown (photo). Alternative centre bearing shells are available if necessary to adjust the endfloat.

Piston rings, pistons and connecting rods

13 Check that the piston ring grooves are thoroughly clean. Always move the rings into position from the top of the piston.

14 The easiest method of fitting piston rings is to use 0.015 inch (0.38 mm) feeler gauges (or similar) around the top of the piston and move the rings into position over the feelers. This sequence is a reversal of the removal procedure detailed in Section 21 of this Chapter.

15 Follow the manufacturer's instructions carefully when fitting rings to ensure that they are correctly fitted. Several variations of compression and oil control rings are available and it is of the utmost importance that they be located correctly in their grooves.

16 When the rings are in position check that the compression rings are free to expand and contract in their grooves. Certain types of multi segment oil control rings are a light interference fit in their grooves and this may not therefore apply to them. When all the rings are in position

26.2 Crankcase main bearing shell

26.5 Centre main bearing shell with thrust flanges

26.7A Installing the crankshaft

26.7B Seating the crankshaft

26.8 Fitting centre main bearing cap

26.9 Crankshaft rear oil seal showing (arrowed) sealant application points

26.11A Crankshaft front main bearing cap correctly located

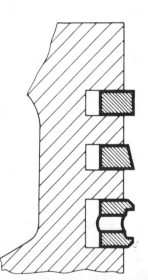

26.11B Tightening a main bearing cap bolt

26.12 Checking crankshaft endfloat

Fig. 1.17 Piston ring fitting diagram (Sec 26)

on the pistons move them around to bring each end gap to be some 120° away from the one on the adjacent ring. This rule applies to the individual rings that comprise the oil control ring where applicable depending on the type fitted.

17 Lay the piston/connecting rod assemblies out in their correct order ready for refitting into thier respective bores in the cylinder block. Remember that the connecting rods have been numbered to indicate to which cylinder they are to be fitted.

18 Clean the cylinder bores with a clean non-fluffy rag.

19 Apply some upper cylinder lubricant to the piston rings and then wrap the piston ring compressor around the first assembly to be fitted.

20 Insert the connecting rod and piston into the top of the cylinder block and gently tap the piston through the ring compressor into the cylinder bore with a wooden or soft-headed mallet. Guide the big-end of the connecting rod near to its position on the crankshaft.

21 Repeat the sequence described for the remaining three piston/connecting rod assemblies.

22 Check that the pistons and connecting rods have been fitted the correct way round in the cylinder block, the connecting rod/cap marking will indicate this.

23 Wipe the shell seat in the big-end of the connecting rod clean, and the underside of the new shell bearing. Fit the shell in position in the connecting rod with its locating tongue engaged with the appropriate groove in the big-end.

24 Generously lubricate the crankpin journals with engine oil and turn the crankshaft so that it is in its most advantageous position for the rod to be drawn onto it.

25 Wipe the bearing shell seat in the bearing cap clean, and then the underside of the new shell. Fit the shell into the cap, engaging the shell tongue with the groove in the cap.

26 Draw the big-end of the connecting rod onto the crankpin and then fit the cap into position. Make sure it is the correct way round, and then insert the two retaining bolts.

27 Tighten the big-end bolts a little at first, and do not tighten fully to the specified torque until all the piston/connecting rod assemblies have been fitted and the rotational freedom of the crankshaft checked.

Camshaft and cam followers

28 Lubricate the respective cam followers and insert them into their positions in the inverted crankcase (photo).

29 Before inserting the camshaft, smear the bearing surfaces and cam lobes with a little coating of molybdenum disulphide grease.

30 Carefully reinstall the camshaft into position and check that it rotates freely (photo).

31 Place the new gasket into position on the front end of the crankcase, smearing evenly and liberally with a suitable sealant on both sides (photo).

32 Locate the front engine plate with the patterned face to the front.

33 Now position the camshaft retaining plate with its forks located

26.28 Cam followers (tappets) in position

26.30 Installing the camshaft

26.31 Engine front plate and gasket

into the groove in the boss in the end of the crankshaft. The fork section faces upwards and the retaining plate is secured with two bolts.

34 Check again that the camshaft can rotate freely.

Oil pump and sump

35 Smear the oil pump gasket with medium grease and place it in position.

36 Refit the oil pump and secure with bolts tightened to the specified torque using the special socket adaptor.

37 Apply a layer of suitable sealant to the corners of the front and rear main bearing caps where they meet the bottom surface of the crankcase.

38 Insert the strip seals into the grooves of the main bearing caps and simultaneously smear their mating corners with sealant (longer strip at front).

39 Smear the sump gaskets on one face with grease and locate on each side of the crankcase.

40 Carefully fit the sump into position and secure with retaining bolts and flat washers. Tighten the bolts to the specified torque and remember that the two rear bolts each side of the rear main bearing have the larger diameter washers fitted. Tighten the bolts in a progressive sequence to prevent distortion.

Flywheel and clutch

41 Offer up the flywheel to the rear flange of the crankshaft, aligning the marks made at dismantling.

42 Insert the special bolts to secure and tighten to the specified torque (photo).

43 If the needle roller bearings on the end of the gearbox input shaft have been removed from the centre of the rear end of the crankshaft, they should now be refitted. Pack the rollers with grease and assemble them into the case before inserting the whole into the crankshaft.

44 The clutch unit can be reassembled to the flywheel as described in Chapter 5.

Timing chain, sprockets and tensioner

45 This section describes the replacement procedure as part of the general overhaul of the engine and assumes that the engine is removed from the car. If, however, the timing gear has been removed with the engine in the car, the following additional points should be noted when refitting the timing case. The front face of the engine and plate must be perfectly clean and all traces of old timing case gasket removed. The same applies to the sealant surface of the cover itself.

46 It is advisable to fit a new oil seal into the timing case, so first of all drive out the old one.

47 Place the new seal in position with the lip facing the inside of the cover.

48 Drive the seal home with a block of wood and a mallet to the correct depth (see Section 7).

49 Position the camshaft and crankshaft timing sprockets on their respective shafts and rotate so that the timing marks are in alignment (see Section 7).

50 Now withdraw the camshaft sprocket.

51 Locate the timing chain over the crankshaft sprocket without moving the sprocket. If the original chain is being refitted, check that the mark made before removal faces outwards.

52 Engage the camshaft sprocket into position in the chain and then with the timing marks in alignment refit the sprocket onto the camshaft.

53 Fit the camshaft sprocket retaining nut and washer and tighten to the specified torque. To prevent the sprocket from turning, insert a screwdriver shaft through a sprocket hole.

54 Position the chain tensioner on the front of the engine plate and tighten the bolts. Flex the chain to ensure the tensioner is operating correctly.

55 Locate the dished washer onto the crankshaft with the concave side to the front.

56 Smear some medium grease around the mating surface of the timing cover and then position the gasket against it.

57 Fit the timing cover to the front engine plate and locate with bolts, but do not fully tighten until the cover has been centralised by fitting the crankshaft pulley. When the cover is centralised, tighten the bolts to secure.

58 Insert the crankshaft pulley retaining bolt (with flat washer) and tighten to the specified torque.

Cylinder head

59 Ensure that all valves and springs are clean and free from carbon deposits and that the ports and valve guides in the cylinder head have no carbon dust or valve grinding paste left in them.

60 Starting at one end of the cylinder head take the appropriate valve, oil the stem and put it in the guide. Place the valve spring over the valve stem (photo).

61 Then place the cap over the spring with the recessed part inside the coil of the spring (photo).

62 Place the end of the spring compressor over the cap and valve stem and with the screw head of the compressor over the valve head screw up the clamp until the spring is compressed past the groove in the valve stem. Then put a little grease round the groove (photo).

63 Place the two halves of the split collar (collets) into the groove with the narrow ends pointing towards the spring. The grease will hold them in the groove (photo).

64 Release the clamp slowly and carefully, making sure that the collets are not dislodged from the groove. When the clamp is fully released the top edges of the collets should be in line with each other. Give the top of each spring a smart tap with a soft-faced mallet when assembly is complete to ensure that the collets are properly settled.

65 Refit the cylinder head as described in Section 4.

66 The rocker gear can be refitted with the head either on or off the engine. The only part of the procedure to watch is that the rocker nuts must not be screwed down too far or it will not be possible to refit the pushrods.

67 First place the washer over the rocker stud and then the light spring, with the tapered narrow end down.

68 Next put the rocker arm over the stud followed by the pivot ball (photo). Make sure that the spring fits snugly round the rocker arm centre section and that the two bearing surfaces of the interior of the arm and the ball face, are clean and lubricated with engine oil.

69 Oil the stud thread with SAE 90 oil and fit the nut with the self-locking collar uppermost (photo). Screw it down until the locking collar is on the stud.

70 Refit the pushrods through the head in the holes in line with each valve and rocker stud. It is easy to drop the pushrods inadvertently and

26.42 Tightening the flywheel bolts

26.60 Inserting a valve

26.61 Fitting a valve spring and cap

26.62 Using a valve spring compressor

26.63 Valve spring compressed and collets located

26.68 Fitting rocker arm pivot ball

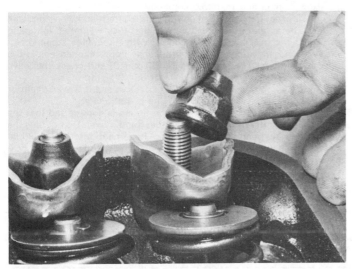

26.69 Fitting rocker arm nut

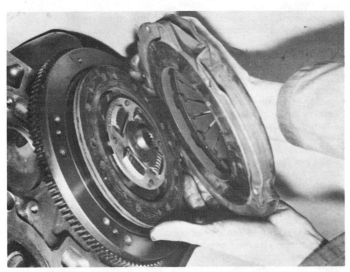

27.2 Assembling clutch to flywheel

27.5 Clutch centralising tool in position as cover bolts are tightened

if they fall at an angle the lower end could get past the tappet and drop down into the crankcase. This would mean certain removal of the head and possible removal of the sump in order to retrieve it. It would be advisable therefore to push the top end through a small 'collar' of stiff cardboard or hold it in a bulldog clip so that it cannot drop through. When the lower end is felt to be firmly seated in the tappet recess the clip or collar may be removed.

71 Next screw down the stud nuts so that the top of the pushrod engages in the recess in the rocker arm and approximately $\frac{1}{8}$th inch of the stud protrudes above the top of each nut. It is as well to check the efficiency of the self-locking ring at this stage.

72 Adjust the valve clearances as described in Section 3.

Manifolds and ancillary components

73 Fit the intake and exhaust manifolds, using new gaskets and tightening bolts and nuts to the specified torque.

74 All the ancillary components should be on the engine where possible before the engine is replaced in the car, as it is generally more easily done at bench level. One possible exception is the carburettor which is somewhat vulnerable and could be damaged when replacing the engine.

75 Even though the valve clearances may not have been finally set, refit the rocker cover for protection. You need not fit the new gasket yet, as the cover will have to be removed once more for final adjustment when hot.

76 When installing the distributor refer to Chapter 4 to ensure correct timing adjustment is obtained.

27 Engine – installation without transmission

1 If the clutch has been disturbed, the friction disc (driven plate) must be centralised before the engine can be coupled to the transmission, otherwise the clutch splined driveshaft will not pass through the hub of the disc.

2 To do this, locate the friction disc against the flywheel so that the greater projecting hub of the disc is away from the flywheel (photo).

3 Bolt on the cover, aligning the marks made before dismantling, but only screw in the bolts finger tight.

4 An alignment tool will now be required to pass through the hub of the friction disc and to engage in the bearing in the end of the crankshaft in order to align the disc. A stepped rod, or one of the clutch alignment tools available at motor stores, should be used to do this.

5 When the disc is aligned, tighten the cover bolts to the specified torque and withdraw the tool (photo).

6 Lower the engine into the engine compartment at an angle so that it can be coupled to the flywheel housing.

7 Screw in the upper connecting bolts.

8 Reconnect the engine front stabiliser and mounting on the right-hand side of the engine compartment and then remove the engine lifting gear.

9 Bolt the exhaust pipe to the manifold.

10 Bolt on the exhaust pipe clamp.

11 Connect the leads to the starter motor.

12 Fit the alternator (if not previously fitted) and connect the electrical leads.

13 Reconnect the clutch driveshaft as described in Chapter 5, having smeared the shaft splines with a little grease.

14 Reconnect the heater coolant hoses.

15 Reconnect all electrical leads, and the control cables to the carburettor.

16 Reconnect the radiator coolant hoses, then fill and bleed the cooling system as described in Chapter 2.

17 Connect the ignition HT and LT leads.

18 Connect the fuel hose to the fuel pump.

19 Connect the engine support to the lower part of the engine.

20 Fit the air cleaner.

21 Reconnect the battery.

22 Fill the engine with the correct grade and quantity of oil.

28 Engine – installation with transmission

The procedure is similar to that described in Section 59, to which reference should be made.

29 Engine – initial start-up after overhaul

1   Make sure the battery is fully charged and that all lubricants, coolant and fuel are replenished.
2   If the fuel system has been dismantled it will require several revolutions of the engine on the starter motor to pump the petrol up to the carburettor.
3   As soon as the engine fires and runs, keep it going at a fast tickover only (no faster), and bring it up to the normal working temperature.
4   As the engine warms up there will be odd smells and some smoke from parts getting hot and burning off oil deposits. The signs to look for are leaks of water or oil which will be obvious if serious. Check also the exhaust pipe and manifold connections, as these do not always 'find' their exact gastight position until the warmth and vibration have acted on them, and it is almost certain that they will need tightening further. This should be done, of course, with the engine stopped.
5   When normal running temperature has been reached adjust the engine idling speed, as described in Chapter 3, and check the valve clearances as described in Section 3 of this Chapter.
6   Stop the engine and wait a few minutes to see if any lubricant or coolant is dripping out when the engine is stationary.
7   Road test the car to check that the timing is correct and that the engine is giving the necessary smoothness and power. Do not race the engine – if new bearings and/or pistons have been fitted it should be treated as a new engine and run in at a reduced speed for the first 500 miles (800 km).

30 Fault diagnosis – ohv engine

Symptom	Reason(s)
Engine fails to turn when starter control operated	
No current at starter motor	Flat or defective battery
	Loose battery leads
	Defective starter solenoid or switch or broken wiring
	Engine earth strap disconnected
Current at starter motor	Jammed starter motor drive pinion
	Defective starter motor
Engine turns but will not start	
No spark at spark plug	Ignition leads or distributor cap damp or wet
	Ignition leads to spark plugs loose
	Shorted or disconnected low tension leads
	Dirty, incorrectly set, or pitted contact breaker points
	Faulty condenser
	Defective ignition switch
	Ignition leads connected wrong way round
	Faulty coil
	Contact breaker point spring earthed or broken
No fuel at carburettor float chamber or at jets	No petrol in petrol tank
	Vapour lock in fuel line (in hot conditions or at high altitude)
	Blocked float chamber needle valve
	Fuel pump filter blocked
	Choked or blocked carburettor jets
	Faulty fuel pump
Engine stalls and will not restart	
Excess of petrol in cylinder or carburettor flooding	Too much choke allowing too rich a mixture to wet plugs
	Float damaged or leaking or needle not seating
	Float lever incorrectly adjusted
No spark at spark plug	Ignition failure – sudden
	Ignition failure – misfiring precedes total stoppage
	Ignition failure – in severe rain or after traversing water splash
No fuel at jets	No petrol in petrol tank
	Petrol tank breather choked
	Sudden obstruction in carburettor
	Water in fuel system
Engine misfires or idles unevenly	
Intermittent spark at spark plug	Ignition leads loose
	Battery leads loose on terminals
	Battery earth strap loose on body attachment point
	Engine earth lead loose
	Low tension leads on coil loose
	Low tension lead to distributor loose
	Dirty or incorrectly gapped plugs
	Dirty, incorrectly set, or pitted contact breaker points
	Tracking across inside of distributor cover
	Ignition too retarded
	Faulty coil

Symptom	Reason(s)
Fuel shortage at engine	Mixture too weak Air leak in carburettor Air leak at inlet manifold to cylinder head, or inlet manifold to carburettor
Lack of power and poor compression Mechanical wear	Burnt out valves Sticking or leaking valves Weak or broken valve springs Worn valve guides or stems Worn pistons and piston rings
Fuel/air mixture leaking from cylinder	Burnt out exhaust valves Sticking or leaking valves Worn valve guides and stems Weak or broken valve springs Blown cylinder head gasket (accompanied by increase in noise) Worn pistons and piston rings Worn or scored cylinder bores
Incorrect adjustments	Ignition timing wrongly set Contact breaker points incorrectly gapped Incorrect valve clearances Incorrectly set spark plugs Carburation too rich or too weak
Carburation and ignition faults	Dirty contact breaker points Fuel filter blocked Air filter blocked Distributor automatic advance and retard mechanisms not functioning correctly Faulty fuel pump giving top end fuel starvation
Excessive oil consumption	Excessively worn valve stems and valve guides Worn piston rings Worn pistons and cylinder bores Excessive piston ring gap allowing blow-by Piston oil return holes choked
Oil being lost due to leaks	Leaking oil filter gasket Leaking rocker cover gasket Leaking timing gear cover gasket Leaking sump gasket Loose sump plug
Unusual noises from engine Excessive clearances due to mechanical wear	Worn valve gear (noisy tapping from rocker box) Worn big-end bearing (regular heavy knocking) Worn timing chain and gears (rattling from front of engine) Worn main bearings (rumbling and vibration) Worn crankshaft (knocking, rumbling and vibration)
Pinking on acceleration	Fuel octane rating too low Ignition timing over-advanced Carbon build-up in cylinder head Valve timing incorrect (after rebuild) Mixture too weak Overheating

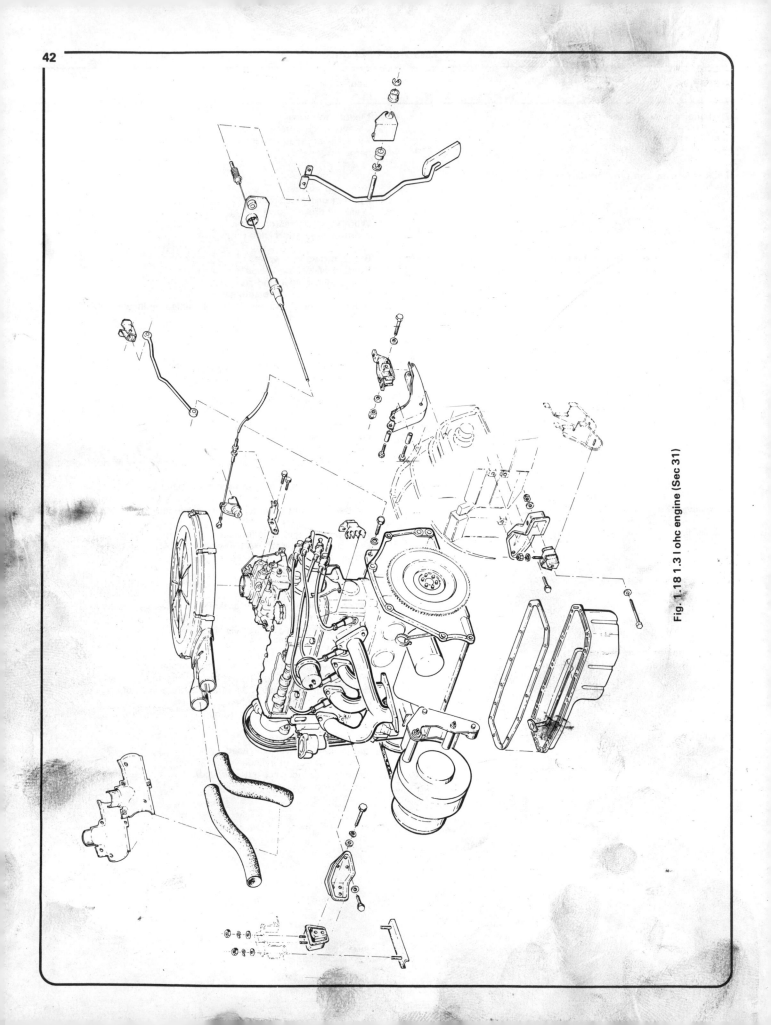

Fig. 1.18 1.3 l ohc engine (Sec 31)

PART B : OHC ENGINE

For modifications, and information applicable to later models, see Supplement at end of manual

31 Description

This engine is of four-cylinder type, with overhead camshaft driven by a toothed belt from a sprocket on the crankshaft.

The crankshaft runs in five main bearings and the camshaft runs in bearings machined directly in the cylinder head.

The cylinder head is of light alloy construction with crossflow design.

Valve adjustment is not required as the valve lifters are of hydraulic type.

32 Operations possible without removing engine

The following operations may be carried out without having to remove the engine from the vehicle.

(a) Removal and refitting of oil pressure regulator valve
(b) Renewal of camshaft toothed timing belt
(c) Removal and refitting of cylinder head
(d) Removal and refitting of sump
(e) Removal and refitting of oil pump
(f) Removal and refitting of pistons/connecting rods
(g) Removal and refitting of flywheel
(h) Renewal of crankshaft front oil seal
(j) Renewal of crankshaft rear oil seal
(k) Removal and refitting of ancillary components (coolant pump, fuel pump, manifolds, distributor, carburettor – refer to appropriate Chapters)

33 Oil pressure regulator valve – removal and refitting

1 From just to the rear of the crankshaft pulley, unscrew the pressure regulator valve plug and extract the spring and plunger.
2 Renew the spring if it is distorted or weak (compare it with a new one if possible).
3 If the plunger is scored, renew it.
4 Clean out the plunger hole and reassemble using a new plug sealing washer.

34 Camshaft toothed belt – renewal

1 Unscrew and remove the belt cover.
2 Apply a spanner to the crankshaft pulley bolt and turn the crankshaft until No 1 piston is on the firing stroke. The BTDC notch on the pulley should be in alignment with the ignition timing pointer, but to ensure that it is No 1 piston that is on the firing stroke and not No 4, either remove the No 1 spark plug and feel the compression being generated as the crankshaft is turned, or remove the distributor cap and check that the rotor is in alignment with No 1 spark plug contact in the cap.
3 Release the alternator adjustment link and mounting bolts, push the alternator in towards the engine and slip the drivebelt from the pulleys.
4 Unscrew the crankshaft pulley bolt without disturbing the set position of the crankshaft. To prevent the crankshaft rotating as the bolt is unscrewed, either engage a gear and apply the handbrake fully, or remove the flywheel housing lower cover and jam the flywheel ring gear with a suitable tool. Withdraw the pulley from the crankshaft.
5 Drain the cooling system.
6 Release the coolant pump mounting bolts just enough to be able to swivel the pump and to release the tension of the toothed belt.
7 If the toothed belt is to be used again, note its running direction before removing it.
8 Take the belt off the sprockets and fit the new one without moving the set position of the camshaft or crankshaft.
9 Engage the new belt over the sprockets and apply some tension by moving the coolant pump (photos).
10 Refit the crankshaft pulley and then check that the pulley notch is still in alignment with the timing pointer and that the camshaft sprocket mark is aligned with the groove in the plate behind it. If not, release the belt tension and readjust the position of the sprockets as necessary (photos).

Fig. 1.19 Location of oil pressure regulator valve (Sec 33)

Fig. 1.20 Components of oil pressure regulator valve (Sec 33)

34.9A Engaging timing belt with sprockets

11 The belt tension should now be adjusted in the following way if the official tool (KM 420) is not available. Tighten the screws on the coolant pump (photo) and using moderate thumb pressure, at the mid-point of the longest run of the belt between the crankshaft and camshaft sprockets, deflect the belt towards the coolant pump sprocket. This deflection should be approximately $\frac{1}{4}$ in (6.35 mm). Adjust the tension as necessary by moving the coolant pump. If the belt is overtight, it will be heard to hum when the engine is running.
12 Refit the belt cover (photo) and the alternator drivebelt.

35 Cylinder head – removal and refitting

1 The cylinder head should only be removed from a cold engine.
2 Disconnect the battery.
3 Drain the coolant (Chapter 2) and retain it for further use if required.
4 Remove the air cleaner (Chapter 3).
5 Disconnect the fuel hoses from the fuel pump and plug their open ends.

34.9B Prising the coolant pump to tension the timing belt

Fig. 1.21 Crankshaft pulley notch and timing pointer (Sec 34)

34.10A Crankshaft pulley timing marks aligned

34.10B Camshaft timing marks (No 1 piston firing)

Fig. 1.22 Coolant pump mounting bolts (Sec 34)

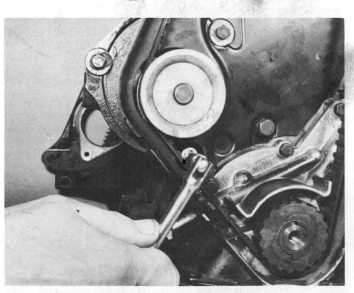

34.11 Tightening a coolant pump mounting screw

34.12 Fitting timing belt cover

35.7 Brake servo connection to intake manifold

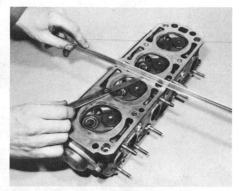

35.19A Checking cylinder head for distortion (transversely)

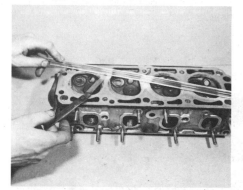

35.19B Checking cylinder head for distortion (lengthways)

35.22A Installing a hydraulic lifter

35.22B Fitting a thrust pad

Fig. 1.23 Cylinder head gasket correctly located. Arrow shows OBEN mark (Sec 35)

6 Disconnect the control cables and electrical leads from the carburettor.

7 Disconnect the heater hose and the vacuum pipe from the intake manifold (photo).

8 Disconnect the lead from the temperature sensor on the intake manifold.

9 Remove the cover from the camshaft belt and then set No 1 piston at tdc on the firing stroke as described in the preceding Section.

10 Remove the distributor (Chapter 4).

11 Remove the coolant pipe bracket from the intake manifold.

12 Remove the alternator drivebelt.

13 Unbolt the exhaust downpipe from the manifold. Unbolt and remove the camshaft cover.

14 Release the coolant pump bolts, move the pump to relieve the tension on the toothed belt and slip the belt from the sprockets.

15 Unscrew the cylinder head bolts and remove them. Work from the ends towards the centre, unscrewing them first by a quarter turn and then by half a turn.

16 Lift off the camshaft housing.

17 Lift off the cylinder head. If it is stuck, tap it gently with a plastic-faced hammer.

18 Peel away the cylinder head gasket and discard it.

19 Remove the rocker arms and thrust pads from the cylinder head. Withdraw the hydraulic valve lifters and immerse them in a container of clean engine oil to avoid any possibility of them draining. Keep all components in their original order. If full dismantling and valve grinding is to be carried out, refer to Section 23. Check the head for distortion (photos).

20 Clean the cylinder block and the cylinder head free from carbon and old pieces of gasket by careful scraping. Take care not to damage the cylinder head, which is made of light alloy and is easily scored. Cover the coolant passages and other openings with masking tape or rag to prevent dirt and carbon falling in. Mop out oil from the bolt holes; hydraulic pressure could crack the block when the bolts are screwed in if oil is left in the holes.

21 When all is clean, locate a new gasket on the block so that the word 'OBEN' can be read from above.

22 Refit the hydraulic lifters, thrust pads and rocker arms to the cylinder head in their original order (photos). If new hydraulic lifters are being used, initially immerse each one in a container of clean engine oil and compress it (by hand) several times to charge it.

23 With the mating surfaces scrupulously clean, locate the cylinder head on the block so that the positioning dowels engage in their holes (photo).

24 Apply jointing compound to the mating flanges of the cylinder head and the camshaft housing and refit the camshaft housing to the cylinder head (camshaft sprocket marks in alignment) (photo).

25 Screw in the cylinder head bolts and tighten first the centre bolts working outwards towards each end of the head. The tightening must be carried out in four stages as given in the Specifications (photo).

35.22C Fitting a rocker arm

35.23 Installing the cylinder head

35.24 Installing the camshaft housing

35.25 Tightening a cylinder head bolt

35.27 Fitting camshaft cover and gasket

35.31 Fitting throttle control cable clip

26 Fit and tension the toothed belt as described in Section 34, then refit the belt cover.
27 Fit the camshaft cover using a new gasket (photo).
28 Fit and tension the alternator drivebelt.
29 Reconnect the vacuum pipe and heater hose.
30 Refit the distributor and time the ignition (Chapter 4).
31 Fit the coolant pipe clamp to the intake manifold and connect the control cables and electrical leads to the carburettor (photo).
32 Reconnect the fuel pipes to the pump.
33 Connect the exhaust pipe to the manifold.
34 Connect the lead to the temperature sensor on the intake manifold (photo).
35 Fill the cooling system and bleed it as described in Chapter 2.
36 Start the engine and bring it to normal operating temperature, then tighten each cylinder head bolt by moving the wrench through an angle of between 30° and 50°. No further tightening will be required until the next overhaul.

36 Sump – removal and refitting

1 Unscrew the drain plug and allow the engine oil to drain from the sump into a container. Refit and tighten the drain plug.
2 Unbolt and remove the guard plate from the front end of the sump.
3 Disconnect the exhaust downpipes from the manifold and at the first coupling, and remove the front exhaust section from the vehicle.

4 Unscrew and remove the sump fixing bolts and lower the sump. Scrape off the old gasket and clean the mating surfaces.
5 To refit the sump, apply jointing compound to the seams in the crankcase jointing face and stick the gasket in position after having applied a thin film of compound to both sides of the gasket.
6 Offer up the sump and screw in the fixing bolts, which should have jointing compound applied to their threads (photos).
7 Refit the exhaust pipe, using a new gasket at the manifold/downpipe flange joint.
8 Fill the engine with oil.
9 Refit the guard plate.

37 Oil pump – removal and refitting

1 Remove the camshaft toothed belt as described in Section 34. Remove the belt cover backplate.
2 Using two screwdrivers as levers, prise off the belt sprocket from the front end of the crankshaft. Remove the Woodruff key.
3 Remove the sump as described in Section 36.
4 Remove the oil pump pick-up pipe and strainer (photos).
5 Unbolt the oil pump from the cylinder block and remove it.
6 Refer to Section 50 for details of oil pump overhaul.
7 Before refitting the oil pump, steps must be taken to protect the seal lips from damage or turning back on the shoulder at the front end of the crankshaft. To do this, grease the seal lips and then bind tape

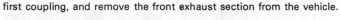

35.34 Temperature sender unit

Fig. 1.24 Oil drain plug (right) and guard plate bolts (Sec 36)

36.6A Sump pan and gasket

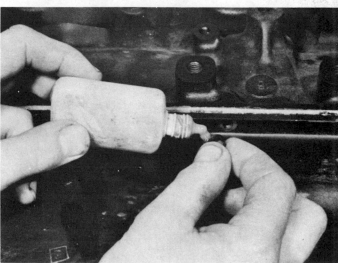

36.6B Applying thread locking compound to sump bolt

37.4A Oil pick-up pipe retaining clip

37.4B Removing oil pick-up pipe

37.7 Crankshaft shoulder taped

37.8 Oil pump installed

37.9 Fitting crankshaft belt sprocket

37.11A Fitting crankshaft pulley and bolt

around the crankshaft to form a gentle taper (photo). Locate a new gasket.

8 Refit the oil pump and unwind and remove the tape (photo).

9 Tighten the bolts to the specified torque and fit the belt sprocket (photo).

10 Refit the pick-up pipe and strainer, the sump and the timing belt as previously described.

11 Refit the crankshaft pulley and the drivebelt and fill the engine with oil (photos).

---

38 Pistons/connecting rods – removal and refitting

---

1 Remove the cylinder head (Section 35).

2 Remove the sump (Section 36).

3 Remove the oil pump pick-up pipe and filter screen.

4 Check that the rods and caps are marked with their position in the crankcase. If they are not, centre-punch them at adjacent points either side of the cap/rod joint. Note to which side of the engine the marks face.

5 Unscrew the big-end cap bolts from the first rod and remove the cap. If the bearing shells are to be used again, tape the cap and shell together.

6 Check the top of the cylinder bores for a wear ridge. If evident, carefully scrape it away with a ridge reaming tool, otherwise as the piston is pushed out of the block, the piston top ring may jam against it.

7 Place the wooden handle of a hammer against the bottom of the connecting rod and push the piston/rod assembly up and out of the cylinder bore (photo).

8 Remove the remaining three assemblies in a similar way. Rotate the crankshaft as necessary to bring the big-end bolts to the most accessible position.

9 If the piston must be separated from its rod, leave this job to your dealer as special tools and a press will be required.

10 Commence reassembly by laying the piston/connecting rod assemblies out in their correct order, complete with bearing shells, ready for refitting into their respective bores in the cylinder block (photo).

11 Wipe out the bores and oil them. Oil the piston rings liberally.

12 Fit a piston ring compressor to the first assembly to be installed.

13 Insert the rod and piston into the top of the bore so that the base of the compressor stands on the block. Check that the rod markings are towards the side of the engine as noted before dismantling. This is very important as the piston crowns do not have front directional marks.

14 Apply the wooden handle of a hammer to the piston crown and tap the assembly into the bore, at the same time releasing the compressor (photo).

15 Guide the big-end of the connecting rod near to the crankpin. Fit and oil the bearing shells, then fit the cap and bolts (photos).

37.11B Tightening the crankshaft pulley bolt

Fig. 1.25 Big-end rod and cap markings (Sec 38)

38.7 Removing a piston/connecting rod

38.10 Piston/connecting rod components

38.14 Installing a piston/connecting rod

38.15A Oiling the big-end crankpins

38.15B Fitting a big-end cap

38.16 Tightening a big-end cap bolt

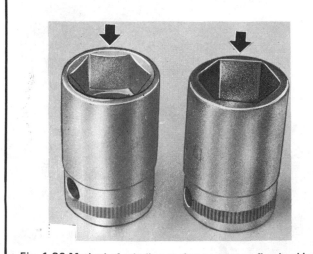

Fig. 1.26 Method of grinding socket to remove flywheel bolts
(Sec 39)

Fig. 1.27 Extracting crankshaft front oil seal (Sec 40)

16 Tighten the bolts to the specified torque (photo).
17 Repeat the operations on the other pistons/rods.
18 Refit the cylinder head, the pick-up pipe and filter and the sump, all as described in earlier Sections of this Chapter.

39 Flywheel – removal and refitting

1 Refer to Chapter 5 and remove the clutch.
2 Mark the position of the flywheel in relation to the crankshaft mounting flange or the drivebelt pulley.
3 Remove the clutch release bearing and guide sleeve, again referring to Chapter 5.
4 Jam the flywheel starter ring gear and using a ring spanner or socket, unscrew the bolts from the flywheel. As the heads of these bolts are very shallow, if a chamfered type of socket is being used, it is best to grind it flat to ensure more positive engagement (Fig. 1.26).
5 Remove the flywheel.
6 Refit by reversing the removal operations, but apply thread locking compound to the bolts.

40 Crankshaft front oil seal – renewal

1 It is possible to renew the oil seal without the need to remove the oil pump.
2 Remove the timing belt as described in Section 34.
3 Using two screwdrivers as levers, prise the sprocket from the crankshaft. Remove the Woodruff key.
4 Punch or drill a small hole in the metal face of the oil seal and screw in a self-tapping screw. Use the head of the screw to lever out the seal.
5 Fill the lips of the new seal with grease and tape the step on the crankshaft as described in Section 37.
6 Using a piece of tubing, tap the oil seal into position. Refit the Woodruff key.
7 Refit the crankshaft sprocket.
8 Refit the timing belt as described in Section 34.

41 Crankshaft rear oil seal – renewal

1 Remove the clutch (Chapter 5).
2 Remove the flywheel (Section 39).
3 The defective rear oil seal can now be prised off the crankshaft using a suitably hooked tool.
4 Grease the lips of the new seal before installing it. As there is very little space to tap the seal into position, it is better to use a bolt with a thick nut and a piece of tubing inserted between the outer face of the seal and the clutch release bearing guide. If the nut is then unscrewed to effectively increase the overall length of the bolt, the seal will be pressed into its seat.
5 Refit the flywheel and clutch by reversing the removal operations.

42 Engine – methods of removal

1 It is possible to remove the engine on its own or to remove it complete with gearbox and final drive.
2 It is much easier to remove the engine independently and this should be done if overhaul of the transmission is not required at the same time.
3 Both methods are however described in the following Sections.

43 Engine – removal without transmission

1 Open the bonnet and prop it wide open.
2 Disconnect the lead from the battery negative terminal. Drain the engine oil.
3 Remove the air cleaner and duct (Chapter 3).
4 Drain the cooling system (Chapter 2).
5 Disconnect the radiator coolant hoses (photo).
6 Disconnect the expansion tank hoses.
7 Disconnect the heater hoses at the manifold and the coolant pump, and the brake servo vacuum hose from the intake manifold (photos).

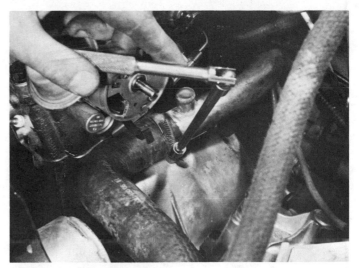

43.5 Disconnecting a hose clip

43.7A Heater hose connection at intake manifold

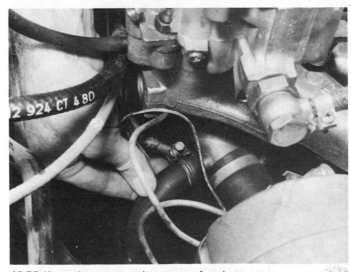

43.7B Heater hose connection at rear of coolant pump

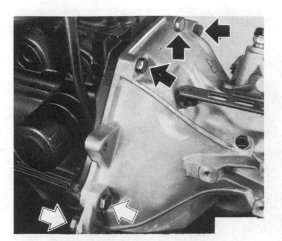

Fig. 1.28 Flywheel housing bolts (Sec 43)

Fig. 1.29 Exhaust attachment to manifold (Sec 43)

43.16 Engine hoist attached to engine

Fig. 1.30 Lifting gear attachment to engine (Sec 43)

Fig. 1.31 Engine swivelled ready for lifting (Sec 43)

Fig. 1.32 Engine being hoisted from vehicle (Sec 43)

8 Disconnect the control cables and the electrical leads from the carburettor, also the fuel hoses from the fuel pump.
9 Remove the alternator electrical plug.
10 Disconnect the HT and LT leads from the ignition coil.
11 Disconnect the leads from the oil pressure switch, the temperature sender and the electric fan switch.
12 Disconnect the leads then unbolt and remove the starter motor.
13 Unscrew and remove the upper bolts from the flywheel housing.
14 Withdraw the splined clutch shaft as described in Section 5 of Chapter 5.
15 Unbolt the exhaust downpipe from the manifold and release the bracket at the engine rear mounting.
16 Attach the slings and hoist to the engine lifting lugs (photo). Take the weight and disconnect the engine front stabiliser and right-hand engine mounting.
17 Unscrew and remove the bolts from the lower part of the flywheel housing.
18 Separate the engine from the transmission enough for it to clear the positioning dowels.
19 Swivel the engine, taking care not to damage the radiator, and lift the unit from the engine compartment.

44 Engine – removal with transmission

1 Carry out the operations described in paragraphs 1 to 12 of the preceding Section.

2 Unbolt the exhaust downpipes from the manifold.
3 Disconnect the clutch operating cable at the release lever on the transmission (photo).
4 Release the pinch-bolt on the gearchange rod clamp.
5 Unscrew the knurled retainer and release the speedometer drive cable from the transmission (photo).
6 Disconnect the electrical leads from the reversing lamp switch on the transmission.
7 Disconnect the earth strap which runs between the transmission and the bodyframe side member.
8 Raise the front of the vehicle and support securely. Remove the front roadwheels.
9 Unscrew the nuts from the suspension lower arm balljoints on both sides of the vehicle and using a suitable separator, disconnect the balljoint taper pins from the hub carrier.
10 Make up a suitable forked tool and insert it between the transmission and the inboard face of one driveshaft. Strike the tool inward to release the driveshaft from the transmission. Repeat the operations on the opposite driveshaft. Be prepared for some loss of oil.
11 Attach the hoist and slings to the engine and take its weight.
12 Disconnect all engine and transmission mountings.
13 Lower the engine/transmission unit until it can be manoeuvred clear of the driveshafts, gearchange rod and mounting brackets and removed from below the engine compartment (photos).
14 Support the transmission and unscrew and remove the starter motor and the flywheel housing bolts. Unbolt and remove the clutch cover plate. Carefully withdraw the transmission from the engine.

44.3 Detaching clutch cable from release lever

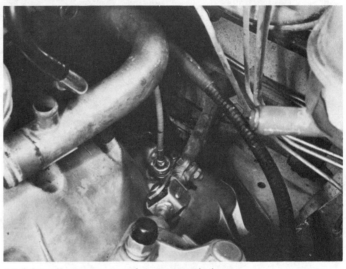

44.5 Speedometer connection to transmission

Fig. 1.33 Gearchange rod clamp and pinch-bolt (Sec 44)

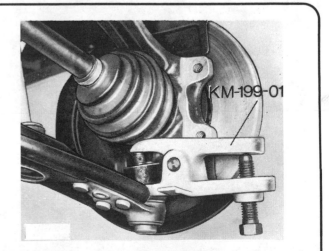

Fig. 1.34 Disconnecting a suspension arm balljoint (Sec 44)

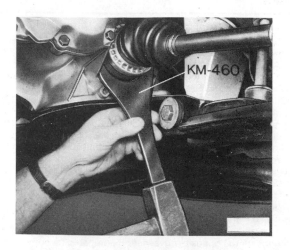

Fig. 1.35 Releasing a driveshaft from the transmission (Sec 44)

44.13A Engine/transmission lowered from vehicle

44.13B Engine compartment after engine/transmission removal

46.3 Removing the intake manifold

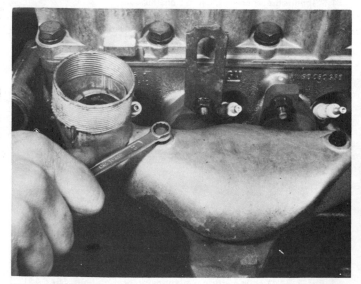

46.4 Unbolting hot air shroud from exhaust manifold

46.5 Unscrewing exhaust manifold nuts

45 Engine dismantling – general

1 Refer to Section 15, paragraphs 1 to 9.
2 Obtain a valve grinding tool and a valve spring compressor.

46 Engine ancillary components – removal

1 Before engine dismantling begins, it is necessary to remove the following ancillary components:

(a) Alternator (Chapter 10)
(b) Fuel pump (Chapter 3)
(c) Thermostat (Chapter 2)
(d) Intake manifold
(e) Carburettor (Chapter 3)
(f) Distributor (Chapter 4)
(g) Coolant pump (Chapter 2)
(h) Exhaust manifold

2 Only the removal of the manifolds is described here, as reference should be made to the Chapters indicated for a full description of the removal procedures for the other components.
3 With the carburettor unbolted and removed, removal of the intake manifold is simply a matter of unscrewing the securing nuts and withdrawing it from the cylinder head (photo).
4 To remove the exhaust manifold, first unbolt and remove the hot air shroud (photo).
5 Unscrew the manifold nuts and withdraw the manifold from the cylinder head (photo).

47 Engine – complete dismantling

1 With the engine removed from the vehicle, clean away external dirt using paraffin and a stiff brush or a water-soluble solvent.
2 Refer to earlier Sections of this Chapter and remove the following in the order shown:

(a) Camshaft toothed belt
(b) Cylinder head
(c) Sump
(d) Oil pump and oil pick-up pipe
(e) Pistons/connecting rods
(f) Clutch and flywheel

3 Invert the engine so that it is standing on the top surface of the cylinder block.
4 Note the markings on the main bearing caps, and from which side of the engine the numbers can be read (photo).
5 Unscrew and remove the main bearing cap bolts and tap off the caps. If the bearing shells are to be used again, keep them with their respective caps.
6 Note that the centre bearing shell incorporates thrust flanges to control crankshaft endfloat.
7 Lift the crankshaft from the crankcase. Extract the upper half shells and again identify their position in the crankcase if they are to be used again.
8 Refer to Sections 51 and 52 for details of dismantling and decarbonising the cylinder head and pistons, and to Section 53 for removal of the camshaft.
9 Unbolt and remove the timing belt rear cover (photo).

48 Oil filter – removal and refitting

1 The oil filter is located adjacent to the exhaust downpipes. An oil filter strap or chain type wrench may be required if it is tight. Alternatively, drive a screwdriver through the oil filter casing near its end and use this as a lever to unscrew it. Be prepared for some loss of oil in this case.
2 Wipe the crankcase mating flange and smear the rubber sealing ring on the filter with grease.
3 Screw on the filter using hand pressure only (photo).

47.4 Main bearing cap markings

47.9 Timing belt rear cover

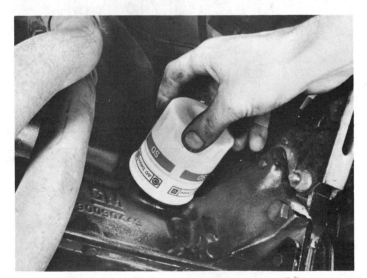
48.3 Screwing on an oil filter

49 Engine lubrication and crankcase ventilation systems – description

1   Oil pressure for all moving components is provided by a gear type oil pump which is driven from the front end of the crankshaft.
2   The pump draws oil from the sump through a pick-up pipe and strainer and pumps it through the oil filter and oil galleries to the engine friction surfaces.
3   A pressure regulator valve is screwed into the body of the oil pump. A relief valve, located in the oil filter, opens should the filter block due to clogging caused by neglected servicing.
4   The cylinder bores are lubricated by oil splash from the sump.
5   The hydraulic valve lifters are pressurised with oil to maintain optimum valve clearance at all times.
6   The crankcase ventilation system is designed to draw oil fumes and blow-by gas (combustion gas which has passed the piston rings) from the crankcase into the air cleaner, whence they are drawn into the engine and burnt during the normal combustion cycle.
7   The oil separator can be unbolted from the crankcase, washed out with paraffin and shaken dry (photo). Clean out the connecting pipes at the same time.

50 Oil pump – overhaul

1   With the oil pump removed from the vehicle, withdraw the rear cover. The cross-head fixing screws are very tight and an impact driver will be required to remove them (photos).
2   Check the clearance between the inner and outer gear teeth and the outer gear and the pump body (photo).
3   Using a straight-edge across the pump cover flange, measure the gear endfloat (photo).
4   If any of the clearances are outside the specified tolerance, renew the components as necessary.
5   The pressure regulator valve can be unscrewed from the oil pump

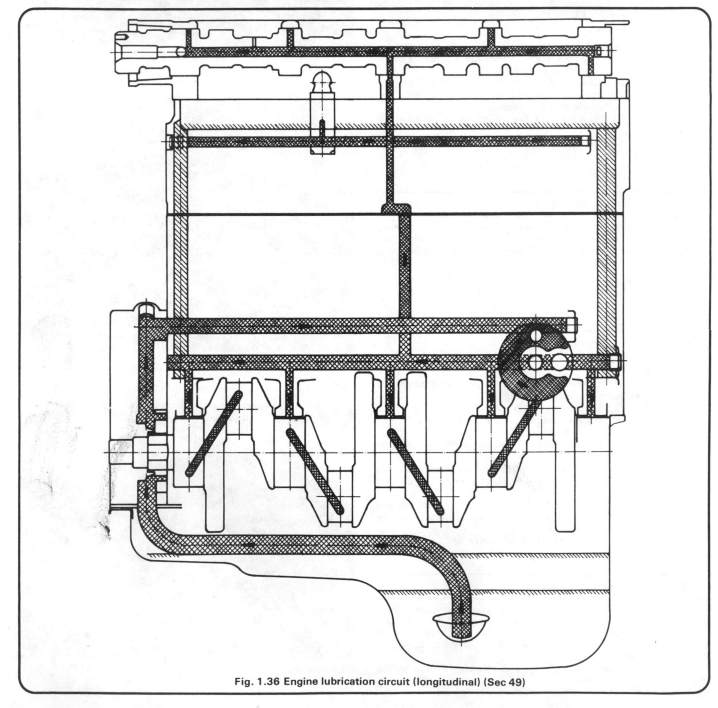

Fig. 1.36 Engine lubrication circuit (longitudinal) (Sec 49)

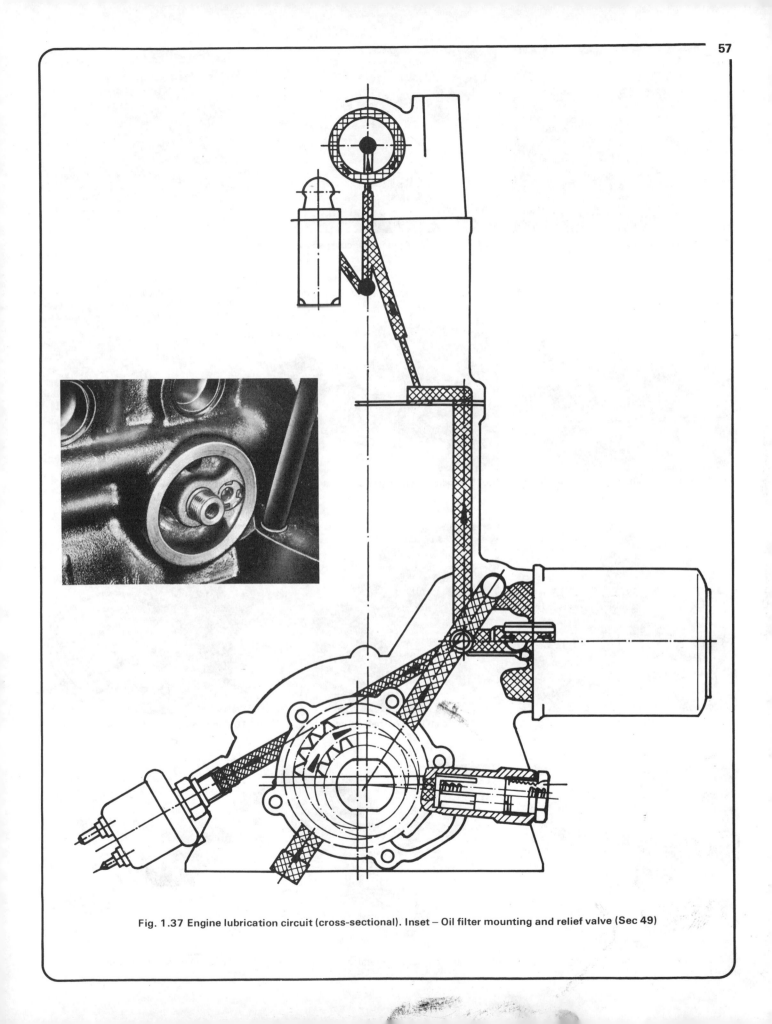

Fig. 1.37 Engine lubrication circuit (cross-sectional). Inset — Oil filter mounting and relief valve (Sec 49)

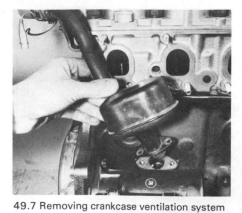
49.7 Removing crankcase ventilation system oil separator

50.1A Extracting oil pump rear cover screws

50.1B Removing oil pump rear cover

50.2 Checking oil pump gear tooth clearance

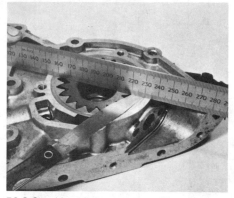
50.3 Checking oil pump gear endfloat

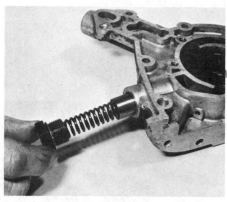
50.5 Oil pump pressure regulator valve

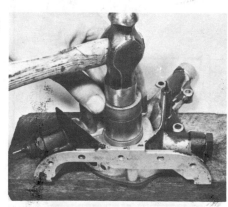
50.6 Installing a new oil pump seal

53.1A Unscrewing camshaft sprocket bolt

53.1B Camshaft sprocket and locating pin

53.2 Unscrewing camshaft retainer plate screws

53.3 Removing camshaft retainer plate

53.4 Withdrawing camshaft from housing

housing and the components cleaned and examined (photo).
6   Always renew the oil seal; a socket is useful to remove and install it (photo).
7   If the gears are removed, make sure that they are installed with their marked sides visible.

51 Cylinder head – dismantling, examination and renovation

1   With the cylinder head removed, clean away external dirt.
2   Remove and recondition the valve components as described in Section 23, paragraphs 2 to 11.

52 Cylinder head and pistons – decarbonising

The operations are as described in Section 24 but as the cylinder head on ohc engines is of light alloy, great care must be taken not to damage it with the tools being used.

53 Camshaft housing – dismantling

1   With the camshaft housing detached from the cylinder head, remove the cover and gasket and then fit an open-ended spanner to the flats on the camshaft and unscrew the sprocket bolt. Remove the sprocket (photos).
2   At the opposite end of the camshaft housing, use an Allen key to unscrew the two screws which retain the camshaft lockplate (photo).
3   Pull out the lockplate (photo).
4   Withdraw the camshaft from the distributor end of the housing (photo).

54 Engine examination and renovation – general

Refer to Section 20.

55 Engine components – examination and renovation

1   The procedures to be followed in respect of the following are as described in Section 21:

(a) Crankshaft and main bearings
(b) Big-end bearings
(c) Cylinder bores
(d) Connecting rods
(e) Pistons and piston rings
(f) Flywheel

Camshaft
2   With the camshaft removed, examine the bearings for signs of obvious wear and pitting. If evident, a new camshaft housing will probably be required.
3   The camshaft itself should show no marks or scoring on the journal or cam lobe surfaces. If evident, renew the camshaft.
4   The retaining plate should appear unworn and without grooves. In any event, check the camshaft endfloat and fit a new plate where necessary.
5   The housing front oil seal should always be renewed at major overhaul (photo).

Camshaft toothed belt
6   Closely inspect the belt for cracking, fraying or tooth deformation. Where evident, renew the belt.
7   If the belt has been in use for 30 000 miles (48 000 km) or more, it is recommended that it is renewed even if it appears in good condition.
8   Whenever the original belt is to be removed but is going to be used again, always note its running direction before removing it. It is even worthwhile marking a few tooth engagement points on each

55.5 Installing the camshaft front oil seal

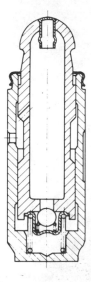

Fig. 1.38 Sectional view of hydraulic valve lifter (Sec 55)

sprocket. As the belt will have worn in to a set position, refitting it in exactly the same way will prevent any increase in noise which might otherwise occur when the engine is running.

Valve lifters, rockers and thrust pads
9   Any signs of wear in a hydraulic valve lifter can only be rectified by renewal, the unit cannot be dismantled.
10   Inspect the rockers and thrust pads for wear or grooving. Again, renew if evident.

Crankshaft
11   If the crankshaft rear flange pilot needle bearing is worn, it can be extracted by filling it with grease and tapping a close-fitting rod into it. Refill with grease and repeat the operation until the bearing is ejected by hydraulic pressure (photos).
12   Tap the new bearing into position using a piece of tubing of suitable diameter (photo).

56 Engine reassembly – general

Refer to Section 25.

55.11A Extracting the crankshaft pilot bearing

55.11B Taking out the crankshaft pilot bearing

55.12 Tapping in a new pilot bearing

57.2 Fitting crankcase main bearing shells

57.6 Oiling crankcase main bearing shells

57.7 Crankshaft rear oil seal in position

57.8 Installing the crankshaft

57.10 Fitting crankshaft rear main bearing cap

57.20 Tightening flywheel bolts

57.23 Fitting oil seals to valve guides

57.24 Oiling a valve stem

57.25A Inlet valve spring seat

57 Engine – complete reassembly

Crankshaft and main bearings

1 Ensure that the crankcase and crankshaft are thoroughly clean and that all oilways are clear. If possible blow the drillings out with compressed air, and then inject clean engine oil through them to ensure they are clear.

2 Wipe the shell seats in the crankcase and bearing caps clean and then fit the upper halves of the main bearing shells into their seats (photo).

3 Note that there is a tab on the back of each bearing which engages with a groove in the shell seating (in both crankcase and bearing cap).

4 Wipe away all traces of protective grease on the new shells.

5 The central bearing shell also takes up the crankshaft endfloat. Note that the half-shells fitted to the cylinder block all have oil duct holes, while only the centre main bearing cap half-shell has an oil duct hole.

6 When the shells are fully located in the crankcase and bearing caps, lubricate them with clean engine oil (photo).

7 Fill the lips of a new crankshaft oil seal with grease and fit it to the end of the crankshaft (photo).

8 Carefully install the crankshaft into position in the crankcase (photo).

9 Lubricate the crankshaft main bearing journals and then refit the centre and intermediate main bearing caps. Tighten the retaining bolts to the specified torque wrench setting.

10 Fill the two grooves in the rear main bearing cap with an RTV type jointing compound, and then fit the cap and retaining bolts. Tighten the bolts to the specified torque, ensuring that the jointing compound exudes from the cap joint, indicating that the grooves are completely filled.

11 Fit the front main bearing cap but before fitting the retaining bolts, smear them with sealant, and then tighten to the specified torque wrench setting. Check that the bearing cap is exactly flush with the end face of the crankcase as it is tightened.

12 Now rotate the crankshaft and check that it turns freely, and shows no signs of binding or tight spots. Check that the crankshaft endfloat is within the limits specified. Alternative centre bearing shells are available if necessary to adjust the endfloat.

Pistons and rings

13 Check that the piston ring grooves are thoroughly clear. Always move the rings into position from the top of the piston.

14 The easiest method of fitting piston rings is to use 0.015 inch (0.38 mm) feeler gauges (or similar) around the top of the piston and move the rings into position over the feelers. This sequence is a reversal of the removal procedure detailed in Section 21 of this Chapter.

15 Follow the manufacturer's instructions carefully when fitting rings to ensure that they are correctly fitted. Several variations of compression and oil control rings are available and it is of the utmost importance that they be located correctly in their grooves.

16 When the rings are in position check that the compression rings are free to expand and contract in their grooves. Certain types of multi-segment oil control rings are a light interference fit in their grooves and this may not therefore apply to them. When all the rings are in position

on the pistons move them around to bring each ring gap to be some 120° away from gap on the adjacent ring. This rule applies to the individual rings that comprise the oil control ring where applicable depending on the type fitted.

17 Refit the pistons/connecting rods as described in Section 38.

Oil pump and oil pick-up pipe

18 Refer to Section 37.

Sump

19 Refer to Section 36.

Flywheel and clutch

20 Refer to Section 39 (photo), and to Chapter 5.

Cylinder head and camshaft housing

21 Fit the camshaft belt rear cover and the thermostat housing.

22 Ensure that all valves and springs are clean and free from carbon deposits and that the ports and valve guides in the cylinder head have no carbon dust or valve grinding paste left in them.

23 Starting at one end of the cylinder head, fit new valve stem oil seals to the ends of the valve guides (photo).

24 Oil the stem of the first valve and insert it into its guide. The valves must be installed into the seats into which they have been ground, which in the case of the original valves will mean that their original sequence of fitting is retained (photo).

25 With inlet valves, fit the spring seat. With exhaust valves fit the valve rotator (photos).

26 Then place the cap over the spring with the recessed part inside the coil of the spring (photo).

27 Place the end of the spring compressor over the cap and valve stem and with the screw head of the compressor over the valve head, screw up the clamp until the spring is compressed past the groove in the valve stem. Then put a little grease round the groove (photo).

28 Place the two halves of the split collar (collets) into the groove with the narrow ends pointing towards the spring. The grease will hold them in the groove (photo).

29 Release the clamp slowly and carefully, making sure that the collets are not dislodged from the groove. When the clamp is fully released the top edges of the collets should be in line with each other. Give the top of each spring a smart tap with a soft-faced mallet when assembly is complete to ensure that the collets are properly settled.

30 Lubricate the hydraulic valve lifters and insert them into their bores in the cylinder head. If new hydraulic valve lifters are being used, initially immerse each one in a container of clean engine oil and compress it (by hand) several times to charge it.

31 Fit the rockers and the thrust pads, also new spark plugs of the specified type.

32 The cylinder head may now be placed to one side ready for installation.

33 Lubricate the camshaft bearings and carefully insert the camshaft into its housing.

34 Fit the retaining plate and fixing screws and then check the camshaft endfloat.

35 Fit a new seal into the seal retainer (if not already done), then hold the camshaft still with an open-ended spanner while the sprocket and its bolt are fitted and the bolt tightened to the specified torque.

57.25B Exhaust valve rotator

57.26 Fitting a valve spring and cap

57.27 Compressing a valve spring

57.28 Inserting valve collets

57.36 Fitting belt cover top bolt

57.37 Locating a new intake manifold gasket

57.39A Fitting an engine mounting bracket

57.39B Fitting a transmission mounting bracket

58.14 Cooling system expansion tank hoses

58.17 Air cleaner hose connections

59.1 Connecting transmission to engine

59.2 Tightening a flywheel housing bolt

59.8 Connecting transmission earth strap

59.9 Fitting flywheel cover plate

36 Refit the cylinder head as described in Section 35. Fit and tension the timing belt (Section 34); fit the belt cover (photo). Fit the camshaft cover using a new gasket.

Manifolds and ancillary components
37 Using new gaskets, bolt on the intake and exhaust manifolds and tighten the nuts to the specified torque (photo).
38 Fit the hot air shroud to the exhaust manifold.
39 Fit the ancillary components, referring as necessary to the appropriate Chapters, but as it is rather vulnerable, leave the fitting of the carburettor until the engine is installed. If the mounting brackets were removed, refit them now (photos).

58 Engine – installation without transmission

1 Make sure that the clutch has been centralised as described in Section 27 and then using the hoist, lower the engine into the engine compartment, taking care not to damage the radiator or adjacent components.
2 Swivel the engine and engage it with the positioning dowels on the flywheel housing.
3 Insert and tighten the connecting bolts.
4 Lower the engine very carefully until the front stabiliser and the right-hand mounting can be connected.
5 Use a new flange gasket and connect the exhaust pipes to the manifold.
6 Engage the clutch splined driveshaft as described in Chapter 5, Section 5, having smeared the shaft splines with a little grease.
7 Connect the starter motor leads.
8 Connect the leads to the oil pressure switch, the temperature sender and the electric fan switch.
9 Connect the ignition leads to the coil.
10 Fit the alternator plug.
11 Reconnect the fuel hose to the fuel pump.
12 Connect the control cables and electrical leads to the carburettor.
13 Connect the heater and brake vacuum hoses to the intake manifold.
14 Connect the hoses to the cooling system expansion tank (photo).
15 Connect the radiator hoses.
16 Refill and bleed the cooling system.
17 Fit the air cleaner and ducting (photo).
18 Connect the battery.
19 Fill the engine with oil.

59 Engine – installation with transmission

1 With the engine located in an upright position and the clutch centralised (refer to Section 27), offer the transmission to the engine until the positioning dowels engage (photo).
2 Insert and tighten the connecting bolts (photo).
3 Hoist the engine from below into the engine compartment and manoeuvre it carefully until the driveshafts can be engaged in the final drive, the gearchange rod coupled and the mounting brackets bolted up.
4 Remove the hoist and slings.
5 Fully connect a driveshaft by applying a chisel to the weld bead of the inner joint and striking it until it locks into position. Repeat on the other shaft.
6 Reconnect the balljoints to the hub carrier.
7 Refit the roadwheels.
8 Connect the transmission earth strap (photo).
9 Fit the flywheel housing cover plate (photo).
10 Connect the reversing lamp leads.
11 Reconnect the speedometer drive cable to the transmission.
12 Connect the clutch operating cable and adjust if necessary (Chapter 5).
13 Connect the exhaust pipes to the manifold.
14 Connect the leads to the starter motor.
15 Connect the leads to the oil pressure switch and the temperature sender.
16 Connect the ignition leads to the coil.
17 Connect the alternator plug.
18 Connect the control cables and electrical lead to the carburettor.
19 Connect the pipes to the fuel pump.
20 Connect the heater and vacuum hoses to the intake manifold.
21 Connect the hoses to the expansion tank.
22 Connect the radiator hoses.
23 Refill and bleed the cooling system (Chapter 2).
24 Fit the air cleaner and duct.
25 Fill the engine with oil and connect the battery.
26 Before attempting to start the engine, adjust the gearchange remote control rod as described in Chapter 6.

60 Engine – initial start-up after overhaul

Refer to Section 29, but ignore all reference to valve clearances. Some valve clatter is to be expected until the hydraulic valve lifters pressurize with oil.

61 Fault diagnosis – ohc engine

Refer to Section 30, but ignore references to valve clearances. Add the following:

Symptom	Reason(s)
Engine misfires	Slack timing belt
Clatter	Faulty hydraulic valve lifter*

*It is normal for a considerable amount of noise to come from hydraulic valve lifters on initial start-up after overhaul. This should only continue until the valve lifters are properly pressurized with oil. Additionally, on a high mileage engine, there may be some initial noise if the engine has not been started for a period of time.

Chapter 2 Cooling and heating system

For modifications, and information applicable to later models, see Supplement at end of manual

Contents

Specifications

System type .... Thermo-syphon with belt-driven pump and electric fan

Coolant
Type/specification .... Antifreeze to BS3151 or 6580 (Duckhams Universal Antifreeze and Summer Coolant)

Capacity:
1196 cc engine .... 10.4 pints (5.9 litres)
1297 cc engine .... 11.1 pints (6.3 litres)

Thermostat
	1196 cc	**1297 cc**
Identification	87/102	92
Begins opening	87°C (189°F)	92°C (198°F)
Fully open	102°C (216°F)	107°C (225°F)

Filler cap
Identification .... Blau 90 096 561
Opening pressure .... 18.13 to 18.85 lbf/in² (1.25 to 1.30 bars)
Boiling point at opening pressure .... 125°C (257°F)

Coolant pump drive
1196 cc engine .... Alternator drivebelt from crankshaft pulley
1297 cc engine .... Timing belt

Torque wrench settings
	lbf ft	Nm
Coolant pump bolts	6	8
Coolant temperature sender	7	10

1 General description

Engine cooling is achieved by a conventional thermo-syphon, pump-assisted system in which the coolant is pressurised. The system consists of a radiator, an engine-driven pump, an electrical fan, a thermostat and connecting hoses. Hoses also conduct coolant to and from a heat exchanger mounted in the car to provide heat for the ventilation and heating system.

The system works in the following way. Cold coolant from one side of the radiator, which is mounted at the front of the engine compartment, is directed to the inlet side of the coolant pump where it is then forced round the cooling passages in the engine cylinder block and the cylinder head. The coolant, now hot, is returned to the other side of the radiator where it flows across the radiator and cools to repeat the cycle.

Air flows through the radiator to cool the coolant as a result of the car's forward motion. However, if the coolant temperature exceeds a given figure, a temperature switch in the radiator switches on an electrical fan to assist and increase the airflow through the radiator. In this way the fan is only driven when it is really needed, with a consequent reduction in noise and energy consumption.

To enable the engine to warm up quickly when starting from cold, the thermostat located in the cylinder head outlet prevents coolant flowing to the radiator until the temperature has risen sufficiently. Instead, the outflow from the cylinder head is redirected around the engine. When hot the thermostat opens to send the coolant to the radiator.

An expansion/header tank is incorporated in the system to accommodate coolant expansion. The system is topped up through a filler cap on this tank.

2 Cooling system – draining

Note: *Take care to protect the hands from escaping steam when removing the expansion tank filler cap if the system is hot.*

1 Before draining the system park the car on level ground, remove the filler cap on the expansion tank and move the heater control to full heat. If the coolant is less than two years old it should be collected for re-use.
2 Position a clean container such as a basin under the radiator bottom hose and loosen a hose clip. If the hose joint has not been disturbed for some time it will be necessary to manipulate the hose to break the joint and allow the coolant to flow into the container. Where fitted, the cylinder block drain plug may be removed to speed draining.
3 On completion of the draining remove the container to a safe place and cover it to prevent contamination of the coolant if it is to be re-used.
4 As no cylinder block drain plug is fitted and the radiator bottom hose may be situated halfway up the radiator, the system will not drain fully. Care should be taken when refilling to maintain antifreeze strength.

3 Cooling system – flushing

1 If effective draining or renewing the coolant has been neglected, then in time the cooling system will gradually lose efficiency as the radiator becomes choked with rust, scale deposits and other sediment from the system. This is one of the main reasons why old cars suffer so much from overheating compared with newer cars. To maintain cooling system efficiency it is necessary to flush the system clean. First drain the system as explained in the previous Section and then remove the thermostat as explained in Section 6. Temporarily refit the thermostat housing and reconnect the hose. Disconnect the radiator top hose at the radiator and cover the engine with a sheet of plastic to prevent it from getting wet during the flushing process.

2 Using a garden hose, direct a flow of clean water through the radiator to wash the system out. Continue flushing until rust-free water emerges. If, after a reasonable period the water still does not run clear, the radiator can be flushed with a good proprietary cleaning agent such as Holts Radflush or Holts Speedflush. If the contamination is particularly bad disconnect the radiator bottom hose and, with suitable connectors, feed the flushing water in at the bottom of the radiator to flush it in reverse. This should dislodge deposits which were not moved by conventional flushing. Repeat the procedure on the engine block. Where any doubt exists about the cleanliness of the radiator after reverse flushing it, it should be removed as explained in Section 5 so that it can be flushed and agitated at the same time. After reverse flushing, carry out a normal flow flush before refitting the thermostat and reconnecting the system hoses.

3 In extreme cases the use of a proprietary de-scaling compound may be necessary. If such a compound is used, adhere to the maker's instructions and satisfy yourself that no damage will be caused to the engine or cooling system components.

4 As the system will not drain fully, flushing should be done every time the coolant is renewed. This will minimise impurities in the system.

4 Cooling system – filling

If renewing the coolant, flush the system (Section 3)

1 Before attempting to fill the cooling system make sure that all the hoses and hose clips are in good condition and that the clips are tight. These cars must have anti-freeze mixture in the system all the year round, to prevent corrosion of light alloys with which the coolant comes into contact as well as preventing the system from freezing in winter.

2 Check that the heater control is in the full heat position and then remove the filler cap from the expansion tank. To release air from the system as it is being filled, slacken the heater hose clip at the connection on the cylinder head (1196 cc engines) or remove the temperature switch from the induction manifold (1297 cc engines). Fill the system slowly (by pouring coolant into the expansion tank) to prevent air locks forming and either tighten the heater hose clip or refit the temperature switch as appropriate when coolant, free of air, emerges. Fill to 0.4 in (10mm) above the level marked KALT (ie COLD) on the expansion tank. Repeated squeezing of the large coolant hoses will induce surging of the mixture in the system which will help to dislodge any air bubbles. Refit the expansion tank filler cap tightly and

mop up any spilt fluid (photo).

3 Run the engine at a fast tickover until the cooling fan motor engages and, particularly if the system has been disturbed in any way, examine carefully for leaks. Stop the engine and allow it to cool before topping up the level in the expansion tank as necessary. Remember that the system must be cold before an accurate level is indicated in the expansion tank.

5 Radiator – removal, inspection and refitting

1 The radiator can be removed complete with the electrically-driven cooling fan if there is no need to disturb the fan. If the fan must be removed, refer to Section 9.

2 Drain the system as described in Section 2 and disconnect the battery earth terminal.

3 Detach the radiator top and bottom hoses, and also the small diameter vent hose between the top of the radiator and the expansion tank (photo).

4 Disconnect the electric wiring from the thermal switch in the radiator at the lower right-hand side (photo). Disconnect the fan motor leads at the connector near the front of the battery.

5 Remove the two clips which secure the radiator located at the top left and right corners of the radiator (photo). Pull the top of the radiator back to free it from the top mountings and then lift it out of the bottom mountings and clear of the car (photo).

6 With the radiator assembly removed it is easier to examine for leaks which will show up as corroded or stained areas. No repairs are possible with this type of radiator, which is made of light alloy and plastic. However a proprietary leak stopping product such as Holts Radweld may be used to cure minor leaks in an emergency, with the radiator still *in situ*. In the long run it is better practice to renew a defective assembly.

7 Clean out the inside of the radiator by flushing as described in Section 3 and also clean the matrix, removing all the dead flies and bugs which reduce the radiator's efficiency. Take this opportunity to inspect the hoses and clips, making sure that all are fit for further use.

8 Refitting the radiator is the reverse of the removal procedure. Check that the rubber mountings are in good condition and ensure that the bottom location pegs fit correctly on installation. Refer to Section 4 for refilling the system.

6 Thermostat – removal, testing and refitting

1 Typical symptoms of thermostat malfunction are either a slow warm-up of the engine, anything in excess of 7 to 8 minutes, or an overheating engine as betrayed by high gauge readings, pinking, running-on or excessive evaporation of coolant.

2 Before removing the thermostat the system will have to be at least partially drained as described in Section 2. The removal and refitting procedure will depend on the type of engine in your car.

1196 cc engine

3 After draining the coolant, disconnect the radiator top hose from the outlet connection at the top of the coolant pump. This will expose the thermostat and it will be seen that it is retained in position by a snap-ring (photo).

4.2 Filling the expansion tank

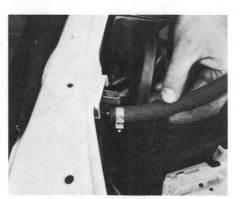
5.3 Radiator vent hose to expansion tank

5.4 Radiator electric fan switch

5.5A Removing radiator securing clip

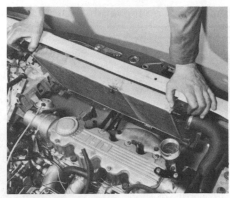

5.5B Removing the radiator

6.3 Thermostat (ohv) showing retaining ring

6.4 Removing the thermostat (ohv)

6.7 Disconnecting radiator hose from thermostat housing (ohc)

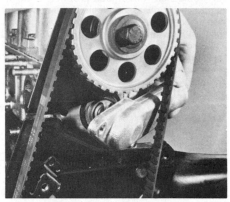

6.8A Removing the thermostat housing (ohc)

6.8B Extracting thermostat and seal (ohc)

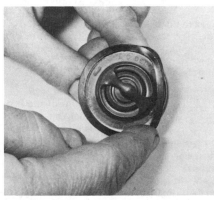

6.10 Fitting a thermostat seal (ohc)

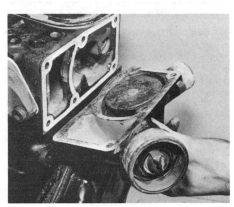

7.6 Fitting coolant pump (ohv)

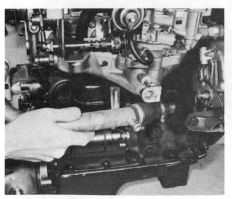

7.10A Coolant hose and pipe connection to rear of pump (ohc)

7.10B Removing coolant pump (ohc) (engine partly dismantled)

7.10C Coolant pump drive sprocket (ohc)

4   Prise the snap-ring free using a suitable screwdriver blade and then remove the thermostat from the pump outlet (photo).

5   The thermostat can be tested easily for correct functioning if this should be in doubt. Boil a pan of water and suspend the thermostat on a piece of cord. Lower the thermostat into the hot water and it should be seen to open on immersion. Remove the thermostat from the water and it should be seen to close. This is only a simple functional test but it will identify a failed thermostat. With a thermometer you can check the correct opening temperature, see Specifications, but the full open temperature will be difficult to check as it is above the boiling point of water. When renewing this component make sure that the replacement item is the correct one for your car as thermostats are made for a wide range of different models and conditions. You can drive without a thermostat in an emergency, no harm will result but the engine will not warm up properly.

6   Refitting the thermostat is the reverse procedure to removal, but use a new rubber seal and install the thermostat with the arrow on the web pointing upwards.

1297 cc engine

7   After draining the coolant, undo the securing bolts and remove the timing belt cover. Disconnect the radiator upper hose at its connection on the engine which is the thermostat housing (photo).

8   Undo the two securing bolts and remove the housing to reveal the thermostat in the cylinder head. Remove the thermostat, noting how it fits in the recesses in the aperture (photos).

9   Testing this thermostat it exactly the same as already described in paragraph 5.

10 Refitting the thermostat is the reverse procedure to removal, but fit a new rubber seal to the thermostat and install it to locate in the two recesses noted during removal (photo).

7 Coolant pump – removal and refitting

1   The procedure for removing and refitting the coolant pump varies with the type of engine fitted in the car but in all cases the coolant system should be drained as described in Section 2.

1196 cc engine

2   Slacken the alternator mounting nuts and bolts, swing the alternator in towards the engine and remove the drivebelt.

3   Undo and remove the three hoses connected to the coolant pump and then remove the six bolts securing the pump to the cylinder head.

4   Carefully separate the pump from the engine, taking care not to damage the casting.

5   The pump unit is not repairable and if it is known to be defective it should be renewed. In this case transfer the thermostat, provided that it is still serviceable, to the replacement unit, referring to Section 6 if necessary.

6   Before fitting the coolant pump, clean the mating surfaces on the pump flange and on the cylinder head free of all traces of the old gasket. Use a new gasket on assembly, using a little grease to hold it in position whilst fitting the pump. Tighten the pump securing bolts to the specified torque (photo).

7   The rest of the reassembly follows the removal procedure in reverse. After fitting the drivebelt, adjust it to the correct tension as described in Section 8. When the coolant system has been refilled run the engine up to its normal operating temperature and check for leaks.

1297 cc engine

8   Slacken the alternator mounting nuts and bolts, swing the alternator in towards the engine and remove the drivebelt.

9   Undo the securing bolts and remove the timing belt cover. Turn the crankshaft to align the timing mark on the camshaft sprocket with the mark at the top of the housing behind the sprocket, and at the same time align the notch in the rim of the crankshaft pulley with the timing pointer.

10 Disconnect the hose at the back of the coolant pump and then slacken the three bolts which hold the pump in the engine block. The pump shaft is eccentric in the pump body so that, by rotating the pump body, the tension in the toothed timing belt can be released. Turn the body of the pump inwards to slacken the toothed timing belt and slip the belt off the pump pulley. Make sure that the crankshaft and the camshaft are not turned while the toothed timing belt is removed as, apart from losing the valve timing, the valves or pistons could be

7.12 Coolant pump O-ring seal (ohc)

damaged. Withdraw the coolant pump from the engine block (photos).

11 Although the pump can be dismantled and reassembled, a press and several special tools are necessary and it is considered that the work is outside the scope of the home mechanic. For this reason a defective pump should be renewed.

12 Before fitting the coolant pump, clean its mounting in the engine block and fit a new O-ring seal to the pump body (photo). Install the pump in the block and fit the three retaining bolts and washers, but only hand tighten them at this stage.

13 Fit the toothed timing belt to the pump pulley and refer to Chapter 1 for the procedure on tensioning the belt. Tighten the three bolts securing the pump to the specified torque.

14 Refit the timing belt cover and then fit the drivebelt to the crankshaft and alternator pulleys. Refer to Section 8 for the procedure for tensioning the belt and tighten the alternator mounting bolts.

15 Reconnect the coolant hose at the back of the pump and then refill the system as described in Section 2. Finally run the engine up to its normal operating temperature and check for leaks.

8 Drivebelt – removal, refitting and tensioning

1   On the 1196 cc engine the drivebelt runs in the crankshaft, coolant pump and alternator pulleys, but on the 1297 cc engine the belt only runs in the crankshaft and the alternator pulleys as the coolant pump is driven by the toothed timing belt. However, the removal, refitting and tensioning procedures on both engines are similar.

2   Correct tensioning of the drivebelt will ensure that it has a long and useful life. Beware, however, of over tightening as this can cause excessive wear in the alternator and/or coolant pump bearings.

3   A regular inspection of the belt should be made and if it is found to be overstretched, worn, frayed or cracked it should be renewed before it breaks in service. To insure against such an event arising it is a good idea to carry a spare belt, of the correct type, in the car at all times.

4   To remove an old belt, loosen the alternator mounting bolts and nuts just sufficiently to allow the unit to be pivoted in towards the engine. This will release all tension from the belt which can now be slipped off the respective pulleys. Fit a new belt after checking that it is of the correct type and take up the slack in the belt by swinging the alternator away from the engine and lightly tightening the bolts just to hold it in that position.

5   Although special tools are available for measuring the belt tension a good approximation can be achieved if the belt is tensioned so that there is 0.5 in (13 mm) of movement at the mid-point position on the longest run of belt between pulleys. With the alternator bolts just holding the unit firm, lever the alternator away from the engine using a wooden lever at the mounting bracket end until the correct tension in the belt is reached and then tighten the alternator bolts. On

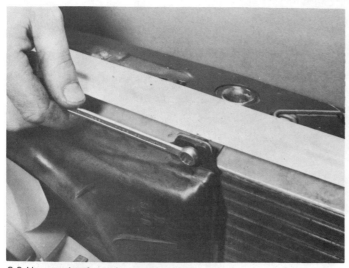

9.2 Unscrewing fan unit mounting bolt

no account apply any loads at the free end of the alternator as serious damage can be caused internally.

6   When a new belt has been fitted it will probably stretch slightly to start with and the tension should be rechecked, and if necessary adjusted, after about 250 miles (400 km).

9   Radiator electric fan – removal and refitting

1   Disconnect the battery earth terminal and then disconnect the fan motor leads at the connector block near the front of the battery.
2   Undo the single securing bolt at the top of the fan mounting assembly and remove the fan assembly from its location (photo).
3   Further dismantling of the assembly depends on the extent of the problem. If the motor is defective it would be better to have it overhauled by a specialist as spare parts for it may be difficult to get hold of. The only other course of action would be to renew the complete motor and this may be cheaper and quicker in the long run.
4   Reassembly, if the unit was dismantled, and refitting to the car are the reverse of the dismantling and removal sequences. On completion run the engine up to normal operating temperature and check the fan for correct functioning.

10   Cooling fan thermal switch – removal and refitting

1   The cooling fan is controlled by a thermal switch which is located in the right-hand rear face of the radiator at the bottom corner. If the fan fails to work when it should, the circuit can be tested by connecting together the two electrical leads serving the switch and turning the ignition on. If the fan now works then the switch is at fault and needs changing.
2   To remove the switch, first drain the coolant from the system as described in Section 2 and then disconnect the battery earth lead.
3   Disconnect the electrical wires from the switch and unscrew it from the radiator.
4   Refitting is the reverse of the removal procedure, but smear a little sealant on the switch threads before installing it. Refill the system and run the engine up to its normal operating temperature to check the fan for correct functioning, and to check for leaks.

11   Coolant temperature sender – removal and refitting

1   The coolant temperature sender unit is located in the cylinder head behind the coolant pump on the 1196 cc engine and on top of the induction manifold at the right-hand end on the 1297 cc engine.
2   Before removing the sender unit drain sufficient coolant from the system to avoid spillage, as described in Section 2, and then disconnect the battery earth lead.

3   Disconnect the electrical wire from the sender unit terminal and unscrew the unit from its location.
4   Refitting is the reverse of the removal procedure. Use sealant on the sender unit threads. Refill the system as described in Section 2 and run the engine to check the functioning of the sender unit, and to check for leaks.

12   Antifreeze mixture

1   In these cars it is important to use an antifreeze mixture in the system all the year round. The mixture should be made up from clean, preferably soft, tap water (or rain water) and a good quality antifreeze liquid containing corrosion inhibitor. The proportions of water to antifreeze will depend on the degree of protection required and listed below are the recommended quantities of antifreeze necessary to give protection for varying degrees of freezing.
Note: some coolant will remain in the system after draining, so it is recommended that the following procedure is used, rather than premixing the coolant.

1196 cc engine °C (°F)	Antifreeze
-10 (+14)	*1.6 pints* *(0.9 litres)*
-20 (-4)	*2.8 pints* *(1.6 litres)*
-30 (-22)	*3.5 pints* *(2.0 litres)*
-40 (-40)	*4.2 pints* *(2.4 litres)*

1297 cc engine °C (°F)	Antifreeze
-10 (+14)	*2.3 pints* *(1.3 litres)*
-20 (-4)	*3.7 pints* *(2.1 litres)*
-30 (-22)	*4.9 pints* *(2.8 litres)*
-40 (-40)	*5.8 pints* *(3.3 litres)*

2   Before filling with fresh antifreeze, drain and flush the system as described in Sections 2 and 3 and check that all the hoses are in good condition and that the clips are all tight. Antifreeze has a searching action and will leak more rapidly than plain water. Pour a couple of pints of water into the system and then add the correct quantity of antifreeze fluid. Then top up with water and, with the filler cap removed, run the engine to mix the coolant. Fit the filler cap and continue to run to warm up to normal temperatures and check for leaks. After allowing the engine to cool down check the level and, if necessary, top up with water. All future topping-up should be done using mixed coolant of the correct proportions.
3   The antifreeze should be renewed every two years as the corrosion inhibitor will then be of little use. Don't attempt to use engine antifreeze in the windscreen wash system; it will attack the car's paintwork and will smear the windscreen. Finally remember that antifreeze is very poisonous and must be handled with due care.
4   In climates where antifreeze is not required, use a corrosion inhibitor in the cooling system water, never use plain water.

13   Heater – description

1   The heater system depends upon fresh air being drawn into the grille at the base of the windscreen and passed through a matrix which is heated from the engine cooling system.
2   Temperature regulation is controlled by mixing cold intake air with warm air, using flap valves both for this function and for the direction of air to the interior, windscreen or side air outlets.
3   An electric booster fan is mounted within the engine compartment to supplement the normal ram effect provided when the vehicle is in forward motion.
4   An independent fresh air ventilation system provides a supply of unheated fresh air at the nozzles on the instrument panel.
5   Stale air is exhausted from the vehicle interior through the slots just to the rear of the rear side windows.

14 Heater components – removal and refitting

Control unit

1 Working under the facia panel inside the vehicle, disconnect the heater control rods from the air distribution levers (photo).

2 Remove the switch panel from the facia. Do this by extracting the retaining screws by passing a screwdriver under the top edge of the cut-outs of the foglamp and rear wash/wipe switches. Pull the switch panel from its holding clips and disconnect the switch plugs from the rear of the panel.

3 Unscrew the heater control panel from the facia (photos).

Heater matrix

4 Clamp the two heater hoses near the engine compartment rear bulkhead. Self-grip wrenches are useful for this.

5 Disconnect the heater hoses from the matrix pipe stubs at the bulkhead. Cap or plug the open stubs to prevent loss of coolant.

6 Working inside the vehicle, remove the heater housing lower cover and section from under the facia. These are held by one screw and six clips (photos).

7 Pull the heater matrix from its location, displacing the bulkhead grommets as it is withdrawn (photo).

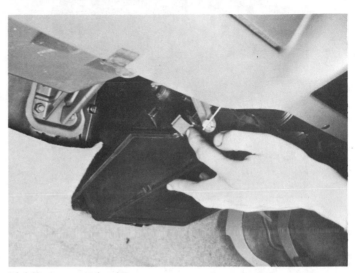

14.1 Heater control rod

Fig. 2.1 Extracting switch panel screws (arrowed) (Sec 14)

14.3A Heater control panel screw

14.3B Heater control panel removed

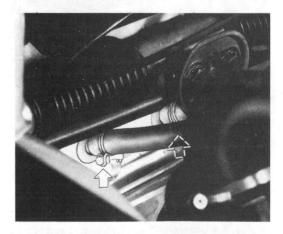

Fig. 2.2 Heater hose connections at engine compartment rear bulkhead (Sec 14)

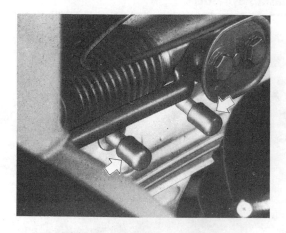

Fig. 2.3 Heater pipe stubs capped (Sec 14)

14.6A Heater housing lower section cover screw

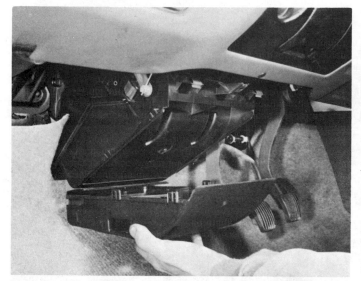

14.6B Removing heater housing lower section cover

14.7 Heater matrix exposed

Fig. 2.4 Heater matrix withdrawn (Sec 14)

E   Matrix   G   Bulkhead
F   Grommets

14.11 Removing insulation sheet

Air distribution housing

8 Remove the heater matrix as previously described.
9 Remove the switch plate as described in paragraph 2.
10 Remove the facia fresh air nozzles from above the switch plate as described in Section 15.
11 Working within the engine compartment, pull off the insulation sheet (photo).
12 Detach the air distribution housing (three screws) from the blower motor housing.
13 Returning to the vehicle interior, disconnect the heater controls from the air distributor housing and remove the two housing mounting screws.
14 Pull the air distribution hoses from the housing, and then withdraw the housing.

Blower motor

15 Working within the engine compartment, unclip the cover of the blower motor housing.
16 Pull off the multi-pin plug connector (photo).
17 Unscrew the blower motor/fan from the housing (photo).
18 If necessary, the motor mounting bracket screws can be extracted to dismantle the assembly (photo).

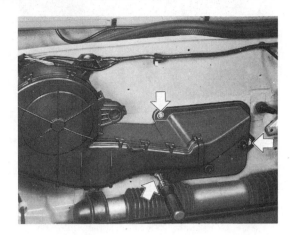

Fig. 2.5 Air distribution housing screws (Sec 14)

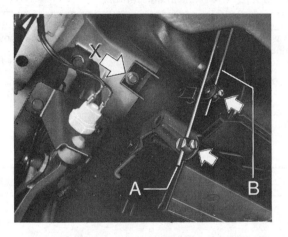

Fig. 2.6 Heater control rods (A and B) and air distribution housing mounting screw (X) (Sec 14)

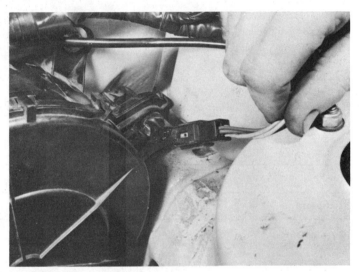

14.16 Blower motor connector plug

14.17 Heater blower motor screws

14.18 Motor mounting bracket removal

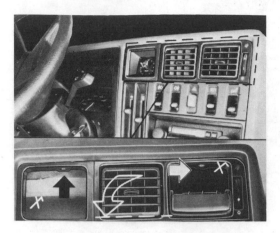

Fig. 2.7 Fresh air nozzle frame securing screws (arrowed) (Sec 15)

Fig. 2.8 Removing a facia side heater nozzle (Sec 15)

Refitting

19 This is a reversal of removal, but observe the following points.

20 When connecting the control rods, set the flaps and the control levers on the facia to the closed position, before tightening the trunnion pinch-bolts.

21 After refitting the matrix, top up the cooling system as described in Section 4.

22 When installing the air distributor housing, make sure that the flange is well sealed with a piece of foam rubber (10 x 8 mm).

15 Facia nozzles – removal and refitting

Centre fresh air nozzle

1 Swing the right-hand nozzle fully down and pull, then remove the blanking plate or clock if fitted (see Chapter 10).

2 Extract the two screws from under the top edge of the grille frame.

Side heater nozzle

3 This is simply removed by prising it out with a thin screwdriver.

All nozzles

4 Refitting is a reversal of removal.

13 Fault diagnosis – cooling and heating system

Symptom	Reason(s)
Overheating	Insufficient coolant in system
	Pump ineffective due to slack drivebelt (ohv)
	Radiator blocked either internally or externally
	Kinked or collapsed hose causing coolant flow restriction
	Thermostat not working properly
	Faulty electric fan
	Faulty fan thermoswitch
	Engine out of tune
	Ignition timing retarded or auto advance malfunction
	Cylinder head gasket blown
	Engine not yet run-in
	Exhaust system partially blocked
	Engine oil level too low
	Brakes binding
Engine running too cool	Faulty, incorrect or missing thermostat
Loss of coolant	Loose hose clips
	Hoses perished or leaking
	Radiator leaking
	Filler/pressure cap defective
	Blown cylinder head gasket
	Cracked cylinder block or head
Heater gives insufficient output	Engine overcooled (see above)
	Heater matrix blocked
	Heater controls maladjusted or broken
	Heater control valve jammed or otherwise defective

Chapter 3 Fuel and exhaust systems

For modifications, and information applicable to later models, see Supplement at end of manual

Contents

Specifications

General

System type	Rear-mounted fuel tank, mechanical fuel pump, single or dual barrel downdraught carburettor
Fuel tank capacity:	
Saloon and Hatchback	42 litres (9.25 gal)
Estate	50 litres (11 gal)
Fuel octane requirements:	
High compression (S) engines	98 RON (UK 4-star)
Low compression engines	91 RON (UK 2-star)
Fast idle speed (1297 cc high compression only, hot)	2000 to 2100 rpm

Fuel pump pressure .... 19.6 to 25.5 kPa (2.8 to 3.7 lbf/in^2) at 2000 engine rpm

Air cleaner type .... With single barrel carburettor, manual air intake temperature control
With dual barrel carburettor, automatic temperature controlled intake

Air cleaner element

1196 cc ohv engine	Champion W101
1297 cc ohc engine (low and high compression)	Champion W103

Carburettors

Solex 35 PDSI

Type	Single barrel downdraught
Application	All 1196 cc engines, and 1297 cc low compression engine
Venturi diameter	26.0 mm (1.024 in)
Fuel inlet needle valve	1.75 mm (0.069 in)
Inlet valve seal thickness	2.5 mm (0.087 in)
Main jet	X125 or X122.5
Air correction jet	80
Idle jet	50
Injection tube	50
Enrichment jet in housing	80 or 100
Enrichment jet in cover	50, 80 or 100
Idle speed	900 to 950 rpm
Exhaust gas emission at idle	1.0 to 2.5% CO

GM Varajet II

	Primary	Secondary
Type	Dual barrel downdraught	
Application	1297 cc high compression engine	
Venturi diameter	28 mm (1.102 in)	–
Throttle plate diameter	35 mm (1.378 in)	46 mm (1.811 in)
Main jet	1.5 mm (0.059 in) press fit	
Partial load needle valve	1.0 mm (0.039 in) not renewable	
Idle jet	0.65 mm (0.026 in) press fit	
Accelerator pump piston setting	10.4 to 10.8 mm (0.410 to 0.425 in)	
Idle speed:		
Manual	900 to 950 rpm	
Automatic	800 to 850 rpm	
Exhaust gas emission at idle	1.0 to 1.5% CO	

Torque wrench settings

	Nm	lbf ft
Fuel pump bolts (ohc)	20	15
Manifold nuts	20	15
Carburettor mounting nuts	20	15

1 Description

The fuel system comprises a fuel tank (mounted under the vehicle floor pan but below the rear seat as a protection against rear end collision), a mechanically-operated fuel pump, a temperature regulated or controlled air cleaner and a carburettor.

The type of carburettor used depends upon the engine (see Specifications).

The exhaust system is of conventional design.

2 Fuel pump – description and maintenance

1   On ohv engines, the fuel pump is located on the side of the crankcase and is driven by a lobe on the camshaft which is in contact with the rocker arm of the pump.

2   On ohc engines, the fuel pump is mounted at the front end of the camshaft housing and is again driven by a lobe on the camshaft, this time through a pushrod.

3   The only maintenance possible on some pumps is to remove the pump cover (one screw), prise out the sealing ring and lift out the filter screen and clean it (photo).

4   Check the condition of the seal when refitting and do not overtighten the cover screw.

5   The pump cannot be further dismantled and if faulty, it must be renewed complete. Note that some pumps are *completely* sealed (photo).

3 Fuel pump – testing, removal and refitting

1   If it is found that the carburettor fuel bowl is dry and yet there is fuel in the tank, test the pump in the following way.

2   Disconnect the fuel hose from the carburettor and place its open end in a container.

3   Disconnect the LT lead which connects the distributor to ignition coil. This will prevent the engine from firing.

4   Turn the ignition key to operate the starter motor through several revolutions and observe the fuel being ejected from the open end of

the fuel hose. It should come out in well-defined spurts, if not, the pump is faulty and must be removed for renewal.

5   To remove the pump, disconnect the hoses from it and unscrew the retaining bolts.

6   Withdraw the pump, retaining any spacer (photo).

7   Refit by reversing the removal operations, but use new flange gaskets. Remember to refit the spacer if one was removed.

4 Air cleaner – description

The provision of air at the correct temperature which is drawn into the carburettor is carried out in the following way.

With single barrel carburettor

Intake air preheating is controlled by a flap valve located either in the air cleaner casing or the intake spout. The valve lever should be moved to WINTER or SUMMER, or the INTERMEDIATE position (1196 cc only) in accordance with the following ambient temperature ranges.

1196 cc engine
SUMMER position: above 10°C (50°F)
INTERMEDIATE position: −5° to 10°C (23°F to 50°F)
WINTER position: below −5°C (23°F)
1297 cc engine
SUMMER position: above 10°C (50°F)
WINTER position: below 10°C (50°F)

The SUMMER position may be retained down to 0°C (32°F) in the interest of fuel economy, but not if the engine is inclined to hesitate as the throttle is opened.

With dual barrel carburettor

A vacuum device holds the air cleaner control damper covering the hot air port, and the cold air port is fully open when the engine is not running.

When the engine is started, the vacuum pressure at the vacuum device is controlled by a temperature sensor in the air cleaner body. This sensor is sensitive to the heated air drawn from within the shroud

2.3 Fuel pump cover, filter and seal

2.5 Completely sealed type fuel pump

3.6 Removing fuel pump (ohc) engine

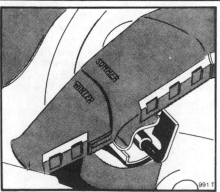

Fig. 3.1 Different types of manually-operated flap air cleaners (Sec 5)

on the exhaust manifold and regulates the damper to vary the mix of hot and cold air to provide air at a predetermined temperature level.

The arrangement is overridden automatically to admit greater cold air inflow at time of maximum acceleration.

A fault in the sensor unit or vacuum device will give rise to hesitatation, surge, stalling or weak mixture, especially in cold weather, and one or both components will have to be renewed.

5 Air cleaner – servicing, removal and refitting

1   At the specified intervals, remove the centre screw from the air cleaner lid and take off the lid. The edge of the lid will require flexing to ease it over the retaining tabs (photos).
2   Remove the filter element and discard it (photo).
3   Wipe out the air cleaner casing and insert the new element.
4   Refit the lid.
5   To remove the air cleaner casing, remove the securing nut (GM Varajet carburettor) or release the securing clip (Solex carburettor) and raise the casing until the air duct can be disconnected and the flexible pipes detached from the underside of the casing. Mark the hoses if there is any doubt as to their attachment points (photos).
6   Refitting is a reversal of removal.

6 Fuel tank – removal, servicing and refitting

1   The fuel tank is located under the floor beneath the rear seats and is held in place by supporting straps (photo).
2   Before removal, the tank should not be more than half full with fuel. Excess fuel should be syphoned out into a container which can be sealed.
3   Disconnect the handbrake cable at the equaliser. Disconnect the battery earth lead.
4   Remove the rear section of the exhaust pipe. If the pipe joints are severely corroded, it will probably be easier to detach the front end of the system from the manifold, release the flexible mountings and lower the complete system.

5   Disconnect the flexible supply hose from the fuel line and quickly plug it to prevent loss of fuel during removal of the tank (photo).
6   Disconnect the electric leads from the tank sender unit.
7   Release the hose clips on the flexible section of the tank filler pipe, apply some lubricant to the metal upper section and slide the flexible pipe upwards (photo).
8   Plug the tank filler pipe opening with a piece of rag to prevent dirt dropping into it.
9   Support the tank on a jack with a piece of wood as an insulator and then unscrew the mounting strap bolts.
10 Lower the tank just enough to be able to detach the vent hoses.
11 Lower the tank completely and withdraw it from under the vehicle.
12 If the tank contains sediment or water, first remove the tank sender unit as described in the next Section.
13 Pour in some paraffin, vigorously shake the tank and then allow to drain. Repeat as necessary until clean.
14 If the tank is leaking due to damage or corrosion, leave any repair to a specialist repairer. *Never attempt to weld or solder an empty tank unless it has been thoroughly purged by steam cleaning.*
15 Temporary repairs using fibreglass or other materials are not satisfactory as a long-term solution.
16 The protection of the tank bottom surface with thick coats of undersealing compound is recommended, even on new vehicles.
17 Refitting the fuel tank is a reversal of removal.
18 The vent container which is located at the upper part of the tank filler pipe has two connecting hoses, one vents to the outside of the vehicle and the other is from the fuel tank. As a safeguard against fuel flowing out of this pipe in the event of the vehicle overturning, the vent container incorporates a ball type flow cut-off valve.
19 When refitting the fuel tank, always make sure that the connecting hoses are in good order and that the clips are secure.

7 Fuel tank sender unit – removal and refitting

1   Drain the fuel from the tank by syphoning. Disconnect the battery earth lead.
2   Disconnect the electrical leads from the sender unit.

5.1A Removing air cleaner centre screw

5.1B Removing air cleaner lid

5.2 Renewing air cleaner filter element

5.5A Underside of air cleaner casing

5.5B Air cleaner hot air pick-up on exhaust manifold

6.1 Fuel tank and mounting straps

6.5 Fuel tank supply hose

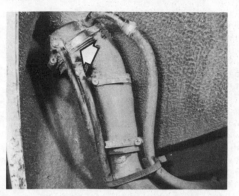

6.7 Fuel tank filler pipe and vent hose. Vent container arrowed

8.6a Varajet carburettor showing cold start fuel enrichment vacuum diaphragm unit

8.6b Varajet carburettor showing automatic choke housing

9.7 Adjusting bypass screw on Varajet carburettor

3   Using a suitable lever engaged in the cut-outs on the surface of the unit, unscrew it until it is released.

4   Carefully withdraw the tank unit with its float.

5   A defective sender unit must be renewed; no repair is possible.

6   Refit by reversing the removal operations. Make sure that the rubber seal is in good condition and that it does not slip during installation.

8   Carburettor – description

1   One of two types of carburettor may be fitted, according to engine type.

2   On all 1.2l and low compression 1.3l engines, a Solex 35 PDSI manual choke carburettor is used.

3   On 1.3l S engines, a Varajet II carburettor with automatic choke is used.

4   The Solex carburettor is of single barrel manual choke down-draught type with fixed jets and a separate idle circuit. A diaphragm-type accelerator pump is used, together with two enrichment systems which support the main jet system.

5   A temperature compensator is provided to give an air bleed into the intake manifold when the engine is hot. The compensator is attached to the side of the throttle flap body and consists of a bi-metal blade and a tapered plug. Opening temperature is 90°C (194°F).

6   The GM Varajet II carburettor is of twin-barrel downdraught type with automatic choke which is operated electrically (photos).

7   Enrichment and compensation systems are incorporated to provide optimum performance under all operating and load conditions, and a mechanically-operated accelerator pump is fitted.

8   A temperature compensator is fitted, its purpose being as described for the Solex carburettor.

9   A fuel cut-off valve is fitted to both carburettors to prevent engine run-on after it is switched off. The valve is of solenoid type, electrically-operated.

9   Carburettor – slow running adjustment

1   Both carburettors are adjusted during production and normally only the bypass screw should be altered to bring the slow running (idle) speed within the specified limits.

Solex

2   Have the engine at normal operating temperature.

3   Connect a tachometer to the engine in accordance with the manufacturer's instructions.

4   Start the engine and turn the bypass screw in or out as necessary to bring the engine speed to the specified level.

5   If the fuel/air ratio (mixture) is thought to be incorrect, indicated by weak or rich idling symptoms, or after carburettor overhaul or changed engine characteristics after a high mileage, the plastic sealing cap can be prised out and the mixture screw turned as necessary (anti-clockwise to enrich, clockwise to weaken).

6   This adjustment should normally only be carried out if an exhaust gas analyser can be used to ensure that the idling exhaust gas CO content is within the specified limits. Fit a new plastic seal on completion.

GM Varajet II

7   The procedure for adjusting the idle speed and mixture is very similar to that described for the Solex carburettor in the preceding paragraphs, but observe the different locations of the adjustment screws (photo).

10   Solex carburettor – in-vehicle adjustments

Note: *For all the following adjustments, remove the air cleaner.*

Fast idle

1   This is set automatically when the choke control is actuated.

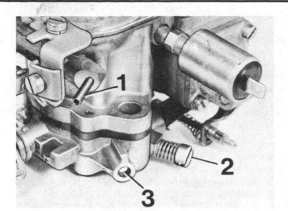

Fig. 3.2A Solex carburettor adjusting screws (Sec 9)

1   *Distributor vacuum connection*   3   *Mixture screw*
2   *Bypass screw*

Fig. 3.2B GM Varajet adjusting screws (Sec 9)

1   *Distributor vacuum connection*   3   *Mixture screw*
2   *Bypass screw*

Fig. 3.3 Accelerator pump rod (Solex) (Sec 10)

2   Correct setting of the fast idle screw can be verified by observing that with the throttle valve plate closed, the screw is just in contact with the throttle spindle lever, the choke control not being in operation.

Accelerator pump stroke

3   When the accelerator pump is correctly adjusted, the volume of fuel ejected from the pump discharge nozzle should be between 0.65 and 0.85 cc during one complete movement of the throttle valve plate from closed to fully open.

4   This discharge can be successfully measured using a small graduated measure. (It may be easier to measure the delivery over, say, 5 strokes, and divide the amount received by the number of strokes).

5   To adjust the quantity of discharged fuel, turn the nut on the rod which effectively increases or reduces the stroke of the pump. Squeeze the slotted end of the nut on completion to prevent it rotating due to engine vibration.

Float level

6   No adjustment tabs are provided on the float arm and provided the arm is not bent, any sign of incorrect fuel level must be due to a deformed or incorrect-thickness sealing washer under the fuel inlet valve.

11 GM Varajet carburettor – in-vehicle adjustments

Note: *For the following adjustments, first remove the air cleaner.*

Automatic choke

1   The normal setting for the automatic choke cover is when the pointer on the cover is one graduation past the centre mark on the scale in the 'R' (rich) direction (Fig. 3.4).

2   At this setting, the choke valve plate should take between 2 and 3 minutes to move from closed to fully open when the ignition is switched on.

Accelerator pump piston

3   The correct setting is as shown in Fig. 3.5 when dimension A (upper edge of pump rod to carburettor cover) is between 10.4 and 10.8 mm (0.410 and 0.425 in). The primary barrel throttle valve plate must be in the idle position when measuring.

4   Bend the pump lever if necessary at point B.

Fig. 3.4 Automatic choke housing (GM Varajet). Alignment marks arrowed (Sec 11)

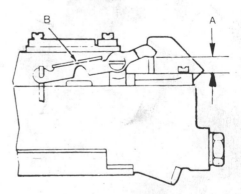

Fig. 3.5 Accelerator pump setting diagram (GM Varajet) (Sec 11)

A   *Pump lever travel*   B   *Adjustment point*

Choke valve plate opening

5   Carrying out this check may be done with the engine stationary or running.

Engine stationary

6   Set the automatic choke linkage so that the choke valve plate is closed and the fast idle screw is located on the centre step of the cam.

7   Using a vacuum source (modified bicycle pump or similar), create sufficient suction at the vacuum unit to move the baffle plate lever against its stop and against the pull of the bi-metal spring in the automatic choke cover.

8   The dimension A (choke valve plate to barrel bore) in Fig. 3.6 should be between 2.8 and 3.4 mm (0.11 and 0.13 in).

9   Adjust if necessary by turning the stop screw on the vacuum unit. Refer also to paragraphs 12 and 13.

Engine running

10   With the engine idling at operating temperature and air cleaner removed, move the fast idle cam so that the fast idle screw is located on the centre step of the cam.

11   Move the choke valve plate to the fully closed position and then check the gap between the edge of the choke plate and the barrel bore. This should be between 2.8 and 3.4 mm (0.11 and 0.13 in). If adjustment is needed, turn the stop screw on the vacuum unit.

12   Where the gap was checked and found to be less than specified, the end of the linkage will probably need bending backwards before turning the stop screw. This will ensure that a clearance is provided between the stop and the baffle plate lever.

13   Once adjustment is complete, check the clearance between the baffle plate lever and the pullrod while the pullrod is held in the fully extended position. The clearance should be between 0.1 and 0.3 mm (0.004 and 0.012 in). If necessary, bend the end of the pullrod to adjust.

Later models

14   In October 1980 a five-step fast idle cam was introduced on this carburettor and to ensure that the fast idle speed is correct at cold starting, the following revised procedure must be followed.

15   Have the engine at normal operating temperature.

16   Open the throttle valve plate slightly and position the fast idle cam so that the fast idle screw locates on the 4th step (2nd highest) when the throttle valve plate is released.

17   Start the engine without touching the accelerator pedal: the engine fast idle speed should be 2100 rpm. If it is not, adjust the fast idle screw and repeat the operation.

Float level

18   Remove the carburettor cover.

19   Using moderate finger pressure, hold the fuel inlet needle valve closed by applying pressure to the float arms and pivot clip.

20   The top surface of the float should be between 7.5 and 8.5 mm (0.295 and 0.334 in) below the carburettor top flange (photo).

21   Where necessary, bend the arms of the float equally at the points indicated (photo).

22   Before refitting the float, check that the clearance between the needle valve retaining spring and the arms of the float (Fig. 3.7) is 0.2 mm (0.008 in). Adjust if necessary by modifying the curvature of the spring.

12 Carburettor – removal and refitting

Solex

1   Remove the air cleaner.

2   Disconnect the vacuum pipe and the electrical lead from the fuel

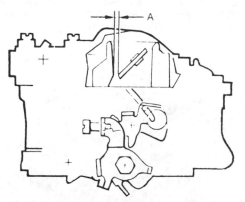

Fig. 3.6 Choke valve plate adjustment diagram (GM Varajet) (Sec 11)

A   Valve plate gap

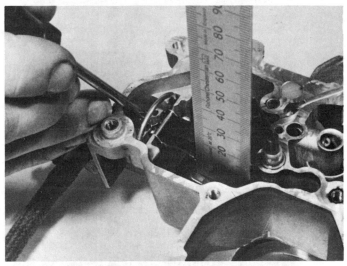

11.20 Checking Varajet float level

11.21 Varajet carburettor float – adjustment points arrowed

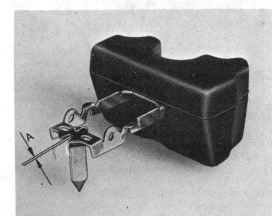

Fig. 3.7 Needle valve spring to float arm clearance A (GM Varajet) (Sec 11)

12.7 Fuel pipe banjo connection to carburettor

12.8 Removing carburettor from manifold

cut-off solenoid valve.
3 Disconnect the fuel supply hose.
4 Disconnect the throttle and choke controls, unscrew the two mounting nuts and remove the carburettor from the intake manifold.
5 Refitting is the reverse of removal. Use a new flange gasket.

GM Varajet
6 The operations are similar to those described for the Solex unit, but the leads from the automatic choke must also be disconnected.
7 The fuel supply pipe is attched by means of a banjo union which is disconnected by unscrewing the hollow centre bolt (photo).
8 The carburettor is held to the manifold by four mounting nuts (photo).
9 Refitting is the reverse of removal. Use a new flange gasket.

Fig. 3.8 Fast idle rod connecting clip (Solex) (Sec 13)

Fig. 3.9 Fuel inlet needle valve (Solex)(Sec 13)

13 Solex carburettor – overhaul

1 Major carburettor overhaul is not a routine operation and should only be carried out when components are obviously worn. Removal of the cover and mopping out the fuel and any sediment from the fuel bowl, and clearing the jets with compressed air, is usually sufficient to keep a carburettor in good working order. When a unit has covered a very high mileage, it will probably be more economical to renew it with a new or exchange rebuilt carburettor rather than to renew individual components.
2 With the carburettor removed from the engine and cleaned externally, remove the clip which retains the fast idle rod to the lever on the choke valve plate spindle.
3 Extract the six screws and remove the cover.
4 Use a socket wrench to unscrew the fuel inlet needle valve.
5 Extract the screw plug and withdraw the metering pin.
6 Extract the spring clip and withdraw the float from the carburettor bowl.
7 The part load enrichment valve is screwed into the base of the float bowl.
8 The main jet can be unscrewed if the plug in the float bowl is extracted and a screwdriver inserted through the hole.
9 The throttle valve housing is held to the main body of the carburettor by two securing screws. To remove the housing, first disconnect the accelerator pump link and then extract the screws.
10 The accelerator pump housing can be dismantled by extracting the four pump housing screws.
11 Clean all components and examine for wear or damage.
12 Blow through all jets and passages with air from a tyre pump; never probe them with wire in an attempt to clean them or their calibration will be ruined.
13 Reassembly is a reversal of removal, but carry out the checks and adjustments as described in Section 10 as work proceeds.

Fig. 3.10 Metering pin and plug (Solex) (Sec 13)

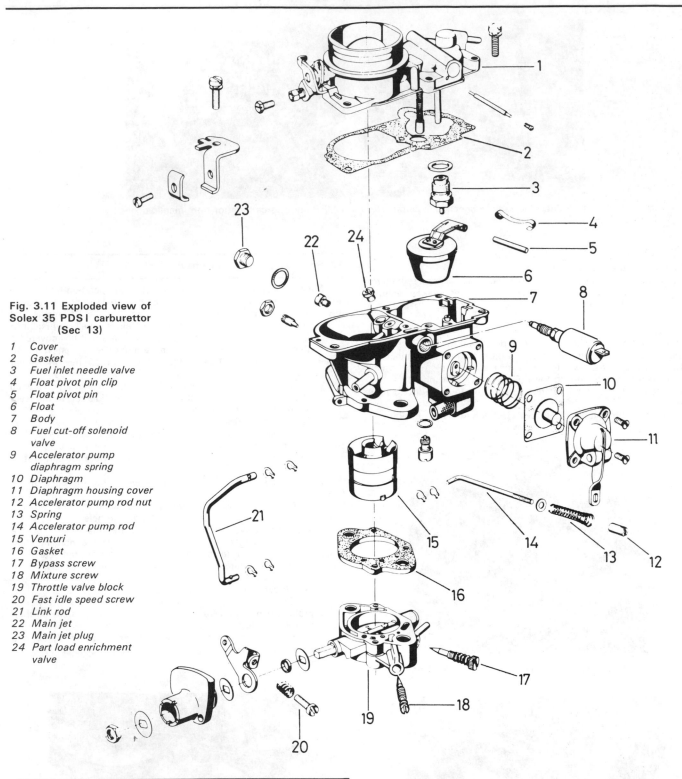

**Fig. 3.11 Exploded view of
Solex 35 PDSI carburettor
(Sec 13)**

1   Cover
2   Gasket
3   Fuel inlet needle valve
4   Float pivot pin clip
5   Float pivot pin
6   Float
7   Body
8   Fuel cut-off solenoid
     valve
9   Accelerator pump
     diaphragm spring
10   Diaphragm
11   Diaphragm housing cover
12   Accelerator pump rod nut
13   Spring
14   Accelerator pump rod
15   Venturi
16   Gasket
17   Bypass screw
18   Mixture screw
19   Throttle valve block
20   Fast idle speed screw
21   Link rod
22   Main jet
23   Main jet plug
24   Part load enrichment
     valve

14 GM Varajet carburettor – overhaul

1   Refer to Section 13, paragraph 1. Note also that on the GM
Varajet carburettor an inlet fuel filter is fitted which should be removed
and cleaned at regular intervals. Access is gained by disconnecting the
fuel delivery pipe and then unscrewing the union (photo).
2   Unscrew the seven screws and withdraw the cover. Do not disturb
the gasket at this stage. Take great care not to knock or bend the tubes
projecting from the cover, and do not attempt to remove them,
otherwise the cover will have to be renewed (photo).
3   Withdraw the accelerator pump piston and return spring (photo).
4   If necessary, the gasket can now be removed. A slit is provided in

the gasket to enable it to pass over the part load needle valve.
5   Withdraw the packing piece from the float chamber and lift out the
float and needle valve (photo).
6   To remove the part load needle valve, unscrew the threaded
retainer. When withdrawing the needle valve, take great care not to
bend or damage it.
7   Remove the pump suction valve spring retainer using a pair of
pliers.
8   Invert the float chamber to remove the check balls from the
accelerator pump bore and the suction valve drilling. If the balls are of
different diameter, note the original locations. On later models the
accelerator pump is retained by a plate and cannot be removed.

Fig. 3.12 Part load enrichment valve (Solex) (Sec 13)

Fig. 3.13 Removing main jet (Solex). Screwdriver arrowed (Sec 13)

14.1 Removing fuel inlet union to expose filter (Varajet)

Fig. 3.14 Cover securing screws (GM Varajet) (Sec 14)

14.2 Removing Varajet carburettor cover

14.3 Withdrawing accelerator pump piston and spring from Varajet carburettor

9   Use a screwdriver to remove the main jet and the float needle valve seat.
10   The throttle valve housing is secured to the float chamber by four screws. Extract the screws and separate carefully to avoid damaging the gasket.
11   Clean all components and examine for wear or damage.
12   Blow through the jets and passages with air from a tyre pump; never probe them with wire in an attempt to clean them or their calibration will be ruined.
13   Commence reassembly by dropping the check balls into the accelerator pump bore (if removed) and the suction valve drilling. If the balls are of different diameter, ensure they are returned to the

Fig. 3.15 Removing cover gasket (GM Varajet)(Sec 14)

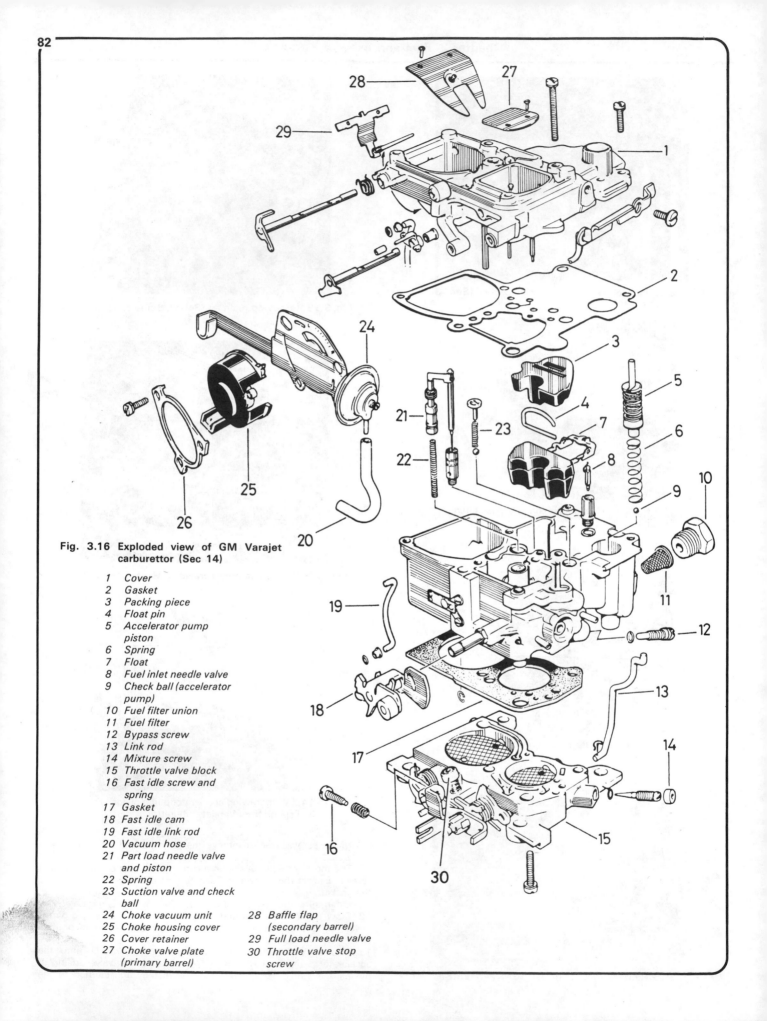

Fig. 3.16 Exploded view of GM Varajet carburettor (Sec 14)

1 Cover
2 Gasket
3 Packing piece
4 Float pin
5 Accelerator pump piston
6 Spring
7 Float
8 Fuel inlet needle valve
9 Check ball (accelerator pump)
10 Fuel filter union
11 Fuel filter
12 Bypass screw
13 Link rod
14 Mixture screw
15 Throttle valve block
16 Fast idle screw and spring
17 Gasket
18 Fast idle cam
19 Fast idle link rod
20 Vacuum hose
21 Part load needle valve and piston
22 Spring
23 Suction valve and check ball
24 Choke vacuum unit
25 Choke housing cover
26 Cover retainer
27 Choke valve plate (primary barrel)
28 Baffle flap (secondary barrel)
29 Full load needle valve
30 Throttle valve stop screw

14.5 Varajet float and fuel inlet valve

Fig. 3.17 Removing part load needle valve (Sec 14)

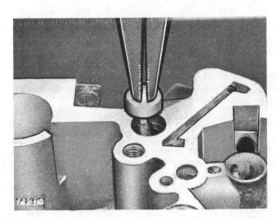

Fig. 3.18 Removing pump suction valve spring retainer (Sec 14)

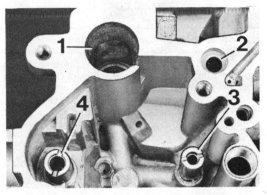

Fig. 3.19 Jet and bore identification (GM Varajet) (Sec 14)

1 Accelerator pump bore	3 Main jet
2 Suction valve spring drilling	4 Fuel inlet needle valve seat

Fig. 3.20 Throttle block securing screws (GM Varajet) (Sec 14)

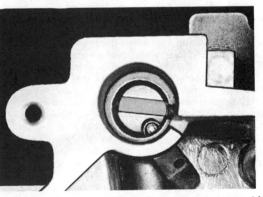

Fig. 3.21 Accelerator pump check ball correctly located (GM Varajet) (Sec 14)

Fig. 3.22 Fuel inlet needle valve secured with spring (GM Varajet) (Sec 14)

correct location. Make sure that the accelerator pump ball locates correctly in its recess.

14 Fit the part load valve assembly.

15 Refit the fuel needle valve, hooking the valve spring onto the platform as shown (Fig. 3.22). Lower the valve into its seat and guide the float pivot clip into the vertical slots in the float chamber. The clip may be fitted either way round.

16 Fit the float chamber packing piece so that its slot is located over the float pivot clip.

17 Fit the carburettor cover and check the free movement of the accelerator pump piston (Section 11) before tightening the securing screws.

18 If the automatic choke cover was removed, make sure when refitting it that the choke flap tang engages in the eye at the end of the bi-metal coil. Set the choke cover as described in Section 11.

19 Carry out the checks and adjustments as described in Section 11 as reassembly progresses.

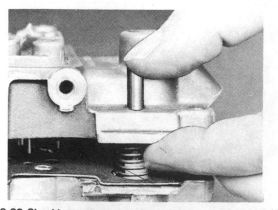

Fig. 3.23 Checking movement of accelerator pump piston (GM Varajet) (Sec 14)

Fig. 3.24 Fitting automatic choke housing (GM Varajet) (Sec 14)

1 Eye	2 Tang

15 Fuel cut-off valve – removal and refitting

1   This valve is fitted to all later model carburettors to prevent running-on by cutting off fuel to the idling circuit as soon as the ignition is switched off.
2   To remove the valve, disconnect the electrical lead from it and using an open-ended spanner, unscrew it from the carburettor.
3   If the valve malfunctions it must be renewed, no repair being possible.

16 Accelerator and choke controls – adjustment and cable renewal

Accelerator
1   The throttle control is of cable-operated type, with a pendant foot pedal.
2   There are two points of adjustment. A screw is located on the pedal arm to control the fully released position of the pedal stop, and locknuts are located on a threaded section of the outer cable at the bracket on the intake manifold.
3   Adjust the cable so that when the accelerator pedal is released, there is just the slightest amount of slackness in the cable at the carburettor end.
4   With the air cleaner removed, check that when the pedal is fully depressed, the throttle valve plate is fully open. Adjust the locknuts and the pedal stop screw to achieve the desired results. On models equipped with a GM Varajet carburettor, it should be noted that the secondary throttle valve plate starts to open when the primary throttle valve plate has opened by $\frac{2}{3}$rds of its travel. Opening of the secondary throttle will not occur at all unless the choke valve plate is fully open (engine hot), so have the engine at normal operating temperature before carrying out accelerator pedal setting on these vehicles.
5   To renew the cable, slacken off all adjustment at the carburettor by unscrewing the locknuts. Pull the cable end fitting away from the pedal arm and pass the inner cable through the slot in the pedal arm tab (photo).
6   Remove the nuts completely at the carburettor end and withdraw the clip from the ball end fitting at the throttle linkage (photos).
7   Withdraw the cable through the bulkhead grommet.
8   Refitting is a reversal of removal. Adjust the cable as described in paragraphs 3 and 4.

Choke control
9   The manual choke cable fitted to Solex carburettor versions is of normal fixing at the instrument panel by means of a bezel nut.
10   Extract the clip, take off the control knob and unscrew the bezel nut.
11   Release the cable at the carburettor and withdraw the cable into the vehicle interior.
12   When refitting, make sure that the choke lever is fully off when the control knob is pushed in.
13   On later 1200 models, the choke control incorporates a warning switch with instrument panel lamp (photo). On this type of control, the knob is simply unscrewed and the switch bezel nut released from the support bracket under the lower edge of the facia panel.

17 Manifolds and exhaust system – removal and refitting

1   The intake and exhaust manifolds are on the same side of the engine on 1.2l models, but on opposite sides (crossflow) on 1.3l models.
2   On 1.2l engines removal and refitting of both manifolds is simply a matter of unscrewing the fixing nuts. The carburettor will have to be removed to give access to the bolt hidden beneath it (see Chapter 1).
3   Always use new gaskets on refitting, and tighten the nuts to the specified torque.
4   To remove the intake manifold from the 1.3l engine, the cooling system must first be drained and the heater hose disconnected from the manifold.

16.5 Accelerator pedal connections

16.6A Accelerator cable attachment to carburettor throttle linkage and support bracket

16.6B Extracting clip from throttle link ball end fitting

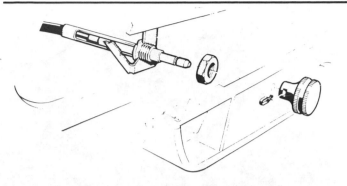

Fig. 3.25 Choke control knob (typical) (Sec 16)

5 Disconnect the lead from the coolant temperature sender and the vacuum pipe from its stub, both of which are screwed into the manifold.

6 The alternator will also have to be moved on its mountings before the manifold can be withdrawn.

7 A new gasket can be fitted to the exhaust manifold without having to disconnect the exhaust downpipes, as there is a flexible joint at the first section coupling of the exhaust system.

8 A heated air shroud for the supply of warm air to the air cleaner is fitted to all exhaust manifolds.

9 The exhaust system comprises twin downpipes, a spring-loaded flexible coupling to absorb the flexing of the power unit on its resilient mountings, a silencer box and an expansion box (photos).

10 The system is suspended on flexible mountings.

11 The sections of the system can be renewed separately by releasing the clamps but as the joints are usually well rusted or corroded, it is recommended that the complete system be removed from under the vehicle and the system dismantled afterwards. The vehicle will have to be well raised to provide clearance for removal.

12 Clean the pipes and sockets and apply a little grease to make connection easier.

13 Fit the clamps, but do not tighten them until the system has been installed and the attitude of the silencer checked for correct alignment. Renew any suspect flexible mounting components and check that any slight deflection of the system will not cause it to knock against adjacent components of the vehicle suspension or bodywork. Tighten the clamp bolts (photo).

14 If the exhaust system is being repaired Holts Flexiwrap and Holts Gun Gum exhaust repair systems can be used for effective repairs to exhaust pipes and silencer boxes, including ends and bends. Holts Flexiwrap is an MOT approved permanent exhaust repair.

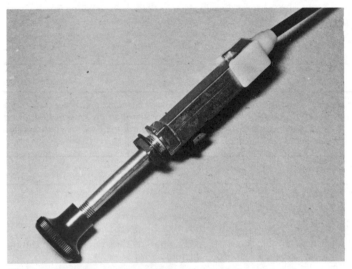

16.13 Choke control with electric warning switch

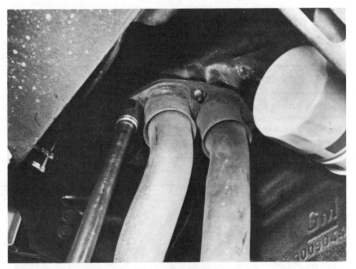

17.9A Unscrewing exhaust downpipe flange nut

17.9B Unscrewing exhaust pipe flexible coupling bolt

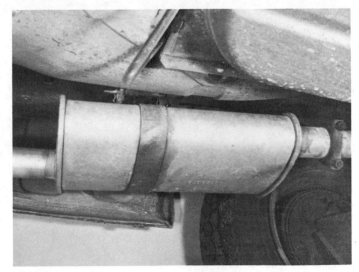

17.9C Exhaust silencer

17.9D Exhaust expansion box

17.13 Exhaust clamp and bracket

18 Fault diagnosis – fuel system

Unsatisfactory engine performance and excessive fuel consumption are not necessarily the fault of the fuel system or carburettor. In fact they more commonly occur as a result of ignition and timing faults. Before acting on the following it is necessary to check the ignition system first. Even though a fault may lie in the fuel system it will be difficult to trace unless the ignition is correct. The faults below, therefore, assume that this has been attended to first (where appropriate).

Symptom	Reason(s)
Smell of petrol when engine is stopped	Leaking fuel lines or unions Leaking fuel tank
Smell of petrol when engine is idling	Leaking fuel line unions between pump and carburettor Overflow of fuel from float chamber due to wrong level setting, ineffective needle valve or punctured float
Excessive fuel consumption for reasons not covered by leaks or float chamber faults	Worn jets Over-rich setting Sticking mechanism Dirty air cleaner element Sticking air cleaner thermostatic mechanism (dual barrel carburettor)
Difficult starting, uneven running, lack of power, cutting out	One or more jets blocked or restricted Float chamber fuel level too low or needle valve sticking Fuel pump not delivering sufficient fuel Faulty solenoid fuel shut-off valve (if fitted) Induction leak
Difficult starting when cold	Choke control or automatic choke maladjusted Insufficient use of manual choke Automatic choke not cocked before starting
Difficult starting when hot	Excessive use of manual choke, or automatic choke malfunction Accelerator pedal pumped before starting Vapour lock (especially in hot weather or at high altitude)
Engine does not respond properly to throttle	Faulty accelerator pump Blocked jet(s) Slack in accelerator cable
Engine idle speed drops when hot	Defective temperature compensator Overheated fuel pump
Engine runs on	Faulty fuel cut-off valve

Chapter 4 Ignition system

For modifications, and information applicable to later models, see Supplement at end of manual

Contents

Specifications

Firing order ....
1-3-4-2, No 1 cylinder at the timing end (right-hand side of the car)

Spark plugs
1196 cc ohv engines .... Champion RL82YCC or RL82YC
1297 cc ohc engines .... Champion RN7YCC or RN7YC
Electrode gap:
  RL82YCC and RN7YCC .... 0.8 mm (0.032 in)
  RL82YC and RN7YC .... 0.7 mm (0.028 in)

HT leads
1196 cc and 1297 cc (to 1982) .... Champion CLS 3, boxed set

Ignition coil

	Delco-Remy	Bosch
Make		
Type	12 VDR 502	DF 0.7 KW 12 V
Code number	3 474 200	0 221 119 023
Primary winding resistance	1.2 to 1.6 ohms	1.2 to 1.6 ohms
Spark measurement gap	14 mm (0.55 in)	14 mm (0.55 in)

Distributor

	Delco-Remy	Bosch
Make		
Code number	340 5488	0 231 186 029
Rotor rotation	Clockwise	Clockwise
Contact breaker gap	0.4 mm (0.016 in)	0.4 mm (0.016 in)
Dwell angle	47° to 53° (53 to 59 %)	47° to 53° (53 to 59%)

Ignition timing
Static or at idle speed (vacuum pipe disconnected):
  12 and 12S engines .... 5° btdc (crankshaft pulley notch opposite mark on timing cover)
  13 and 13S engines .... 10° btdc (crankshaft pulley notch opposite pointer on oil pump housing)

Centrifugal advance (engine rpm, crankshaft degrees):

	12/12S engine	13 engine	13S engine
1000 rpm	0° to 2°	0°	0°
1500 rpm	9° to 17°	2° to 10°	2° to 10°
3800 rpm	24° to 30°	22° to 29°	19° to 22°
4000 rpm	–	25° to 31°	19° to 24°

Torque wrench settings

	lbf ft	Nm
Spark plugs:		
1196cc ohv engines	29	40
1297cc ohc engines	15	20

1 General description

In order that the engine can run correctly it is necessary for an electrical spark to ignite the fuel/air mixture in the combustion chamber at exactly the right moment in relation to engine speed and load. The ignition system is based on feeding low tension voltage from the battery to the coil where it is converted to high tension voltage. The high tension voltage is powerful enough to jump the spark plug gap in the cylinders many times a second under high compression, providing that the system is in good condition and that all adjustments are correct.

The ignition system is divided into two circuits, low tension and high tension.

The low tension circuit (sometimes known as the primary) consists of the battery, lead to the ignition switch, lead from the ignition switch to the low tension or primary coil windings, and the lead from the low tension coil windings to the contact breaker points and condenser in the distributor.

The high tension circuit consists of the high tension or secondary coil winding, the heavy ignition lead from the centre of the coil to the centre of the distributor cap, the rotor arm, and the spark plug leads and spark plugs.

The system functions in the following manner. Low tension voltage is changed in the coil into high tension voltage by the opening and closing of the contact breaker points in the low tension circuit. High tension voltage is then fed via the carbon brush in the centre of the distributor cap to the rotor arm of the distributor cap, and each time it comes in line with one of the four metal segments in the cap, which are connected to the spark plug leads, the opening and closing of the contact breaker points causes the high tension voltage to build up, jump the gap from the rotor arm to the appropriate metal segment and so via the spark plug lead to the spark plug, where it finally jumps the spark plug gap before going to earth.

The ignition is advanced and retarded automatically, to ensure that the spark occurs at just the right instant for the particular load at the prevailing engine speed.

The ignition advance is controlled both mechanically and by a vacuum operated system. The mechanical governor comprises two weights, which move out from the distributor shaft as the engine speed rises due to centrifugal force. As they move outwards they rotate the cam relative to the distributor shaft, and so advance the spark. The weights are held in postion by two light springs and it is the tension of the springs which is largely responsible for correct spark advancement.

The vacuum control consists of a diaphragm, one side of which is cconnected via a small bore tube to the carburettor, and the other side to the contact breaker plate. Depression in the inlet manifold and carburettor, which varies with engine speed and throttle opening, causes the diaphragm to move, so moving the contact breaker plate, and advancing or retarding the spark.

A resistance wire in the low tension feed to the coil keeps the coil voltage down to 6V during normal running. This wire is bypassed when the starter motor is operating, to compensate for reduced battery voltage.

2 Routine maintenance

1 *Spark plugs:* Remove the plugs and thoroughly clean away all traces of carbon. Examine the porcelain insulator round the central electrode inside the plug. If damaged discard the plug. Reset the gap between the electrodes. Do not use a set of plugs for more than 12 000 miles (20 000 km) — it is false economy.
2 *Distributor:* Every 6000 miles (10 000 km) remove the cap, rotor arm, cover and bearing plates (ohc) and put one or two drops of engine oil into the centre of the cam recess where appropriate (photo). Smear the surfaces of the cam itself with petroleum jelly. Do not over-lubricate as any excess could get onto the contact point surfaces and cause ignition difficulties. At the same time examine the contact point surfaces. If there is a build-up of deposits on one face and a pit in the other it will be impossible to set the gap correctly and they should be refaced or renewed. Set the gap when the contact surfaces are in order.
3 *General:* Examine all leads and terminals for signs of broken or cracked insulation. Also check all terminal connections for slackness or signs of fracturing of some strands of wire. Partly broken wire should be renewed. The HT leads are particularly important as any insulation faults will cause the high voltage to 'jump' to the nearest earth and this will prevent a spark at the plug. Check that no HT leads are loose or in a position where the insulation could wear due to rubbing against part of the engine.

3 Distributor contact breaker points – gap and dwell angle adjustment

1 Prise the distributor cap cover apart and hinge open to remove (photo).
2 Unclip the distributor cap and lift the cap clear. On Delco-Remy distributors the cap is retained by two screws (photo).
3 Wipe the inside and outside of the cap clean with a dry cloth. Scrape away any small deposits from the four studs and inspect the cover for cracks or surface deterioration. Check the brush in the centre of the cap, it should protrude about $\frac{1}{4}$ in (6 mm). Renew the cap if cracked or if any of the HT studs are corroded, worn away or cracked.
4 Lift the distributor rotor arm from the central shaft and wipe the metal tip clean (photo).
5 Remove the plastic cover which protects the contact breaker and prevents condensation from settling on the mechanism and reducing its effectiveness (photo). Unscrew and remove the rotor shaft bearing plates (ohc) (photos).
6 Now that the contact breakers are exposed, gently prise the contacts apart and examine the condition of their faces. If they are rough, pitted or dirty, it will be necessary to remove them for resurfacing or for new points to be fitted.
7 Presuming the points are satisfactory, or they have been cleaned or replaced, the points gap must now be correctly set. With the Bosch distributor fitted to ohc engines, it is essential that the rotor shaft bearing plates are refitted before this operation. Unless the rotor shaft is positively located, an accurate points gap cannot be set. Measure the gap between the points by turning the engine until the contact breaker arm is on the peak of one of the four cam lobes. Refer to the Specifications for the size of the feeler gauge to use when measuring the gap. Take care not to contaminate the point faces with oil.
8 If the points are too close or too far apart, slacken the contact breaker mounting screw. Move the stationary point until the correct gap has been achieved and then secure by tightening the setscrew in

the breaker set mounting plate (photo).
9 Check the gap once again to ensure the adjustment was not disturbed when the set screw was tightened.
10 Refit the plastic cover, then the rotor arm and finally the distributor cap with its plastic cover.
11 On modern engines, setting the contact breaker gap in the distributor using feeler gauges must be regarded as a basic adjustment only. For optimum engine performance, the dwell angle must be checked. The dwell angle is the number of degrees through which the distributor cam turns during the period between the instance of closure and opening of the contact breaker points. Checking the dwell angle not only gives a more accurate setting of the contact breaker gap but also evens out any variations in the gap which could be caused by wear in the distributor shaft or its bushes, or difference in height of any of the cam peaks.
12 The angle should be checked with a dwell meter connected in accordance wth the maker's instructions. Refer to the Specifications for the correct dwell angle. If the dwell angle is too large, increase the points gap, if too small, reduce the points gap.
13 The dwell angle should always be adjusted before checking and adjusting the ignition timing.

4 Distributor contact breaker points – removal and refitting

1 If the contact breaker points are burned, pitted or badly worn, they must be removed and either be renewed or have their faces filed smooth and flat if they are still serviceable.
2 Remove the distributor cover, the cap, rotor arm, and contact breaker mechanism cover.
3 *Bosch distributors:* Where a rotor spindle outer bearing plate is fitted, undo the two screws and remove the plate. Remove the LT spade connector, then remove the setscrew retaining the contact breaker mechanism to the baseplate and lift out the complete assembly (photos).
4 *Delco-Remy distributors:* Undo and remove the setscrew retaining the contact mechanism to the baseplate. Ease the moving contact arm spring from the insulator assembly on the fixed contact plate and remove the condenser and LT spade terminals (photo).
5 Lift off the moving contact arm and spring followed by the fixed contact plate (photo).
6 It is possible to reface the contact points using a fine carborundum stone or emery paper. However, if the points show signs of burning or pitting, it is strongly recommended that they are replaced with a new set. Clean the faces of new points with methylated spirit before fitting.
7 Refitting of the points follows the reverse sequence to removal. When refitting the Delco-Remy type points, ensure that the LT and condenser terminals are fitted in the correct order on the insulator post (photo).
8 Finally, adjust the points gap, as described in Section 3.

5 Condenser – removal, testing and refitting

1 The purpose of the condenser (sometimes known as the capacitor) is to ensure that when the contact breaker points open there is no sparking across them which would waste voltage and cause wear.
2 On the Bosch distributor the condenser is mounted on the outside of the distributor body whilst on Delco-Remy models it is fitted on the contact breaker baseplate. If it develops a short-circuit it will cause ignition failure as the points will be prevented from interrupting the low tension circuit.
3 If the engine become very difficult to start or begins to miss after several miles running and the breaker points show signs of excessive burning, then the condition of the condenser must be suspect. A further test can be made by separating the points by hand with the ignition switched on. If this is accompanied by a strong blue flash it is indicative that the condenser has failed in the open circuit mode.
4 Without special equipment the only sure way to diagnose condenser trouble is to replace a suspected unit with a new one and note if there is any improvement.
5 To remove the condenser from the distributor take off the distributor cap, rotor arm and cover.

Bosch distributor
6 Remove the bearing plates, then pull off the contact points LT lead

2.2 Oiling distributor felt pad (Delco Remy)

3.1 Removing Bosch distributor cap cover (ohc)

3.2 Removing distributor cap screw (Delco Remy)

3.4 Removing the rotor arm – Bosch distributor (ohc)

3.5A Removing Bosch distributor plastic cover (ohc)

3.5B Bosch rotor shaft upper bearing plate (ohc)

3.5C Bosch rotor shaft lower bearing plate (ohc)

3.8 Adjusting contact breaker points gap (Delco Remy)

4.3A Releasing contact breaker screw – Bosch distributor (ohc)

4.3B LT spade connector to contact breaker – Bosch distributor (ohc)

4.4 Releasing wires from distributor terminal block (Delco Remy)

4.5 Removing contact breaker set (Delco Remy)

4.7 Delco Remy LT wires correctly fitted to terminal

5.10 Releasing condenser screw (Delco Remy)

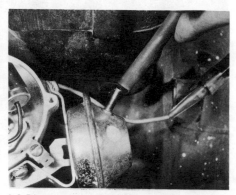
6.8 Disconnecting distributor vacuum pipe (Delco Remy)

6.9A Unbolting distributor (ohc)

6.9B Removing distributor (ohc)

6.9C Removing Delco Remy distributor from (ohv) engine

from the spade terminal located inside the distributor casing.

7   Remove the LT lead connecting the coil to the distributor, from the ignition coil.

8   Undo and remove the screw securing the condenser and LT lead assembly to the distributor case. Note that the condenser is supplied complete with the LT lead to the coil and the LT spade tag and mounting grommet.

Delco-Remy distributor

9   Ease out the moving contact arm spring from the insulating post and lift out the condenser spade terminal.

10   Remove the condenser retaining screw and lift out the condenser (photo).

All distributors

11   Refitting of the condenser follows the reverse procedure to removal.

6   Distributor – removal and refitting

1   Disconnect the battery earth terminal.

2   Remove the distributor cap and place it aside and out of the way.

3   If the cap and leads are to be dismantled then number the leads by putting tags on them to avoid mixing them up on reassembly.

4   Remove the spark plugs and check that the transmission is in neutral. This will enable the engine to be turned over by hand without resistance from compression.

5   Rotate the engine by means of the crankshaft-pulley bolt until the engine is at tdc on the compression stroke on No 1 cylinder. When a Bosch distributor is fitted the distributor rotor arm line and the corresponding mark on the top of the distributor body will be in alignment. For Delco-Remy distributors align the rotor arm and earth connection screw. In addition the timing marks on the crankshaft pulley and the timing case will be in alignment.

6   Once the engine has been set in this position ensure that the engine is not disturbed from this position whilst the distributor is

removed. This will make the installation task easier.

7   Detach the LT lead from the coil.

8   Disconnect the vacuum advance tube from the distributor (photo).

9   Unscrew and remove the distributor clamp plate bolt or nut and withdraw the distributor from the engine (photos).

10   Refitting the distributor is a direct reversal of the removal sequence. Check that the engine has not been disturbed from the position set before removal. If the engine was turned over for any reason reset it to the position given in paragraph 5 (No 1 piston at tdc on the firing stroke).

11   *1196cc ohv engine:* The distributor on this engine is driven by a skew gear from the camshaft and because of this the distributor shaft will turn slightly whenever the distributor is removed or refitted. To counter this the shaft must be pre-positioned so that, on assembly, it will turn to the correct position. Turn the shaft forward in the direction of rotation for about 20° beyond the alignment marks noted in paragraph 5, check that the oil pump drive slot is still in the correct mating position as shown (photo), and then insert the distributor into its location.

12   *1297 cc ohc engine:* Fit a new O-ring seal to the distributor flange and then align the groove in the rotor drive spindle with the timing mark on the edge of the case. Check that the slot in the camshaft drive is in the correct relative position and engage the distributor in its location (photos).

13   On either type of engine when the distributor has been engaged with the drive check that rotor is in the correct position as noted in paragraph 5 and, if all is well, refit the distributor clamp and tighten the bolt or nut as appropriate.

14   Reconnect the LT lead to the coil and the vacuum tube to the vacuum unit. Refit the cap, leads, plugs and battery earth terminal to complete.

15   Check the timing using a stroboscope as described in Section 8.

7   Distributor – dismantling, inspection and reassembly

1   Before dismantling the distributor, check on the availability of parts which may be necessary. If the distributor has seen a lot of

Are your plugs trying to tell you something?

Normal.
Grey-brown deposits, lightly coated core nose. Plugs ideally suited to engine, and engine in good condition.

Heavy Deposits.
A build up of crusty deposits, light-grey sandy colour in appearance.
Fault: Often caused by worn valve guides, excessive use of upper cylinder lubricant, or idling for long periods.

Lead Glazing.
Plug insulator firing tip appears yellow or green/yellow and shiny in appearance.
Fault: Often caused by incorrect carburation, excessive idling followed by sharp acceleration. Also check ignition timing.

Carbon fouling.
Dry, black, sooty deposits.
Fault: over-rich fuel mixture.
Check: carburettor mixture settings, float level, choke operation, air filter.

Oil fouling.
Wet, oily deposits. Fault: worn bores/piston rings or valve guides; sometimes occurs (temporarily) during running-in period.

Overheating.
Electrodes have glazed appearance, core nose very white – few deposits. Fault: plug overheating. Check: plug value, ignition timing, fuel octane rating (too low) and fuel mixture (too weak).

Electrode damage.
Electrodes burned away; core nose has burned, glazed appearance. Fault: pre-ignition. Check: for correct heat range and as for 'overheating'.

Split core nose.
(May appear initially as a crack). Fault: detonation or wrong gap-setting technique. Check: ignition timing, cooling system, fuel mixture (too weak).

WHY DOUBLE COPPER IS BETTER FOR YOUR ENGINE.

Unique Trapezoidal Copper Cored Earth Electrode — 50% Larger Spark Area — Copper Cored Centre Electrode

Champion Double Copper plugs are the first in the world to have copper core in both centre _and_ earth electrode. This innovative design means that they run cooler by up to 100°C – giving greater efficiency and longer life. These double copper cores transfer heat away from the tip of the plug faster and more efficiently. Therefore, Double Copper runs at cooler temperatures than conventional plugs giving improved acceleration response and high speed performance with no fear of pre-ignition.

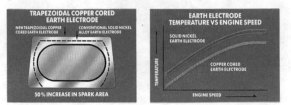

Champion Double Copper plugs also feature a unique trapezoidal earth electrode giving a 50% increase in spark area. This, together with the double copper cores, offers greatly reduced electrode wear, so the spark stays stronger for longer.

- **FASTER COLD STARTING**
- **FOR UNLEADED OR LEADED FUEL**
- **ELECTRODES UP TO 100°C COOLER**
- **BETTER ACCELERATION RESPONSE**
- **LOWER EMISSIONS**
- **50% BIGGER SPARK AREA**
- **THE LONGER LIFE PLUG**

Plug Tips/Hot and Cold.
Spark plugs must operate within well-defined temperature limits to avoid cold fouling at one extreme and overheating at the other.
Champion and the car manufacturers work out the best plugs for an engine to give optimum performance under all conditions, from freezing cold starts to sustained high speed motorway cruising.
Plugs are often referred to as hot or cold. With Champion, the higher the number on its body, the hotter the plug, and the lower the number the cooler the plug. For the correct plug for your car refer to the specifications at the beginning of this chapter.

Plug Cleaning
Modern plug design and materials mean that Champion no longer recommends periodic plug cleaning. Certainly don't clean your plugs with a wire brush as this can cause metal conductive paths across the nose of the insulator so impairing its performance and resulting in loss of acceleration and reduced m.p.g.
However, if plugs are removed, always carefully clean the area where the plug seats in the cylinder head as grit and dirt can sometimes cause gas leakage.
Also wipe any traces of oil or grease from plug leads as this may lead to arcing.

CHAMPION

DOUBLE **CC** COPPER

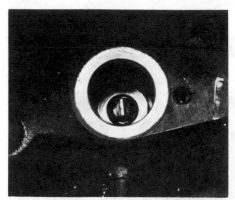
6.11 Oil pump driveshaft setting (ohv)

6.12A Fitting distributor O-ring seal (ohc)

6.12B Distributor drive slot on camshaft (ohc)

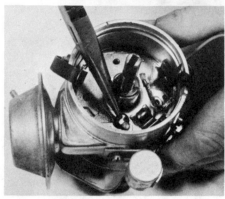
7.6 Extracting vacuum rod circlip (Bosch)

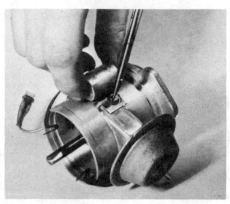
7.7A Condenser/vacuum unit fixing screw (Bosch)

7.7B Removing vacuum unit (Bosch)

7.8A Baseplate/clip securing screw (Bosch)

7.8B Removing baseplate (Bosch)

7.8C Releasing baseplate screw (Delco Remy)

7.8D Baseplate ready for removal (Delco Remy)

7.9A Centrifugal weights and springs (Bosch)

7.9B Baseplate removed (Delco Remy)

service then the chances are that it is generally worn and should be renewed.

2   If the distributor is to be dismantled, the work should be carried out on a clean workbench where the respective components can be laid out in order as they are removed.

3   If it has not already been removed, disconnect the distributor cap and cover together with the leads (see Section 3). Withdraw the rotor arm and damp proof cover.

4   Remove the contact breaker set as described in Section 4.

5   Remove the condenser as described in Section 5.

6   On Bosch distributors prise the circlip from the vacuum control rod-to-timing plate spindle (photo).

7   Unscrew the vacuum control unit retaining screws and remove the unit, unhooking the control rod (photos).

8   Unscrew and lift out the baseplates (photos).

9   The centrifugal weights and springs can now be inspected and removed if required, but take note of the respective spring and weight positions (photos).

10   To withdraw the spindle, the drivegear or drive dog must be removed. Use a small punch and drive out the retaining pin and then extract the spindle upwards.

11   Clean all parts in an oil and grease solvent and wipe/blow dry ready for inspection.

12   Inspect all components for obvious signs of excessive wear or damage. Check the spindle play and drivegear teeth or drive dog faces for wear. Renew as applicable any parts which are defective or suspect.

13   Prior to reassembly smear all sliding parts and the centrifugal weight springs with a small amount of medium grease.

14   Slide the spindle into position and relocate the drivegear or dog. Drive a new retaining pin into position to secure the gear or dog.

15   Reassemble the centrifugal weights and springs, ensuring that they are securely located.

16   Refit the contact plates and tighten screws to secure.

17   Refit the vacuum control unit, relocating the control rod and tightening the screws to secure. On the Bosch distributor relocate the circlip to retain the rod on the plate spindle. Apply a little grease to the plate spindle.

18   Refit the condenser as described in Section 5.

19   Refit the contact breaker set as described in Section 4 and readjust the contact gap in accordance with Section 3.

20   Lubricate the sliding parts of the contact breaker base plate assembly with some clean oil and smear a small amount of high melting-point grease onto the cam surface.

21   Check the spindle for freedom of rotation and the contact points for correct operation. Support the gear and apply finger pressure to the rotor arm in the reverse direction to that in which it operates. It should spring back freely to its static position.

22   The distributor is now ready for refitting.

8   Ignition timing – adjustment

1   It is necessary to time the ignition when it has been upset due to overhauling or dismantling which may have altered the relationship between the position of the pistons and the moment at which the distributor delivers the spark. Also, if maladjustments have affected the engine performance it is very desirable, although not always essential, to reset the timing starting from scratch. In the following procedures it is assumed that the intention is to obtain standard performance from the standard engine which is in reasonable condition. It is also assumed that the recommended fuel octane rating is used.

2   Set the transmission to neutral and remove all four spark plugs.

3   Place a thumb over No 1 cylinder spark plug hole (right-hand cylinder), and rotate the engine clockwise by means of the crankshaft pulley bolt until pressure is felt building up in No 1 cylinder. This indicates that the No 1 cylinder piston is approaching top dead centre (tdc) on the firing stroke.

4   Continue to rotate the crankshaft until the BTDC notch in the pulley is directly opposite the timing cover mark or the pointer as appropriate.

5   Remove the distributor cap and check that the rotor is opposite the No 1 cylinder segment in the cap.

6   Slacken the distributor clamp bolt or nut and rotate the distributor body until the contact breaker points are just opening and then tighten the clamp bolt or nut.

7   Difficulty is sometimes experienced in determining exactly when the contact breaker points open. This can be ascertained most accurately by connecting a 12V bulb in parallel with the contact breaker points (one lead to earth and the other from the distributor low tension terminal). Switch on the ignition and turn the distributor body until the bulb lights up, indicating that the points have just opened.

8   If it was found impossible to align the rotor arm correctly one of two things is wrong. Either the distributor driveshaft has been incorrectly fitted in which case the distributor must be removed and replaced as described in Section 6 of this Chapter, or the distributor cam assembly has been incorrectly fitted on the driveshaft. To rectify this, it will be necessary to partially dismantle the distributor and check the position of the cam assembly on the centrifugal advance mechanism; it may be 180° out of position.

9   As a final check on the ignition timing the best method is to use a strobe lamp.

10   Put a spot of white paint on the notch in the crankshaft pulley and the timing mark or the pointer and connect the strobe light into the No 1 cylinder HT circuit following the maker's instructions. Disconnect and plug the distributor vacuum pipe.

11   Run the engine at idling speed and point the strobe lamp at the timing marks. At idling speed the white paint marks should appear to be immediately opposite each other; open the throttle slightly and check that as the engine revolutions rise the spot on the crankshaft pulley moves anti-clockwise. This indicates the centrifugal advance mechanism is operating correctly.

12   If the timing marks do not line up under the strobe light, slightly slacken the distributor clamp bolt or nut and carefully turn the distributor in its location to bring the marks into line and then retighten the clamp bolt or nut.

13   Reconnect the distributor vacuum pipe and check that a small advance occurs to the ignition timing, indicating that the vacuum unit is operating correctly.

9   Spark plugs and HT leads – general

1   The correct functioning of the spark plugs is vital for the correct running and efficiency of the engine. It is essential that the plugs fitted are appropriate for the engine, and the suitable type is specified at the beginning of this chapter. If this type is used and the engine is in good condition, the spark plugs should not need attention between scheduled replacement intervals. Spark plug cleaning is rarely necessary and should not be attempted unless specialised equipment is available as damage can easily be caused to the firing ends.

2   At intervals of 6000 miles (10 000 km) the plugs should be removed and examined. The condition of the spark plug will also tell much about the overall condition of the engine. Renew the plugs every 12 000 miles (20 000 km).

3   If the insulator nose of the spark plug is clean and white, with no deposits, this is indicative of a weak mixture, or too hot a plug (a hot

Fig. 4.1 Timing marks (Sec 8)
Left - ohc engine   Right - ohv engine

plug transfers heat away from the electrode slowly, a cold plug transfers heat away quickly).

4   The plugs fitted as standard are specified at the beginning of this Chapter. If the top and insulator nose are covered with hard black-looking deposits, then this is indicative that the mixture is too rich. Should the plug be black and oily, then it is likely that the engine is fairly worn, as well as the mixture being too rich.

5   If the insulator nose is covered with light tan to greyish brown deposits, then the mixture is correct and it is likely that the engine is in good condition.

6   The spark plug gap is of considerable importance, as, if it is too large or too small, the size of the spark and its efficiency will be seriously impaired. For the best results the spark plug gap should be set in accordance with the Specifications at the beginning of this Chapter.

7   To set it, measure the gap with a feeler gauge, and then bend open, or close, the outer plug electrode until the correct gap is achieved. The centre electrode should never be bent as this may crack the insulation and cause plug failure if nothing worse.

8   When fitting new plugs, remember to refit the leads from the distributor in the correct firing order, which is 1-3-4-2, No 1 cylinder being at the timing end (right-hand side of the car).

9   The plug leads require no routine attention other than being kept clean and wiped over regularly. At intervals of 6000 miles (10 000 km), however, pull each lead off the plug in turn and remove it from the distributor. Water can seep down into the joints giving rise to a white corrosive deposit which must be carefully removed from the end of each cable.

10 Coil – general

1   The coil is an auto-transformer and has two sets of windings wound around a core of soft iron wires. The resistance of the primary winding is given in the Specifications at the beginning of this Chapter.

2   If the coil is suspect then the resistance may be checked by an auto electrician and if faulty it may readily be renewed after undoing the mounting bolts.

11 Fault diagnosis – ignition system

1   By far the majority of breakdown and running troubles are caused by faults in the ignition system either in the low tension or high tension circuits.

2   There are two main symptoms indicating faults. Either the engine will not start or fire, or the engine is difficult to start and misfires. If it is a regular misfire, (ie the engine is running on only two or three cylinders), the fault is almost sure to be in the secondary or high tension circuit. If the misfiring is intermittent the fault could be in either the high or low tension circuits. If the car stops suddenly, or will not start at all, it is likely that the fault is in the low tension circuit. Loss of power and overheating, apart from faulty carburation settings, are normally due to faults in the distributor or to incorrect ignition timing.

Engine fails to start

3   If the engine fails to start and the car was running normally when it was last used, first check that there is fuel in the petrol tank. If the engine turns over normally on the starter motor and the battery is evidently well charged, then the fault may be in either the high or low tension circuits. First check the HT circuit.

4   One of the commonest reasons for bad starting is wet or damp spark plug leads and distributor. Remove the distributor cap. If condensation is visible internally dry the cap with a rag and also wipe over the leads. A moisture dispersant, such as Holts Wet Start, can be very effective. To prevent the problem recurring, Holts Damp Start can be used to provide a sealing coat, so excluding any further moisture from the ignition system. In extreme difficulty, Holts Cold Start will help to start a car when only a very poor spark occurs. Refit the cap.

5   If the engine still fails to start, check that voltage is reaching the plugs by disconnecting each plug lead in turn at the spark plug end, and holding the end of the cable with rubber or an insulated tool about $\frac{1}{4}$ in (6 mm) away from the cylinder block. Spin the engine on the starter motor.

6   Sparking between the end of the cable and the block should be fairly strong with a regular blue spark. If voltage is reaching the plugs, then remove them and clean and regap them, The engine should now start.

7   If there is no spark at the plug leads, take off the HT lead from the centre of the distributor cap and hold it to the block as before. Spin the engine on the starter once more. A rapid succession of blue sparks between the end of the lead and the block indicates that the coil is in order and that the distributor cap is cracked, the rotor arm is faulty or the carbon brush in the top of the distributor cap is not making good contact with the spring on the rotor arm.

8   If there are no sparks from the end of the lead from the coil, check the connections at the coil end of the lead. If it is in order start checking the low tension circuit. Possibly, the points are in bad condition. Clean and reset them as described in this Chapter, Section 3.

9   Use a 12V voltmeter or a 12V bulb and two lengths of wire. With the ignition switched on and the points open, test between the low tension wire to the coil and earth. No reading indicates a break in the supply from the ignition switch. Check the connections at the switch to see if any are loose. Refit them and the engine should run. A reading shows a faulty coil or condenser, or broken lead between the coil and the distributor.

10 Take the condenser wire off the points assembly and with the points open test between the moving point and earth. If there is now a reading then the fault is in the condenser. Fit a new one and the fault is cleared.

11 With no reading from the moving point to earth, take a reading between earth and the distributor terminal of the coil. A reading here shows a broken wire which will need to be replaced between the coil and the distributor. No reading confirms that the coil has failed and must be renewed, after which the engine will run once more. Remember to refit the condenser wire to the points assembly. For these tests it is sufficient to separate the points with a piece of dry paper while testing with the points open.

Engine misfires

12 If the engine misfires regularly run it at a fast idling speed. Pull off each of the plug caps in turn and listen to the note of the engine. Hold the plug cap in a dry cloth or with a rubber glove as additional protection against a shock from the HT supply.

13 No difference in engine running will be noticed when the lead from the defective circuit is removed. Removing the lead from one of the good cylinders will accentuate the misfire.

14 Remove the plug lead from the plug which is not firing and hold it about $\frac{1}{4}$ in (6 mm) away from the block. Restart the engine. If the sparking is fairly strong and regular, the fault must lie in the spark plug.

15 The plug may be loose, the insulation may be cracked, or the points may have burnt away giving too wide a gap for the spark to jump. Worse still, one of the points may have broken off. Either renew the plug, or clean it, reset the gap, and then test it.

16 If there is no spark at the end of the plug lead, or if it is weak and intermittent, check the ignition lead from the distributor to the plug. If the insulation is cracked or perished, renew the lead. Check the connections at the distributor cap.

17 If there is still no spark, examine the distributor cap carefully for tracking. This can be recognised by a very thin black line running between two or more electrodes, or between an electrode and some other part of the distributor. These lines are paths which now conduct electricity across the cap thus letting it run to earth. The only answer is a new distributor cap.

18 Apart from the ignition timing being incorrect, other causes of misfiring have already been dealt with under the Section dealing with the failure of the engine to start. To recap, these are that

(a)   The coil may be faulty giving an intermittent misfire
(b)   There may be a damaged wire or loose connection in the low tension circuit
(c)   The condenser may be faulty
(d)   There may be a mechanical fault in the distributor (broken driving spindle or contact breaker spring)

19 If the ignition timing is too far retarded, it should be noted that the engine will tend to overheat, and there will be a quite noticeable drop in power. If the engine is overheating and the power is down, and the ignition timing is correct, then the carburettor should be checked, as it is likely that this is where the fault lies.

20 If the ballast resistor wire is broken or disconnected, the engine will fire when the starter motor is operating but will refuse to run. Renewal of the resistor wire will cure the problem. Do not bypass the resistor wire with ordinary wire, or overheating of the coil will occur.

Chapter 5 Clutch

For modifications, and information applicable to later models, see Supplement at end of manual

Contents

Specifications

General

Type	Single dry plate, diaphragm spring, cable operated
Clutch pedal free play	No play. As clutch wears, pedal moves up
Adjustment (only after cable or driven plate renewal)	Clip and nut at engine end of cable

Friction disc

Diameter:

Saloons and Hatchback	12 engine: 6.7 in (170.18 mm); 12S, 13, and 13S engines: 7.5 in (190.5 mm)
Estate	7.5 in (190.5 mm)
Identification	LUK or GM
Thickness (not loaded)	0.367 to 0.390 in (9.3 to 9.9 mm)
Allowable lateral run-out	0.016 in (0.4 mm)

Torque wrench settings

	lbf ft	Nm
Clutch cover plate-to-transmission case bolts	5	7
Clutch-to-flywheel bolts	11	15
Release fork clamp bolt	26	36
Release bearing guide-to-transmission case bolts	4	5
Transmission cover sealing plug	37	51
Flywheel housing-to-engine bolts (ohv)	16	22
Flywheel housing to engine bolts (ohc)	55	75
Reverse lamp switch	15	20
Clutch driveshaft screw	11	15

1 General description

All models covered by this manual are fitted with a single plate diaphragm spring clutch which is enclosed in a pressed steel cover bolted to the flywheel. The gearbox input shaft projects through the clutch and is located at its forward end in a needle roller spigot bearing within the centre of the crankshaft (photo).

The clutch friction disc is located between the flywheel and the clutch pressure plate and it can slide on splines on the gearbox input shaft. When the clutch is engaged, the diaphragm spring forces the pressure plate to grip the friction disc against the flywheel and drive is transmitted from the crankshaft, through the friction disc to the gearbox input shaft. On disengaging the clutch the pressure plate is lifted to release the friction disc with the result that the drive to the gearbox is disconnected.

The clutch is operated by a foot pedal suspended under the facia and a cable connected to the clutch release lever mounted on the clutch bellhousing. Depressing the pedal causes the release lever to move the thrust bearing against the release fingers of the diaphragm spring in the pressure plate assembly. The spring is sandwiched between two rings which act as fulcrums. As the centre of the spring is moved in, the periphery moves out to lift the pressure plate and disengage the clutch. The reverse takes place when the pedal is released.

As wear takes place on the friction disc with usage, the foot pedal will rise progressively relative to its original position. Periodic adjustment is not required.

An unusual feature of the design of this particular clutch is that the friction disc, release bearing and seal can be renewed without having to remove either the engine or the transmission from the car.

1.1 Clutch driven plate and cover

Fig. 5.1 Clutch cable adjuster nut at release lever. Spring clip arrowed (Sec 2)

2 Clutch – adjustment

1   The clutch is normally self-adjusting, but if the cable or driven plate are renewed, the following initial adjustment will be required.
2   Take a measurement from the edge of the steering wheel to the centre of the clutch pedal and then take another measurement with the pedal fully depressed. These measurements can be taken using a suitable strip of wood or metal as the important figure is the difference between the two measurements, that is, the movement of the pedal itself. This should be 5.4 in (138 mm) and if this is not the case, the nut on the threaded end of the cable where it fits into the clutch release lever must be adjusted to obtain the correct pedal movement. Before adjusting the nut, remove the spring clip, and refit it after the adjustment has been made. Recheck the pedal movement on completion.
3   After some period in use, it will not be possible to adjust the cable in this fashion and it will be necessary to renew the clutch friction disc. Note that when correctly adjusted, the clutch pedal will be slightly higher than the brake pedal and it is incorrect for the two pedals to be in alignment. If they are aligned the clutch cable needs adjusting. Note also that there should be no play in the clutch pedal of these cars.

3 Clutch cable – removal and refitting

1   The most obvious reason for having to renew the clutch cable is breakage, but it may also be necessary if the pedal action is stiff or jerky.
2   Before disturbing the installation, take a measurement of the length of the threaded end of the cable fitting protruding through the adjusting nut at the release lever end. This will enable you to preset the new cable and so simplify its installation.
3   Remove the spring clip from the cable, slacken the adjusting nut and disconnect the cable from the release lever. The cable assembly can now be extracted from the lug on the bellhousing case.
4   Working inside the car, unhook the return spring from the clutch foot pedal and disconnect the cable from the pedal lever.
5   The cable assembly can now be withdrawn into the engine compartment by pulling it through the bulkhead.
6   Refitting the clutch cable assembly is the reverse of the removal procedure. On completion, adjust as described in the previous Section.

4 Clutch pedal – removal and refitting

1   Refer to the previous Section and disconnect the clutch cable from the release lever and the clutch pedal, but there is no need to remove the assembly from the lug on the bellhousing case or withdraw the assembly from the car.
2   Remove the wire locking clip from the pedal pivot retaining nut,

then remove the nut and washer.
3   Push the pivot out of the support bracket and remove the clutch pedal and the return spring.
4   Refitting is the reverse of the removal procedure. Before inserting the pedal pivot, lightly smear the bearing surface with a molybdenum disulphide grease. Refit the cable as described in the previous Section and adjust if necessary.

5 Clutch unit – removal and refitting

1   A novel feature of these models is the ability to renew the clutch pressure plate, the friction disc, the release bearing, the release lever pivot bushes, and the clutch/transmission seal without having to remove either the engine or the clutch bellhousing. Although the maker's procedure requires the use of special tools these are not essential and the work can be done with the tools available to the average home mechanic.
2   As it is easier to do some of the work under the front of the car, apply the handbrake firmly, jack up the front of the car and support it on ramps or axle stands.
3   Using a 36 mm spanner, preferably a socket, undo and remove the plug in the transmission case end cover (photos). Remove the circlip located in the end of the clutch driveshaft using a pair of circlip pliers (photo). Underneath is a screw with a recess in the head which requires a key having twelve drive splines to undo it. Accessory shops can supply a socket adaptor for this purpose. Undo and remove this screw (photos).
4   The clutch shaft can be slid out of engagement with the clutch friction disc, and to do this the manufacturers provide a special tool. To overcome this problem, borrow one of the four bolts securing the gearchange mechanism cover to the top of the transmission case, screw the bolt into the end of the clutch shaft, and then pull the shaft out of engagement with the clutch disc using a pair of grip pliers (photos). Don't forget to refit the bolt to the gearchange mechanism cover.
5   Undo and remove the four bolts securing the cover to the bottom of the clutch bellhousing and remove the cover (photo). This will expose the clutch unit, which is bolted to the flywheel. Next remove the spark plugs in order to make turning the crankshaft easier.
6   Before the clutch assembly can be removed, the pressure plate must be compressed to provide sufficient clearance for removal. For this the manufacturers provide three special clamps which are used to hold the pressure plate in the compressed state. Alternatively, similar clamps can be made up using scrap metal as shown in Fig. 5.2. The clamps are fitted securely over the rims of the clutch cover and pressure plate while the clutch is fully disengaged. To do this, turn the crankshaft pulley bolt until one of the three apertures in the clutch cover becomes accessible from below. An assistant will now be needed to depress the clutch pedal while one of the clamps is fitted as shown in Fig. 5.3. With the clutch pedal still depressed, turn the crankshaft and fit the remaining two clamps to the apertures.
7   With the clutch pedal released and the clamps holding the pressure plate compressed against the tension of the diaphragm spring, progressively loosen and finally remove the six bolts securing the clutch assembly to the flywheel (photo). While doing this note the coloured spot on the flywheel aligned with the notch in the clutch cover, as these must be refitted in the same position. Finally lower the clutch unit out of the bellhousing case. After removal it will be necessary to compress the clutch cover and pressure plate in a vice, using two suitable blocks of wood to prevent damage, to enable the clamps to be withdrawn.
8   Refitting is basically the reverse of the removal procedure. In some instances new cover assemblies will be supplied with retaining clips in place, but where this is not the case the previously used clamps must be refitted prior to reassembly. Make sure that the extended side of the clutch disc hub faces towards the gearbox, and apply a very light film of graphite grease to the splines in the hub. Avoid overdoing it at all costs as the friction faces must be kept free of grease. Manoeuvre the clutch assembly to align the splines in the friction disc hub with those on the clutch shaft and press the shaft home into the bearing in the end of the crankshaft. Screw the recessed screw into the end of the shaft and press the gear cluster up to the stop in the gearbox before fitting a new circlip to retain the screw. Apply a film of sealant to the threads on the sealing plug and screw it into position in the transmission case (photo). This plug must be tightened to the specified

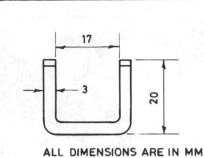

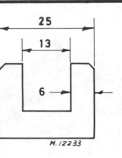

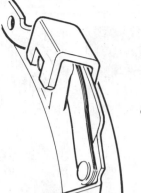

ALL DIMENSIONS ARE IN MM

H.12233

Fig. 5.3 Fitted position of clutch cover/pressure plate clamps (Sec 5)

H.12234

Fig. 5.2 Clutch cover/pressure plate retaining clamp dimensions (Sec 5)

5.3A Threaded plug (arrowed) in transmission end cover

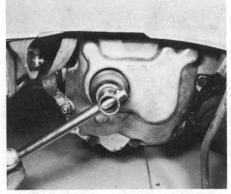

5.3B Unscrewing cover plug

5.3C Removing clutch driveshaft circlip

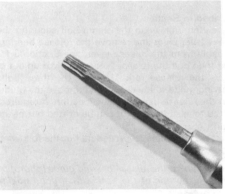

5.3D Special splined screw removal tool

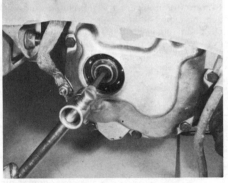

5.3E Removing clutch driveshaft screw

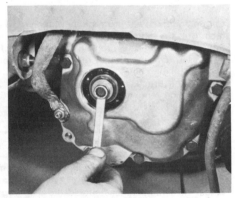

5.4A Screwing a bolt into the clutch shaft

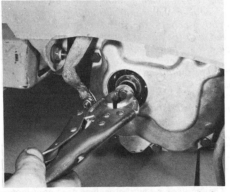

5.4B Using grips to withdraw the clutch shaft

5.5 Removing clutch housing lower cover plate

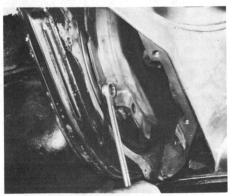

5.7 Unscrewing clutch bolts

5.8 Applying sealant to end cover threaded plug

7.3A Removing clutch release fork locking bolt. Gearbox is removed from vehicle for clarity

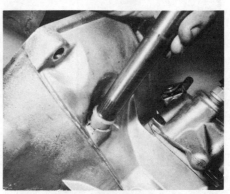

7.3B Withdrawing release lever shaft

7.3C Release lever shaft bushes

7.3D Clutch release bearing

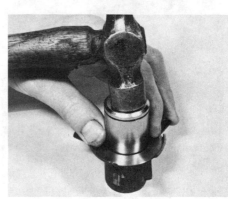

7.4 Fitting new oil seal to release bearing guide

torque and must not protrude more than 0.16 in (4 mm) from the case face. Bolt the clutch cover to the flywheel. Remove the clips one at a time by turning the crankshaft with the clutch pedal again held depressed. On completion refit the clutch housing lower cover plate and adjust the clutch as described in Section 2.

9   For the procedure for removing the clutch with the engine and transmission removed from the car, refer to Chapter 1.

6   Clutch unit – inspection

1   In the normal course of events, clutch dismantling and reassembly involves simply fitting a new clutch pressure plate and friction disc. Under no circumstances should the diaphragm spring clutch unit be dismantled. If a fault develops in the pressure plate assembly, an exchange replacement unit must be fitted.

2   If a new clutch disc is being fitted it is a false economy not to renew the release bearing at the same time. This will preclude having to replace it at a later date when wear on the clutch linings is very small.

3   Examine the clutch disc friction linings for wear or loose rivets, the disc for rim distortion, cracks and worn splines. If any of these faults are evident the disc must be replaced with a new one.

4   Check the machined faces of the flywheel and the pressure plate. If either is badly grooved it should be machined until smooth, or replaced with a new item. If the pressure plate is cracked or split it must be renewed.

5   Examine the clutch disc hub splines for wear and also make sure that the centre hub is not loose.

7   Release lever bushes, release bearing and seal – renewal

1   Wear of the clutch release bearing is indicated by a squealing noise when the clutch pedal is depressed with the engine running.

2   To gain access to the release bearing it is necessary first to remove the clutch unit as described in Section 5.

3   After removing the clutch unit, undo the clamp bolt securing the release fork to the release lever pivot and remove the release bearing. Disconnect the clutch cable from the release lever, see Section 3 for details if necessary, and then pull the release lever and pivot up out of the housing and remove the release fork. Unscrew the three bolts securing the release bearing guide to the casing and remove the guide. Prise the old seal out of the release bearing guide location. If required, the bushes supporting the release lever pivot can be drifted out of the case using a suitable drift (photos).

4   Refitting is the reverse of the removal procedure but the following points should be noted:

    (a) *After fitting a new seal to the release bearing guide (photo) fill the space between the lips of the seal with a good quality general purpose grease*

    (b) *When fitting the new O-ring seal to the casing at the release bearing guide location do not use any grease or oil as this seal should be fitted dry*

    (c) *Lightly smear the release bearing guide surface on which the bearing slides with molybdenum disulphide grease and tighten the securing bolts to the specified torque*

    (d) *If being renewed, drift the new release lever bushes into their housings, ensure that their locating tongues are engaged in the slots in the case, and coat the inner surfaces of the bushes with molybdenum disulphide grease*

    (e) *Fit the release bearing and the release fork together and tighten the release fork clamp bolt to the specified torque*

    (f) *Refit the clutch as described in Section 5*

8   Fault diagnosis – clutch

There are four main faults to which the clutch and release mechanism are prone. They may occur by themselves or in conjunction with any of the other faults. They are clutch squeal, spin, slip and judder.

Clutch squeal – diagnosis and cure

1   If on taking up the drive or when changing gear, the clutch squeals, this is a sure indication of a badly worn clutch release bearing.

2   As well as regular wear due to normal use, wear of the clutch release bearing is much accentuated if the clutch is ridden, or held down for long periods with the engine running. To minimise wear of this component the car should always be taken out of gear at traffic lights and for similar delays.

Clutch slip – diagnosis and cure

3   Clutch slip is a self-evident condition which occurs when the clutch friction plate is badly worn, when oil or grease have got onto the flywheel or pressure plate faces, or when the pressure plate itself is faulty.

4   The reason for clutch slip is that, due to one of the faults listed above, there is either insufficient pressure from the pressure plate, or insufficient friction from the friction plate, to ensure solid drive.

5   If small amounts of oil get onto the clutch, they will be burnt off under the heat of clutch engagement, and in the process, gradually darken the linings, excessive oil on the clutch will burn off leaving a carbon deposit which can cause quite bad slip, or fierceness, spin and judder.

6   If clutch slip is suspected, and confirmation of this condition is required, there are several tests which can be made.

7   With the engine in top gear and pulling lightly up a moderate incline sudden depression of the accelerator pedal may cause the engine to increase its speed without any increase in road speed.

8   In extreme cases of clutch slip the engine will race under normal acceleration conditions.

9   If slip is due to oil or grease on the linings a temporary cure can sometimes be effected by squirting a degreasing solvent into the clutch. The permanent cure is, of course, to renew the clutch driven plate and trace and rectify the oil leak.

Clutch spin – diagnosis and cure

10   Clutch spin is a condition which occurs when the release arm travel is excessive, there is an obstruction in the clutch either on the primary gear splines or in the operating lever itself, or oil may have partially burnt off the clutch linings and have left a resinous deposit which is causing the clutch to stick to the pressure plate or flywheel. This condition may also be due to the driven plate being rusted to the flywheel or pressure plate.

11   The reason for clutch spin is that due to any, or a combination, of the faults just listed, the clutch pressure plate is not completely freeing from the centre plate even with the clutch pedal fully depressed.

12   If clutch spin is suspected, the condition can be confirmed by extreme difficulty in engaging first gear from rest, difficulty in changing gear, and very sudden take up of the clutch drive at the fully depressed end of the clutch pedal travel as the clutch is released.

13   Check that the clutch cable is correctly adjusted and, if in order, the fault lies internally in the clutch. If the centre (driven) plate is sticking to the pressure plate or flywheel it is possible to free it by applying the handbrake, engaging top gear and operating the starter motor. If really badly corroded, then the engine will not turn over, but in the majority of cases the driven plate will free. Once the engine starts, rev it up and slip the clutch several times to clear the rust/resin deposits. If this does not provide a lasting remedy it will then be necessary to remove the clutch for examination, and to check the gearbox input shaft.

Clutch judder – diagnosis

14   Clutch judder is a self-evident condition which occurs when the gearbox or engine mountings are loose or too flexible, when there is oil on the faces of the clutch friction plate, or when the clutch pressure plate has been incorrectly adjusted during assembly.

15   The reason for clutch judder is that due to one of the faults just listed, the clutch pressure plate is not freeing smoothly from the friction disc, and is snatching.

16   Clutch judder normally occurs when the clutch pedal is released in first or reverse gears, and the whole car shudders as it moves backwards or forwards.

Chapter 6 Manual transmission

For modifications, and information applicable to later models, see Supplement at end of manual

Contents

Specifications

Transmission type .... F10. Four forward speeds and one reverse. Forward speeds all with synchromesh. Unit integral with differential/final drive. Floor-mounted remote control type gearchange.

Gear ratios
1st	3.636 : 1
2nd	2.188 : 1
3rd	1.429 : 1
4th	0.969 : 1
Reverse	3.182 : 1

Final drive ratio
Except Estate models
1.2 l (ohv), and 1.3 l (ohc) except S models:
To Sept 1980	4.29 : 1
Sept 1980 to Aug 1981	4.18 : 1
Aug 1981 on	3.94 : 1

1.3 l (ohc) S models:
To Aug 1981	4.18 : 1
Aug 1981 on	3.94 : 1

Estate models
1.2 l (ohv) ... 4.53 : 1

1.3 l (ohc):
To Sept 1980	4.29 : 1
Sept 1980 on	4.18 : 1

Oil type/specification .... Gear oil, viscosity SAE 80 to API GL3 or GL4 (Duckhams Hypoid 80)

Oil capacity .... 1.7 litres (3.0 pts)

Torque wrench settings
	Nm	lbf ft
Flywheel housing-to-engine bolts (ohv)	22	16
Flywheel housing-to-engine bolts (ohc)	75	55
Reversing lamp switch	20	15
Selector cover housing bolts	15	11
Transmission end cover bolts	22	16
End cover threaded cap	50	37
Final drive pressed steel cover bolts	30	22
Crownwheel bolts	85	62

1 Description

The manual transmission is of four-speed synchromesh type, combined in one housing with the differential and final drive.

The transmission unit transmits power to the front roadwheels through open driveshafts which incorporate homokinetic joints.

A floor-mounted gearchange lever operates through a remote control rod.

2 Maintenance

Routine maintenance is restricted to checking the oil level; draining and refilling with fresh lubricant is not specified. Refer also to Section 6, paragraph 24. However, if the lubricant must be drained for any reason, most of it can be removed if the pressed steel cover plate is unbolted and pulled away.

3 Gearchange lever – removal and refitting

1 Set the control lever in neutral.
2 If a centre console is fitted, remove it (see Chapter 12).
3 Release the rubber boot at the base of the lever and slide it upwards (photo).
4 Extract the circlip from its groove in the housing.
5 Withdraw the gearchange lever.
6 If the boot is to be renewed, the knob can be pulled off if it is first heated in very hot water.
7 Refitting is a reversal of removal, but observe the following points:

(a) *Apply grease to the pivot ball and socket*
(b) *Note that the tab on the underside of the boot is towards the front of the vehicle*
(c) *When fitting the gear lever knob, align it as shown (Fig 6.3) with the stop on reverse gear sleeve*

3.3 Gear lever gaiter withdrawn

Fig. 6.1 Gearchange lever circlip (arrowed) (Sec 3)

Fig. 6.2 Gear lever boot alignment tab (Sec 3)

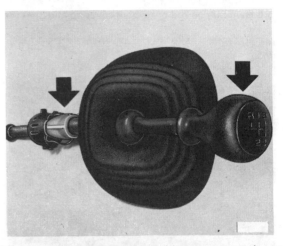

Fig. 6.3 Gear lever knob alignment with reverse gear sleeve (Sec 3)

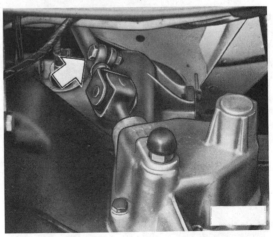

Fig. 6.4 Gearchange rod coupling pinch-bolt (Sec 4)

4.2 Gear lever rubber cover under vehicle

4 Gearchange linkage – removal and refitting

1 Working at the transmission, slacken the pinch-bolt at the gearchange rod coupling.

2 Remove the screws which hold the gearchange rod protective housing and detach the rubber cover at the end of the housing (photo).

3 Separate the base of the gearchange lever from the eye in the gearchange rod and then withdraw the linkage assembly from the vehicle.

4 Withdraw the bellows and boot from the protective housing.

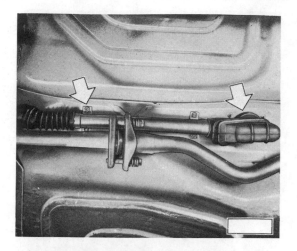

Fig. 6.5 Gearchange rod protective covering and boot (Sec 4)

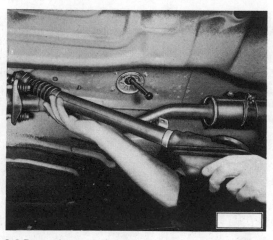

Fig. 6.6 Removing gearchange rod protective covering (Sec 4)

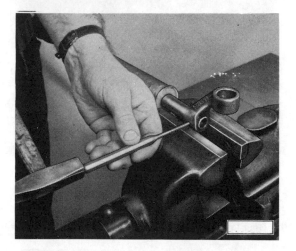

Fig. 6.7 Gearchange rod intermediate lever roll pin (Sec 4)

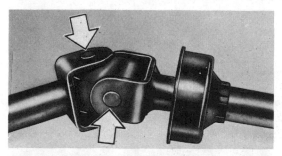

Fig. 6.8 Gearchange rod universal joint pins (Sec 4)

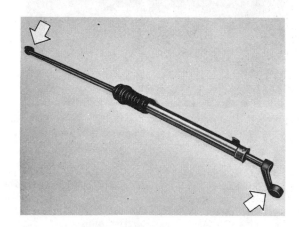

Fig. 6.10 Gearchange rod intermediate lever alignment
with clamp (Sec 4)

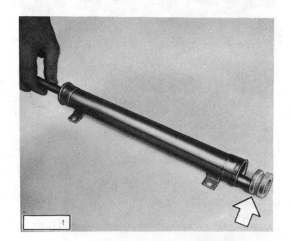

Fig. 6.9 Removing bushes from gearchange rod protective housing
(Sec 4)

9   Commence reassembly by filling the protective housing sleeve
bush grooves with grease and inserting the bushes into the housing.
10 Special pins are available with circlips to replace the original rivets
when reassembling the universal joints.
11 Connect the intermediate lever to the control rod using a new pin,
but make sure that it is aligned with the clamp as shown (Fig. 6.10).
12 Fit the bellows and boot to the protective housing and apply
silicone grease liberally inside the boot.
13 Slide the gearchange rod into the housing and fit to the floor pan.
14 Adjust the linkage as described in the next Section.

5   The assembly may be further dismantled to renew worn components by driving out the retaining pin from the intermediate lever and
control rod.
6   Tap the rod out of the lever.
7   The universal joint may be dismantled by grinding off the rivet
heads.
8   Use a rod to remove the bushes from the protective housing.

5   Gearchange linkage – adjustment

1   Set the gearchange hand control lever in neutral.
2   If fitted, remove the centre console.
3   Slacken the pinch-bolt on the gearchange rod coupling.

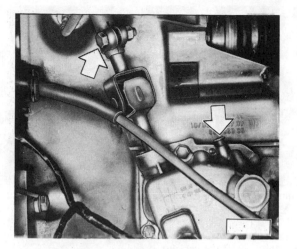

Fig. 6.11 Transmission adjuster hole blanking plug and clamp pinch-bolt (Sec 5)

5.5 Setting gearchange rod (gearbox removed for clarity)

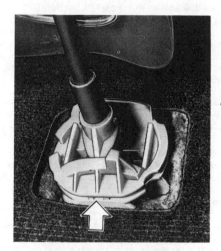

Fig. 6.12A Gearchange lever alignment during adjustment (Sec 5)

Fig. 6.12B Gearchange mechanism guard tube fitted dimension (A) – see text (Sec 5)

4   Prise out the small blanking plug from the transmission cover.

5   Looking towards the front of the vehicle, grip the gearchange rod and twist it in an anti-clockwise direction until a 5.0 mm (0.2 in) diameter twist drill can be inserted into the hole left by removal of the plug. Insert the drill until it contacts the stop (photo).

6   The help of an assistant will now be required to withdraw the gearchange lever boot upwards and to move the lever across the neutral gate until it is aligned with the 1st/2nd (centre) point of the gate.

7   Without moving the set position of the gearchange lever, tighten the rod coupling pinch-bolt.

8   Withdraw the twist drill and refit the plug. To prevent oil leakage when the vehicle is operating, it is vital that this plug seals perfectly, if not, renew it.

9   Refit the gear lever boot and the centre console.

10 From Chassis No 12766342 a rubber-mounted gearchange lever has been introduced. The modified component may be fitted to earlier models.

11 On certain models it is possible for the shift finger to become disconnected from the intermediate shift lever. Should this happen, measure the distance (A) between the lower edge of the remote gearchange mechanism guard tube and the floor pan (Fig. 6.12B). This should be between 38.5 mm (1.516 in) and 40.0 mm (1.574 in).

12 If the dimension is incorrect, remove the bolts from the guard tube rear mounting bracket, loosen the front mounting bracket and then bend the rear bracket as necessary.

6   Transmission – removal and refitting

1   Disconnect the clutch operating cable from the release lever on the transmission.

2   Slacken the pinch-bolt on the gearchange rod coupling.

3   Disconnect the speedometer drive cable from the transmission casing by unscrewing the knurled ring.

4   Disconnect the leads from the reversing lamp switch.

5   Disconnect the earth strap which runs between the transmission casing and the body side frame (photo).

6   Raise the front of the vehicle and remove the front roadwheels.

7   Using a balljoint separator, disconnect the suspension arm ball-joint from the hub carrier on both sides of the vehicle.

8   Using a forked lever as described in Chapter 1, Section 44, disconnect both driveshafts from the transmission and support them by tying them up. Be prepared for some loss of oil.

9   Withdraw the clutch splined shaft as described in Chapter 5, Section 5.

10 On ohv engines, remove the air cleaner.

11 Support the engine either on a jack and insulating wooden block, or by attaching a hoist.

12 Remove the centre mounting, the front left-hand and the rear mounting (photos).

13 Unscrew and remove the bolts which hold the flywheel housing to the engine.

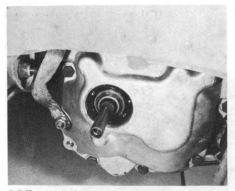

6.5 Transmission earth strap

6.12A Removing centre mounting

6.12B Removing transmission left-hand mounting

14 Pull the transmission slightly away from the engine and lower it on a jack. Withdraw it from under the vehicle.
15 Take care not to damage projecting components when placing the transmission on the floor.
16 Refit the transmission by offering it up to the engine and inserting the connecting bolts. Tighten the bolts to the specified torque. If the clutch has been disturbed, make sure that it has been centralised as described in Chapter 1, Section 27.
17 Reconnect the driveshafts to the transmission. The shafts should have been fitted with new circlips. Snap the shafts fully into engagement by applying a driver to the weld bead of the inner joint, **not** its metal cover.
18 Press the clutch shaft in to its stop and fit a new retaining ring.
19 Apply sealant to the threads and screw in the seal cover to the specified torque.

Fig. 6.13 Location of oil filler (A), oil level plug (B) and adjuster plug hole (C) (Sec 6)

20 Reconnect the suspension arm balljoints and fit the roadwheels. Lower the front of the vehicle.
21 Reconnect the speedometer drive cable, the reversing lamp switch, the clutch operating cable and the earth strap.
22 Refit the air cleaner (if removed).
23 Adjust the gearchange linkage as described in Section 5.
24 Fill the transmission with the correct grade and quantity of oil. Oil is poured into the hole left by removal of the vent plug in the selector cover. A level plug is fitted into the left-hand side of the transmission (looking towards the front of the vehicle). Remove this and as soon as oil flows out, refit both plugs (photo). **Do not** fill the transmission through the level plug hole.

7 Transmission – dismantling into major assemblies

Gearbox

1 With the transmission removed from the vehicle, clean away external dirt using paraffin and a stiff brush or a water-soluble solvent. Drain the lubricant by removing the pressed steel cover plate on the differential.
2 Unbolt and remove the selector cover from the transmission casing (photos).
3 Unbolt the retaining plate and withdraw the speedometer driven gear (photos).
4 Unscrew and remove the reversing lamp switch and allow the oil to drain out (photo).
5 Using a screwdriver as a lever, engage 2nd gear by moving the selector fork nearest the end cover.
6 Unscrew and remove the end cover bolts and nuts (photo).
7 Withdraw the main casing from the end cover and geartrains (photo).
8 Prise out the detent plugs from the end cover and extract the springs and detent plungers (photos).
9 Drive out the roll pins which secure the selector forks to the selector rods.
10 Move the synchro sleeve back to the neutral position and then

6.24 Filling transmission with oil

7.2A Unbolting selector cover

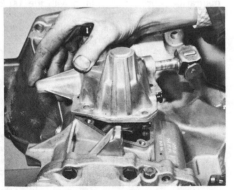

7.2B Removing selector cover

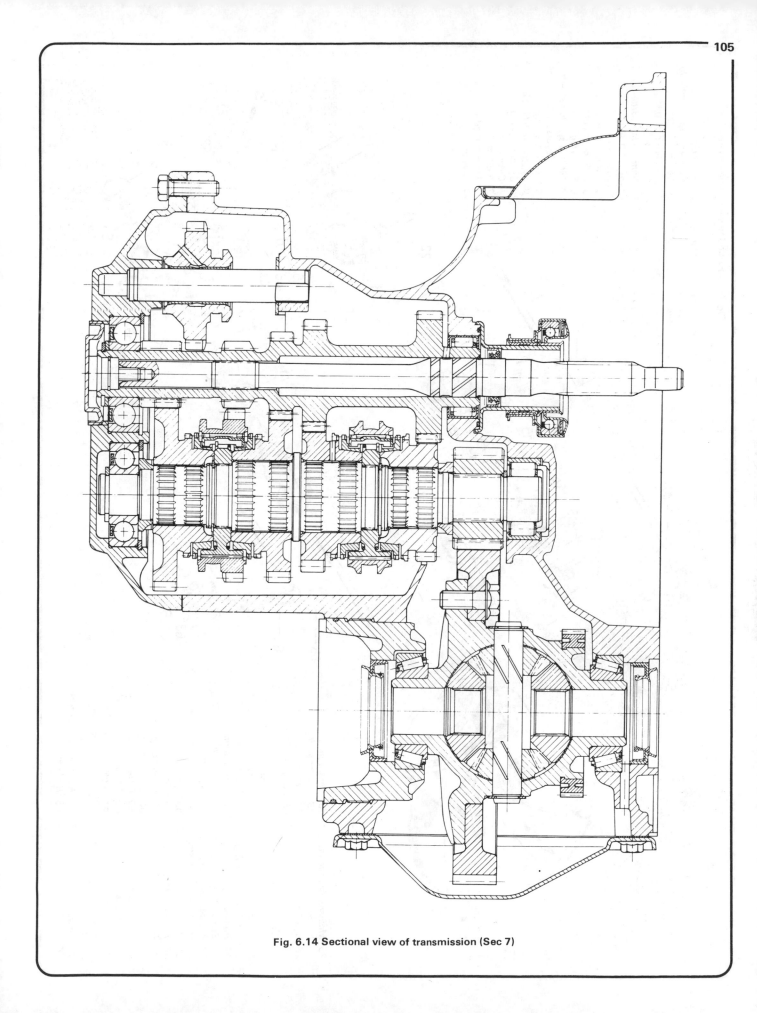

Fig. 6.14 Sectional view of transmission (Sec 7)

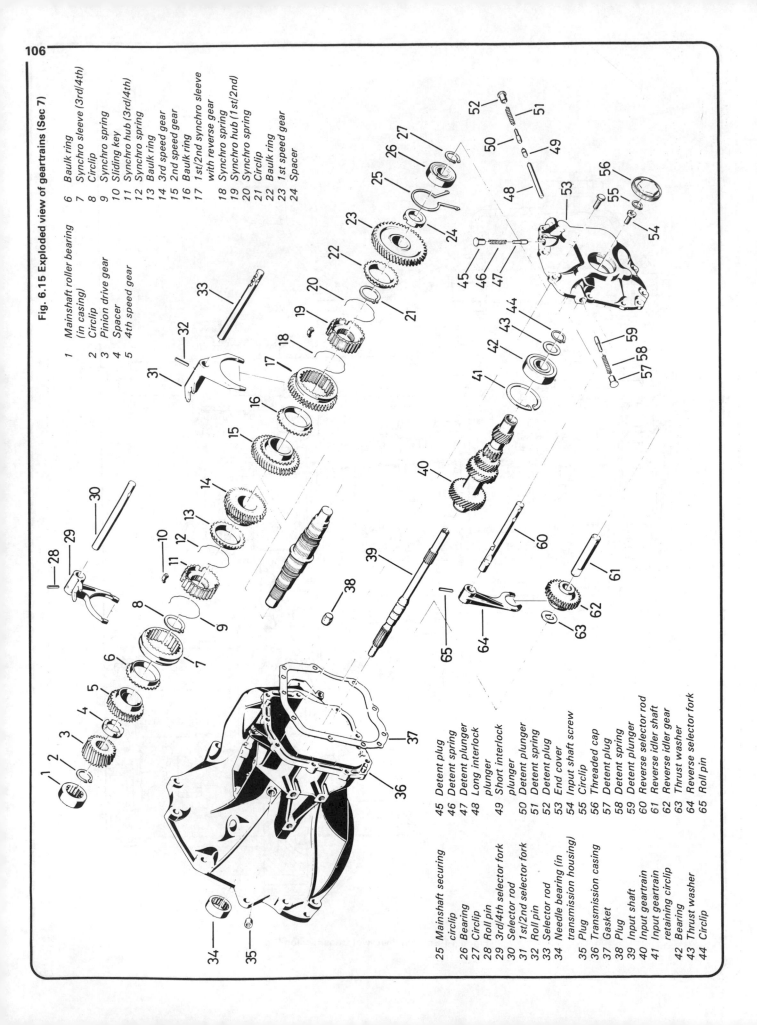

Fig. 6.15 Exploded view of geartrains (Sec 7)

1 Mainshaft roller bearing (in casing)
2 Circlip
3 Pinion drive gear
4 Spacer
5 4th speed gear
6 Baulk ring
7 Synchro sleeve (3rd/4th)
8 Circlip
9 Synchro spring
10 Sliding key
11 Synchro hub (3rd/4th)
12 Synchro spring
13 Baulk ring
14 3rd speed gear
15 2nd speed gear
16 Baulk ring
17 1st/2nd synchro sleeve with reverse gear
18 Synchro spring
19 Synchro hub (1st/2nd)
20 Synchro spring
21 Circlip
22 Baulk ring
23 1st speed gear
24 Spacer

25 Mainshaft securing circlip
26 Bearing
27 Circlip
28 Roll pin
29 3rd/4th selector fork
30 Selector rod
31 1st/2nd selector fork
32 Roll pin
33 Selector rod
34 Needle bearing (in transmission housing)
35 Plug
36 Transmission casing
37 Gasket
38 Plug
39 Input shaft
40 Input geartrain
41 Input geartrain retaining circlip
42 Bearing
43 Thrust washer
44 Circlip

45 Detent plug
46 Detent spring
47 Detent plunger
48 Long interlock plunger
49 Short interlock plunger
50 Detent plunger
51 Detent spring
52 Detent plug
53 End cover
54 Input shaft screw
55 Circlip
56 Threaded cap
57 Detent plug
58 Detent spring
59 Detent plunger
60 Reverse selector rod
61 Reverse idler shaft
62 Reverse idler gear
63 Thrust washer
64 Reverse selector fork
65 Roll pin

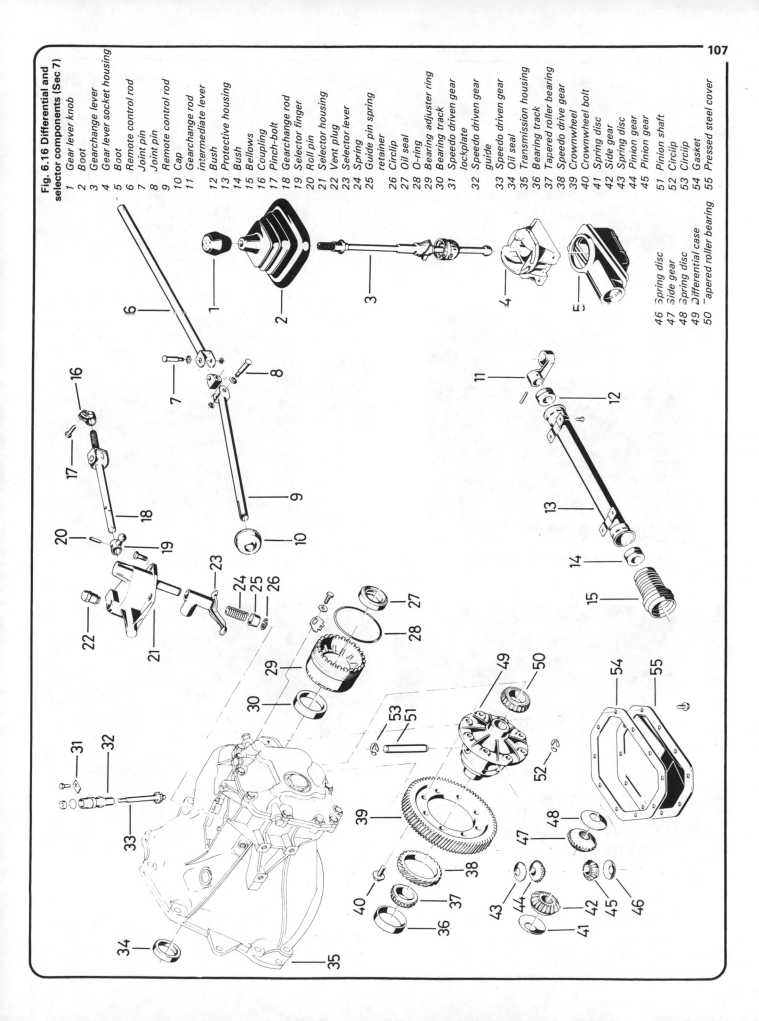

Fig. 6.16 Differential and selector components (Sec 7)

1 Gear lever knob
2 Boot
3 Gearchange lever
4 Gear lever socket housing
5 Boot
6 Remote control rod
7 Joint pin
8 Joint pin
9 Remote control rod
10 Cap
11 Gearchange rod intermediate lever
12 Bush
13 Protective housing
14 Bush
15 Bellows
16 Coupling
17 Pinch-bolt
18 Gearchange rod
19 Selector finger
20 Roll pin
21 Selector housing
22 Vent plug
23 Selector lever
24 Spring
25 Guide pin spring retainer
26 Circlip
27 Oil seal
28 O-ring
29 Bearing adjuster ring
30 Bearing track
31 Speedo driven gear lockplate
32 Speedo driven gear guide
33 Speedo driven gear
34 Oil seal
35 Transmission housing
36 Bearing track
37 Tapered roller bearing
38 Speedo drive gear
39 Crownwheel
40 Crownwheel bolt
41 Spring disc
42 Side gear
43 Spring disc
44 Pinion gear
45 Pinion gear
46 Spring disc
47 Side gear
48 Spring disc
49 Differential case
50 Tapered roller bearing
51 Pinion shaft
52 Circlip
53 Circlip
54 Gasket
55 Pressed steel cover

7.3A Unscrewing speedometer gear retainer

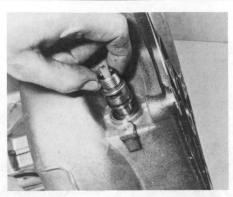
7.3B Withdrawing speedometer driven gear

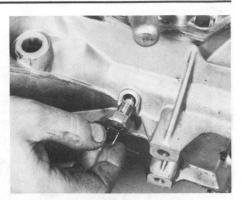
7.4 Removing reversing lamp switch

Fig. 6.17 Engaging 2nd gear (Sec 7)

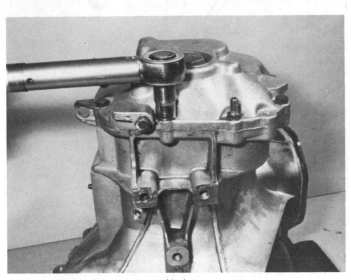
7.6 Removing end cover nuts and bolts

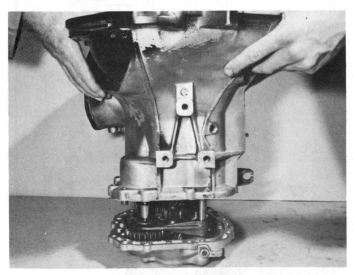
7.7 Withdrawing transmission main casing

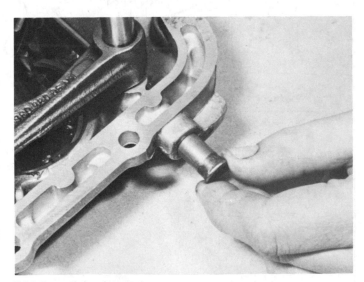
7.8A Removing a detent plug

withdraw 3rd/4th and reverse selector forks and their rods from the end cover.

11 Extract the circlips which retain the mainshaft and input shaft gear trains. Extract the swarf collecting magnet (photos).

12 Remove the geartrain assemblies together with the 1st/2nd selector fork and rod simultaneously (photo).

13 Extract the selector rod interlock pins from the end cover.

14 Remove the reverse idler shaft from the end cover. To do this, grip the shaft in the jaws of a vice fitted with soft metal protectors and using a brass drift, gently tap the cover off the shaft. Take care not to lose the locking ball (photo).

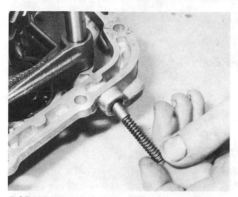

7.8B Withdrawing detent plunger and spring

7.11A Mainshaft securing circlip

7.11B Swarf collecting magnet

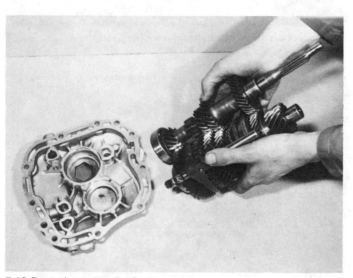

7.12 Removing geartrains from end cover

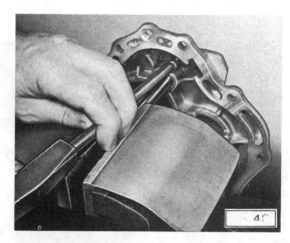

Fig. 6.18 Tapping off end cover (Sec 7)

7.14 Reverse idler shaft and locking ball

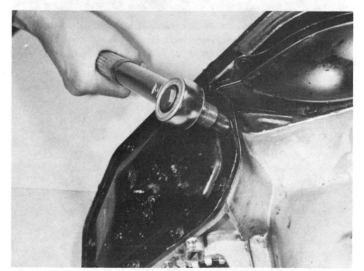

7.15 Unbolting transmission cover

Differential

15 Unbolt and remove the pressed steel cover from the transmission casing (photo).

16 Mark the position of the bearing adjuster ring in relation to the transmission casing. Unbolt the ring lock (photos).

17 Unscrew the bearing adjuster ring. A piece of flat steel bar will act as a suitable wrench (photo).

18 Withdraw the differential/crownwheel assembly (photo).

19 Depending upon the need for further dismantling due to leaking oil seals or worn bearings, proceed in the following way.

20 Renew the oil seals and bearings in the adjuster ring and transmission casing using a piece of tubing to remove the old

7.16A Marking bearing adjuster ring setting

7.16B Bearing ring/casing alignment mark (arrowed)

7.16C Unbolting bearing adjuster ring lockplate

7.17 Unscrewing bearing adjuster ring

7.18 Removing differential/final drive

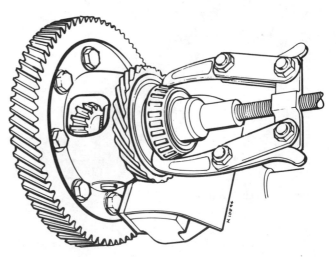

Fig. 6.19 Removing a differential bearing (Sec 7)

components and to install the new (photos).

21 Using a suitable puller remove the tapered roller bearings from the differential.

22 Unbolt the crownwheel and tap it from its register using a brass drift. If the crownwheel or pinion gear are to be renewed, they must always be renewed as a matched pair.

23 Split the speedometer drivegear and discard it.

24 Extract the circlips from the differential pinion shaft.

25 Use a drift to remove the pinion shaft from the differential case.

26 Screw the differential pinions and side gears out of the differential case. Remove the spring discs.

7.20A Installing bearing adjuster ring oil seal

7.20B Installing driveshaft oil seal

Fig. 6.20 Unscrewing crownwheel bolts (Sec 7)

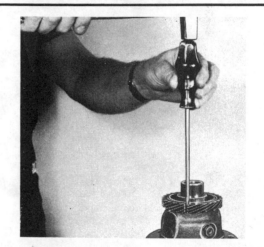

Fig. 6.21 Splitting the speedometer drivegear (Sec 7)

Fig. 6.22 Removing pinion shaft circlips (Sec 7)

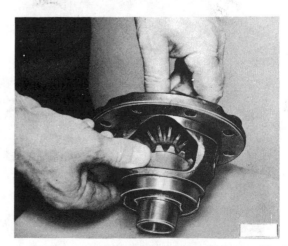

Fig. 6.23 Removing differential pinions and gears (Sec 7)

8.1 Vent plug on selector housing

8.3A Removing retainer from selector guide pin

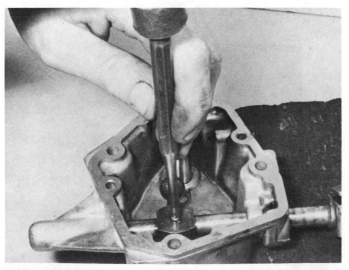

8.4 Removing selector finger roll pin

8 Selector housing cover – overhaul

1   Unscrew and remove the vent plug (photo).
2   Remove the circlip from the top of the guide pin (photo).
3   Take off the retainer, coil spring and intermediate selector lever (photos).
4   Drive out the retaining pin to release the selector finger from the rod and withdraw both components from the cover (photo).
5   If the flexible joint on the selector rod is worn, grind off the rivet to dismantle it and to fit new components. A pin and circlip are

8.2 Extracting circlip from selector guide pin

8.3B Removing selector lever

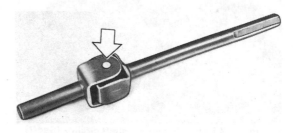

Fig. 6.24 Flexible joint rivet (arrowed) (Sec 8)

supplied as replacements.

6   Renew the oil seal in the selector cover.

9 Transmission housing – overhaul

1   Inspect the housing for cracks, especially around the bolt holes.
2   Mop out any oil and swarf.
3   Prise out the speedometer driven gear and its guide.
4   Always renew the O-ring and oil seal before refitting (photos).
5   Within the bellhousing, check the needle bearing for wear. If it requires renewal, remove the clutch release mechanism as described in Chapter 5.
6   Remove and install the needle bearing using a suitable drift (photo).
7   Inspect the mainshaft supporting roller bearing in the transmission housing and if worn remove it using a puller or a bolt, nut and distance piece.

10 Input shaft – overhaul

1   Support the end of the geartrain and tap the shaft from it.
2   Extract the circlip which secures the bearing to the end of the shaft. Take off the washer (photo).

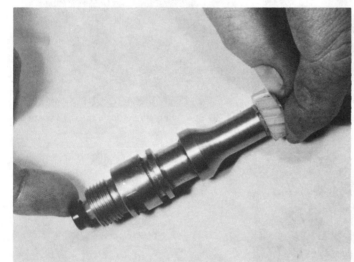

9.4B Speedometer driven gear end seal

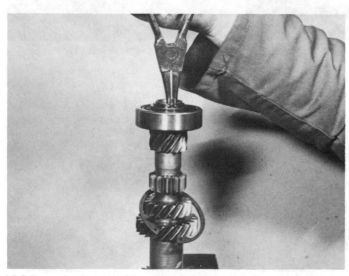

10.2 Removing input shaft bearing retaining circlip. Note geartrain retaining circlip loose on shaft

3   Using a piece of tubing, drive the geartrain out of the bearing.
4   If any of the gears are damaged, the geartrain complete will have

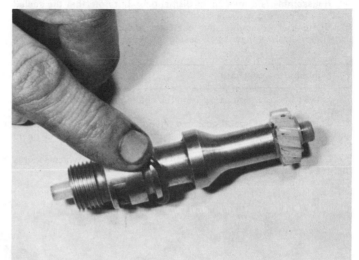

9.4A Speedometer driven gear O-ring

9.6 Transmission casing needle bearing

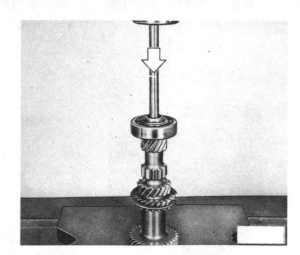

Fig. 6.25 Removing input shaft from geartrain (Sec 10)

to be renewed. This will mean that the matching gears on the mainshaft will also have to be renewed.

5 Reassembly is a reversal of dismantling, but note that the sealed side of the bearing is away from the gear.

6 Remember to locate the geartrain securing circlip ready for installation in its transmission casing groove.

11 Mainshaft – overhaul

1 Extract the retaining circlip from the bearing at the end of the shaft (photo).

2 Support the 1st speed gear and drive the shaft out of the bearing and gear. Note the spacer washer between the bearing and gears (photos).

3 Support 2nd speed gear and then extract the circlip which secures the 1st/2nd synchro (photo).

4 Take the synchro baulk ring from the shaft (photo).

5 Take the 1st/2nd synchro unit from the shaft. Note the reverse gear teeth on the sleeve (photo).

6 Remove the next baulk ring (photo).

7 Remove 2nd speed gear (photo).

8 Now turn your attention to the opposite end of the mainshaft. Extract the circlip which secures the pinion drivegear to the shaft (photo).

9 Remove the pinion gear (photo).

10 Remove the spacer washer (photo).

11 Remove 4th gear (photo).

12 Remove the baulk ring (photo).

13 Extract the circlip which secures the 3rd/4th synchro unit to the mainshaft (photo).

14 Remove 3rd/4th synchro unit (photo).

15 Remove the next baulk ring (photo).

16 Remove 3rd speed gear (photo).

17 If any of the foregoing components cannot be removed from the shaft by hand, use a puller or press, or drive the shaft out of them

11.1 Removing mainshaft bearing circlip

11.2A Removing mainshaft bearing

11.2B Removing spacer from face of 1st speed gear

11.2C Removing 1st speed gear

11.3 Extracting circlip from 1st/2nd synchro

11.4 Removing 1st/2nd baulk ring

11.5 Removing 1st/2nd synchro

11.6 Removing baulk ring from 2nd speed gear

11.7 Removing 2nd speed gear

11.8 Extracting pinion drivegear circlip

11.9 Removing pinion gear

11.10 Removing spacer from face of 4th speed gear

11.11 Removing 4th speed gear

11.12 Removing the baulk ring

11.13 Extracting circlip from 3rd/4th synchro

11.14 Removing 3rd/4th synchro

11.15 Removing baulk ring from 3rd speed gear

11.16 Removing 3rd speed gear

provided the gear is adequately supported at its lower face.

18 With the mainshaft completely dismantled, examine the gears for chipped or worn teeth and the shaft for deformation of splines. Renew all circlips (photo).

19 If there has been a history of noisy gear changing or if the synchromesh could be easily beaten during changes, renew the synchro unit complete or overhaul as described in the next Section.

20 With all parts clean and oiled, reassemble in the following sequence.

21 Fit 3rd speed gear to the drivegear end of the mainshaft.

22 Place the baulk ring on the cone of 3rd gear.

23 Fit the 3rd/4th synchro unit, applying pressure to the hub (photo).

24 Secure the synchro unit with a new circlip.

25 Fit a baulk ring.

26 Fit 4th speed gear.

27 Fit the spacer washer.

28 Fit the pinion drivegear and circlip.

29 Now commence work on the opposite end of the mainshaft.

30 Fit 2nd speed gear.

31 Fit the baulk ring to the cone of 2nd gear.

32 Fit 1st/2nd synchro unit (reverse gear teeth towards 2nd speed gear).

33 Fit the baulk ring.

34 Fit the circlip to secure the synchro unit.

35 Fit 1st speed gear (photo).

36 Fit the spacer washer.

37 Fit the bearing and secure it with its circlip.

38 Remember to locate the geartrain securing circlip ready for installation in its transmission casing groove.

12 Synchroniser units – overhaul

1 Components of 1st/2nd and 3rd/4th synchro units are interchangeable.

2 It is not good practice however to mix parts which have been in

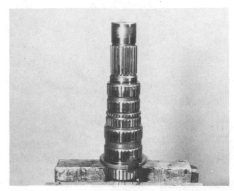

11.18 Mainshaft dismantled

11.23 Using tubing to install 3rd/4th synchro

11.35 Using tubing to install 1st speed gear to mainshaft

use for a high mileage and which have run-in together.

3   If either the hub or sleeve show signs of wear in their teeth, the individual part may be renewed, but general wear is best rectified by complete renewal of the unit.

4   To dismantle, push the sleeve off the hub, taking care not to allow the sliding keys to fly out.

5   Extract the circular springs and keys.

6   Reassembly is a reversal of dismantling. Make sure that the hooked ends of the springs engage in the same sliding key but run in opposite directions in relation to each other (photos).

7   To check the baulk rings for wear, twist them onto the gear cones. The ring should 'stick' to the cone and show a definite clearance between the ring and the gear shoulder. If these conditions are not met, renew the baulk rings.

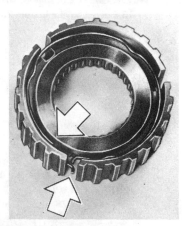

Fig. 6.26 Synchro spring locations (Sec 12)

13 Transmission – reassembly

1   Liberally oil the differential components.

2   Install the side gears and pinions, the spring discs and the pinion shaft into the differential case.

3   Fit new retaining circlips.

4   If the speedometer drivegear was removed, warm the new gear in hot water (80°C/176°F) and tap it onto the differential case with a piece of tubing until it snaps into position. Make sure that the lugs on the gear are aligned with the cut-outs in the differential case.

5   Warm the crownwheel to 80°C (176°F) and locate it on the differential case. Use new bolts and tighten them to the specified torque.

6   Fit the tapered roller bearings to the differential case (if removed at dismantling).

7   If not already done, fit the bearing outer tracks to the transmission casing.

8   Fit new driveshaft seals into the transmission casing (if not already done) and fill the lips with grease.

9   Lower the differential into the transmission casing.

10   Fit a new O-ring and oil seal to the bearing adjuster ring. Apply grease to the seal lips and to the screw threads (photos).

11   Screw the adjust ring into the transmission casing, hand tight at this stage (photo).

12   Adjust the bearing in one of the following ways, depending upon whether the original bearings have been refitted or new ones installed.

13   **Original bearing:** Simply screw in the adjuster ring until the alignment marks made before dismantling are opposite to each other. Should any axial play exist, the ring may be further adjusted to give a turning torque of between 0.6 and 1.01 Nm (5.3 and 8.9 lbf in) as described for new bearings in the following paragraph.

14   **New bearings:** The bearing preload must be adjusted by means of the adjuster ring so that a torque of 1.50 to 1.80 Nm (13.3 to 15.9 lbf in) is required to keep the crownwheel and bearings turning slowly. Unless a special torsion or friction gauge is available, push a tapered

12.6A Synchro hub and sleeve

12.6B Fitting a synchro sliding key

12.6C Fitting a synchro spring

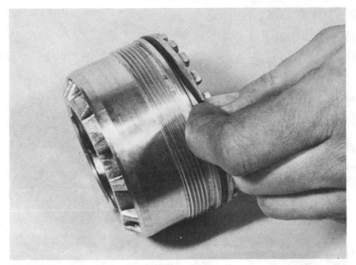

13.10A Bearing adjuster ring O-ring

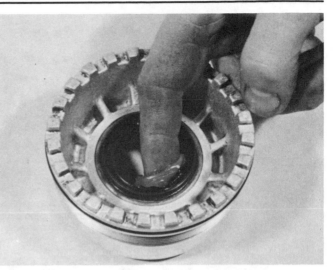

13.10B Filling oil seal lips with grease

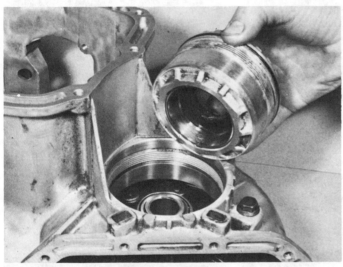

13.11 Installing bearing adjuster ring

13.16 Fitting pressed steel cover and gasket

13.20A Fitting short interlock plunger

softwood rod into the splined side gear and then wrap a cord round it and attach it to a spring balance. Provided the cord leaves the rod at a point about 25.4 mm (1.0 in) from the centre point of its cross section, the torque will be fairly accurate. Adjust the ring until the turning torque is within the specified range.

15 Fit the adjuster ring lockplate without moving the position of the ring. The lockplate bolt hole is elongated to make this possible.

16 Use a new gasket and bolt the pressed steel cover to the transmission housing (photo).

17 Fit the reverse idler shaft to the transmission end cover, making sure that the locking ball is in position.

18 Pin the 1st/2nd selector fork to its rod, but leave the pin projecting by approximately 2.0 mm (0.08 in).

19 Hold the mainshaft, input shaft and reverse gear trains meshed together, with the 1st/2nd selector fork and rod engaged in the groove of 1st/2nd synchro.

20 Locate the assembly into the end cover. The help of an assistant will facilitate the work. Fit the selector rod interlock plungers (photos).

21 Fit the circlips which retain the mainshaft and input shaft assemblies to the transmission casing. Make sure that they engage positively in their grooves. Fit the thrust washer to the reverse idler gear, also the swarf collecting magnet (photos).

22 Check that the sleeve on 1st/2nd synchro is in neutral then fit the 3rd/4th and reverse selector forks and rods (photos).

23 Pin the forks to the rods (photos).

13.20B Fitting long interlock plunger

13.21A Engaging input shaft circlip to transmission housing

13.21B Reverse idler thrust washer

13.22A Fitting 3rd/4th selector fork and rod

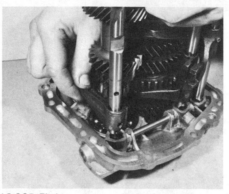

13.22B Fitting reverse selector fork and rod

13.23A Pinning 1st/2nd selector fork to rod

13.23B Pinning reverse selector fork to rod

13.26 Fitting transmission housing gasket

13.29 Locating selector housing gasket

24 Refit the detent plungers and springs. If the sealing plugs are not a really tight fit, oversize ones should be obtained and driven in.

25 Using a screwdriver, move the sleeve of the appropriate synchro unit to engage 2nd gear.

26 Stick a new gasket, with grease, to the transmission casing and then insert the geartrains with end cover into the casing until the fixing bolts and nuts can be screwed in to the specified torque (photo).

27 Fit the speedometer driven gear and bolt on its retainer plate.

28 Screw in the reversing lamp switch to the specified torque.

29 Set the transmission in neutral and stick a new selector housing gasket in position (photo).

30 Bolt on the selector housing, tightening the bolts to the specified torque.

31 The transmission can be filled with oil now as described in Section 6, provided it is held in the in-vehicle attitude, otherwise wait until it has been refitted to the vehicle.

14 Fault diagnosis – manual transmission

Symptom	Reason(s)
Weak or ineffective synchromesh	Synchro baulk rings worn, split or damaged Synchromesh units worn, or damaged
Jumps out of gear	Gearchange mechanism worn Synchromesh units badly worn Selector fork badly worn
Excessive noise	Incorrect grade of oil in gearbox or oil level too low Gearteeth excessively worn or damaged Intermediate gear thrust washers worn allowing excessive end play Worn bearings
Difficulty in engaging gears	Clutch pedal adjustment incorrect
Noise when cornering	Wheel bearing or driveshaft fault Differential fault

Note: *It is sometimes difficult to decide whether it is worthwhile removing and dismantling the gearbox for a fault which may be nothing more than a minor irritant. Gearboxes which howl, or where the synchromesh can be 'beaten' by a quick gearchange, may continue to perform for a long time in this state. A worn gearbox usually needs a complete rebuild to eliminate noise because the various gears, if re-aligned on new bearings, will continue to howl when different wearing surfaces are presented to each other. The decision to overhaul therefore, must be considered with regard to time and money available, relative to the degree of noise or malfunction that the driver has to suffer.*

Chapter 7 Driveshafts

For modifications, and information applicable to later models, see Supplement at end of manual

Contents

Specifications

Type .... Open with homokinetic joint at each end. Right-hand shaft 343 mm (13.5 in) longer than left-hand shaft

Grease type .... GM grease, part No 194 1521/90 094 176 (Duckhams LBM 10)

Torque wrench settings

	Nm	lbf ft
Driveshaft/hub carrier nut:		
Stage 1	100	74
Release, then Stage 2	20	15
Stage 3	turn through 90°	
Roadwheel bolt	90	66
Suspension arm balljoint nut	50	37

1 Description and maintenance

The driveshaft are of open type, having a homokinetic joint at each end. The right-hand shaft is longer than the left-hand one.

Maintenance consists of regularly inspecting the bellows for splits or damage. Renew if evident (Section 3).

2 Driveshaft – removal and refitting

1   Raise the front of the vehicle and support it securely.
2   Remove the front roadwheel.
3   Extract the split pin and unscrew the castellated nut from the end of the driveshaft. This nut is very tight and will require the use of a long knuckle bar to release it. To prevent the driveshaft turning, have an assistant apply the brake pedal or bolt a bar to two of the wheel bolt holes as shown (Fig. 7.1). There is no need to remove the brake caliper, although in the illustration this has been done in the interest of clarity.
4   Extract the split pin from the castellated nut on the suspension arm-to-hub carrier balljoint.
5   Unscrew the castellated nut and then use a suitable balljoint separator to disconnect the balljoint.
6   A forked tool will now be required for insertion between the transmission casing and the inner driveshaft joint. In the absence of the official tool (KM-460-1/2) a flat steel bar with a good chamfer on one end will serve as a substitute. Drive the tool into the gap between the joint and casing to release the shaft snap-ring from the differential. Be prepared for some loss of oil and plug the hole (even with a piece of rag) to prevent loss of oil and entry of dirt.
7   It should now be possible to push the driveshaft out of the hub using finger pressure. If it is not, use a hub puller.
8   Before refitting a driveshaft, make sure thet the contact surfaces of the shaft joint and hub bearing are absolutely clean.
9   Apply some grease to the shaft splines and insert into the hub carrier. Screw on the shaft nut finger tight.

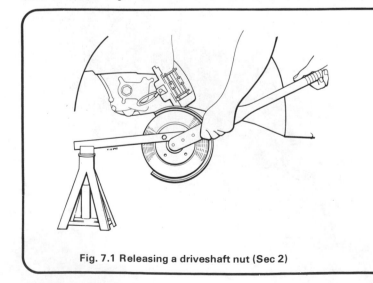

Fig. 7.1 Releasing a driveshaft nut (Sec 2)

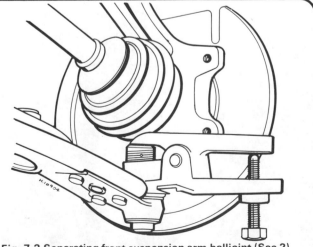

Fig. 7.2 Separating front suspension arm balljoint (Sec 2)

Fig. 7.3 Releasing a driveshaft from the transmission (Sec 2)

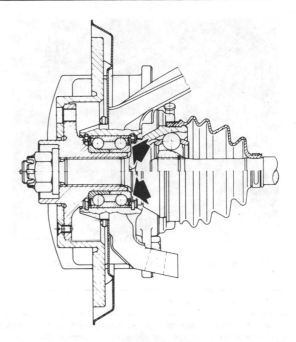

Fig. 7.4 Sectional view of front hub. Clean mating surfaces arrowed (Sec 2)

3.1 Driveshaft bellows securing band (arrowed)

3 Driveshaft joint – bellows renewal

1   With the driveshaft removed from the vehicle as described in the preceding Section, remove the retaining band and slide the bellows from the joint (photo).
2   Expand the retaining circlip and remove the joint from the splines of the driveshaft.
3   Slide the defective bellows from the driveshaft.
4   Clean away the old grease from the joint and repack liberally with the specified grease.
5   Slide the bellows over the joint and squeeze them to expel as much air as possible.
6   Set the bellows on the shaft, making sure that the smaller diameter opening is located in the groove on the driveshaft.
7   Fit new bellows retaining bands. There are many suitable types of band available but those used as original equipment will require the use of special pliers to tighten them.

10 Fit a new snap-ring to the inboard end of the driveshaft.
11 Insert the inboard end of the driveshaft into the transmission as far as it will go.
12 Now apply a screwdriver to the weld bead of the inboard joint, **not** the metal cover, and drive the driveshaft into the differential until the retaining ring engages positively. Pull on the driveshaft to check the engagement.
13 Reconnect the suspension balljoint and tighten the castellated nut to the specified torque.
14 Insert a new split pin and bend over the ends.
15 It is most important that the driveshaft nut is tightened by using the following method.
16 With the brake applied or the hub locked with a bar (see paragraph 3), screw on a new driveshaft nut to the specified Stage 1 torque.
17 Loosen the driveshaft nut and tighten again to specified Stage 2 torque.
18 Tighten the nut through a further 90°. Check this by observing the travel of the knuckle bar wrench.
19 If the slots in the castellated nut do not line up with the split pin hole in the shaft, unscrew the nut slightly, **do not** tighten further to align.
20 Insert a new split pin.
21 Refit the roadwheel and lower the vehicle.
22 Top up transmission oil (see Chapter 6).

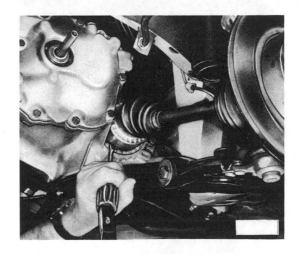

Fig. 7.5 Engaging driveshaft with transmission (Sec 4)

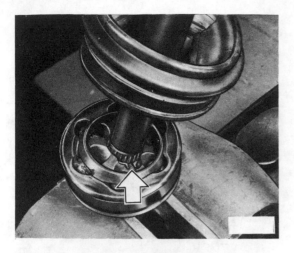

Fig. 7.6 Driveshaft joint retaining circlip (Sec 4)

Fig. 7.7 Tapping joint from driveshaft (Sec 4)

4 Driveshaft joint – renewal

1   A worn driveshaft joint cannot be overhauled, only renewed as a complete assembly. Remove the driveshaft (Section 2).
2   Release the securing band and slide the bellows off the worn joint.
3   Expand the circlip which secures the joint to the driveshaft.

4   Using a plastic-faced hammer, tap the joint from the driveshaft.
5   Tap on the new joint until the securing circlip engages in its groove.
6   Repack the joint with the specified grease.
7   Refit the bellows as described in the preceding Section.
8   Fit the driveshaft to the vehicle.

5 Fault diagnosis – driveshafts

Symptom	Reason(s)
Vibration	Driveshaft bent Worn universal joints Out-of-balance roadwheels
'Clonk' on taking up drive or on overrun	Worn universal joints Worn splines on shaft, hub carrier or differential side gears Loose driveshaft nut Loose roadwheel bolts

Chapter 8 Steering

For modifications, and information applicable to later models, see Supplement at end of manual

Contents

Specifications

General

Type	Rack-and-pinion with safety column
Ratio	22 : 1
Turns of steering wheel (lock-to-lock)	3.9
Turning circle:	
Between kerbs	9.76 m (32 ft)
Between walls	10.52 m (34.5 ft)
Front wheel alignment	
Camber (non-adjustable) – laden*:	
Hatchback and Saloon	– 1° to 0°
Estate	– 1° 15′ to + 0° 15′
Castor (non-adjustable) – laden*:	
Hatchback and Saloon	+ 0° 30′ to + 2° 30′
Estate	0° to + 2°
Toe:	
Laden*	0.5 to 2.5 mm toe-out
Unladen	0 to 2.0 mm toe-in
Rack grease type	GM grease, part No 194 8558/90 018 813 (Duckhams Adgear 00)

Laden indicates a vehicle containing two front seat occupants and the fuel tank half full

Torque wrench settings

	lbf ft	Nm
Balljoint (tie-rod) nut	37	50
Steering wheel nut	18	25
Tie-rod clamp pinch-bolt	15	20
Steering gear mounting nuts	15	20
Steering shaft coupling pinch-bolts	15	20
Rack damper locknut	32	44

1 Description

The steering gear is of rack-and-pinion type, movement being transmitted to the front wheels through tie-rods which are connected to the rack through a sliding sleeve.

The steering column consists of an outer column which incorporates a deformable section and a shaft connected to a flexible coupling at its lower end.

2 Maintenance

1 At regular intervals inspect the flexible bellows on the steering rack housing, and the tie-rod end balljoint gaiters, for splits or damage. Renew as necessary as described in later Sections of this Chapter.

2 Check the tie-rod end balljoints for wear. This is best done by having an assistant move the steering wheel from side to side through an arc of travel of about 20° while the balljoint connection to the steering arm on the front hub carrier is observed. Any loss of movement or shake in the balljoint will indicate wear and a new tie-rod end will have to be fitted (see Section 3).

3 Tie-rod end – removal and refitting

1 Extract the split pin from the castellated nut on the balljoint and unscrew the nut until it is level with the top of the ball-pin.

2 Using a suitable balljoint separator, disconnect the balljoint from the steering arm (photo).

3 Release the pinch-bolt on the tie-rod end clamp and slide the clamp towards the balljoint.

4 Now measure the distance between the bolt which secures the inboard end of the tie-rod to the rack and the end of the threaded socket of the tie-rod end. Record this as an aid to positioning the new tie-rod end.

5 Unscrew and remove the tie-rod end from the tie-rod.

6 The tie-rod ends are handed left (L) and right (R), make sure that you have the correct replacement part for the side being worked upon.

7 Apply grease to the tie-rod threads and screw on the end fitting until it takes up its original recorded position. Make sure that the clamp is located on the tie-rod end.

8 Connect the balljoint to the eye of the steering arm, screw on the nut and fit a new split pin.

9 Set the clamp so that its opening is aligned with the slot in the

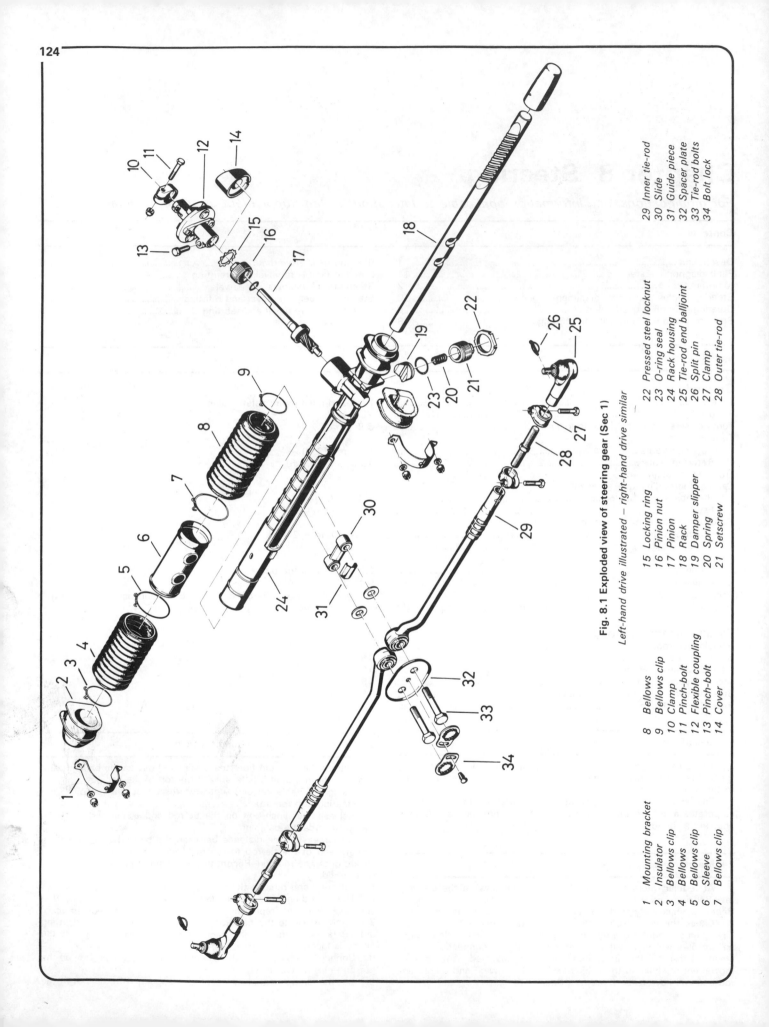

Fig. 8.1 Exploded view of steering gear (Sec 1)

Left-hand drive illustrated — right-hand drive similar

1 Mounting bracket	8 Bellows	15 Locking ring	22 Pressed steel locknut	29 Inner tie-rod
2 Insulator	9 Bellows clip	16 Pinion nut	23 O-ring seal	30 Slide
3 Bellows clip	10 Clamp	17 Pinion	24 Rack housing	31 Guide piece
4 Bellows	11 Pinch-bolt	18 Rack	25 Tie-rod end balljoint	32 Spacer plate
5 Bellows clip	12 Flexible coupling	19 Damper slipper	26 Split pin	33 Tie-rod bolts
6 Sleeve	13 Pinch-bolt	20 Spring	27 Clamp	34 Bolt lock
7 Bellows clip	14 Cover	21 Setscrew	28 Outer tie-rod	

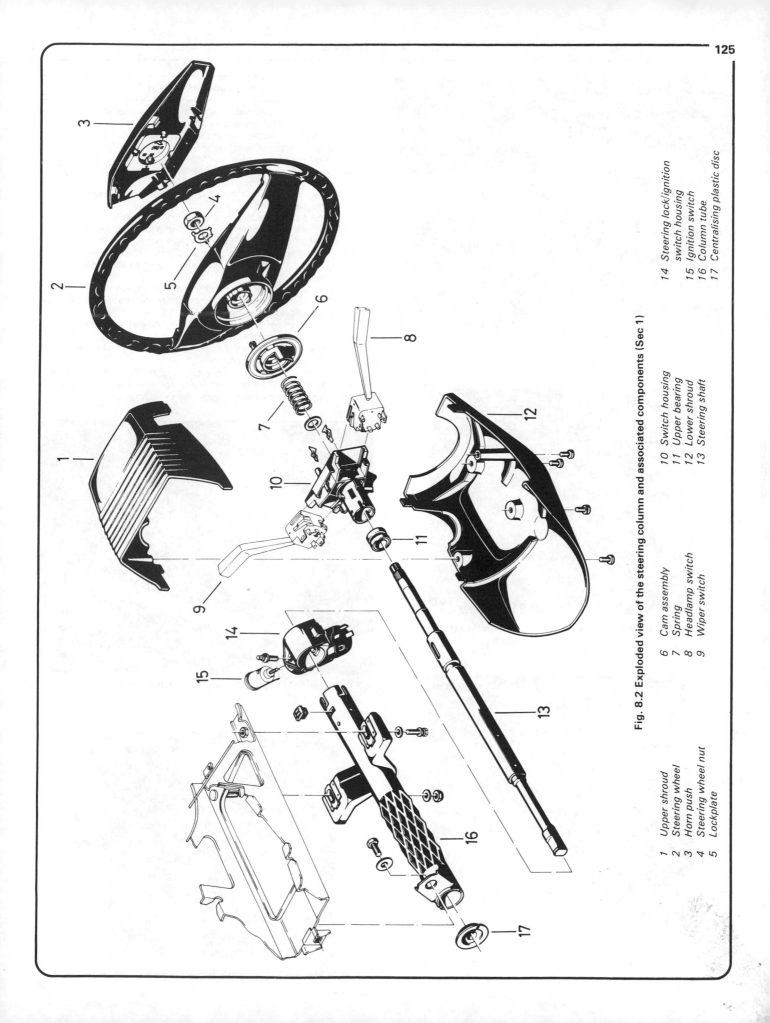

Fig. 8.2 Exploded view of the steering column and associated components (Sec 1)

1 Upper shroud
2 Steering wheel
3 Horn push
4 Steering wheel nut
5 Lockplate

6 Cam assembly
7 Spring
8 Headlamp switch
9 Wiper switch

10 Switch housing
11 Upper bearing
12 Lower shroud
13 Steering shaft

14 Steering lock/ignition switch housing
15 Ignition switch
16 Column tube
17 Centralising plastic disc

3.2 Typical balljoint separator in use

Fig. 8.3 Tie-rod end with clamp (arrowed) (Sec 3)

Fig. 8.4 Tie-rod end balljoint marking (Sec 3)

threaded part of the tie-rod end. The welded pinch-bolt nut should be at the top. Tighten to the specified torque.
10 Check and adjust the front wheel alignment (toe) as described in Section 10.

4 Steering gear – removal and refitting

1   On 1.3 l models only, remove the air cleaner from the engine. Set the steering in the straight-ahead position.
2   Disconnect the battery earth lead.
3   Working at the centre of the steering rack housing, remove both tie-rod bolts and remove the bolt locks and the spacer plate (photo).
4   Unscrew and remove the pinch-bolt from the flexible coupling at the base of the steering column.
5   Unscrew the pinch-bolt which secures the flexible coupling to the pinion of the steering gear.
6   Slide the flexible coupling upwards off the pinion.
7   Unbolt the steering gear mounting clamps and withdraw the rack-and-pinion housing through the front right-hand wheel arch.
8   Refitting is a reversal of removal, but before connecting the flexible coupling to the pinion, the steering must be centred in the following way.
9   Jack up the front of the car and turn the pinion on the steering gear until the distance between the centre of the spacer plate and the rib on the mounting is as shown in Fig. 8.8.
10 Set the steering wheel in its straight-ahead position with the spokes pointing downward.
11 Push the flexible coupling down and connect it with the pinion, then tighten the coupling bolt.
12 The upper clamp should now be lying so that the pinch-bolt is parallel with the steering housing. If it is not, this will indicate that the pinion is out of phase with the rack and the components will have to

4.3 Tie-rod connections at rack (right-hand drive shown)

Fig. 8.5 Tie-rod attachment to rack slide (Sec 4)

Fig. 8.6 Flexible coupling upper and lower pinch-bolts (Sec 4)

Fig. 8.7 Rack housing mounting nut (Sec 4)

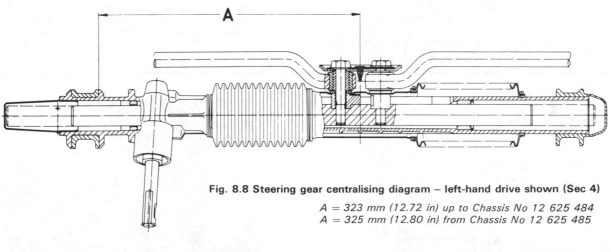

Fig. 8.8 Steering gear centralising diagram – left-hand drive shown (Sec 4)

A = 323 mm (12.72 in) up to Chassis No 12 625 484
A = 325 mm (12.80 in) from Chassis No 12 625 485

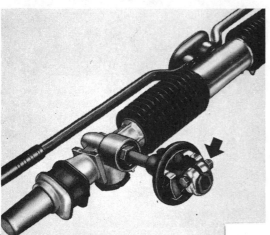

Fig. 8.9 Parallel setting of flexible coupling pinch-bolt when steering centralised – left-hand drive shown (Sec 4)

Fig. 8.10 Mounting bracket and pinion sealing cap correctly installed – left-hand drive shown (Sec 5)

be repositioned in relation to each other as described in Section 6.
13 Refer to the next Section for details of the mounting brackets.

---

5 Steering rack bellows – renewal

1 To renew a faulty bellows, the steering gear must first be removed

from the vehicle as described in the preceding Section.
2 Remove the mounting bracket and its rubber insulator from the housing.
3 Remove the bellows clamp wires and pull the bellows from the housing. If both bellows are to be renewed, the complete bellows/sleeve assembly may be slid from the housing.
4 Refitting is a reversal of removal, but observe the following essential requirements.

5   The concave end of the mounting bracket bolt hole flange must be pointing down when the steering gear is installed.

6   If the pinion sealing cap has been removed, make sure that its notch is engaged with the rib on the steering gear housing.

6   Steering gear – overhaul

1   Remove the steering gear from the vehicle as previously described.

2   Clean away external dirt.

3   Remove the bellows and housing sleeve.

4   Remove the slide and guide piece from the rack.

5   Release the pressed steel locknut from the rack adjuster setscrew.

6   Unscrew and remove the setscrew and extract the coil spring, seal and damper slipper.

7   Extract the locking ring from around the pinion nut, unscrew the nut and extract the seal.

8   Withdraw the rack and the pinion.

9   Push out the cap from the end of the housing using a long rod.

10 Further dismantling is not possible. If the rack bushes or pinion needle bearing are worn, renew the housing complete. The pinion can only be renewed complete with the ball-bearing.

11 Clean away old lubricant and apply the specified grease to internal components. Insert 50g (1¾ oz) of the grease between the rack bushes in the inside of the housing.

12 Insert the rack into the housing and locate it so that its end furthest from the pinion is set as shown in Fig. 8.13.

13 Now insert the pinion so that when its gear is finally meshed with the rack teeth, the cut-out on the pinion shaft is at right-angles to the rack and located as shown (Fig. 8.13).

14 Apply specified grease to the pinion ball-bearing and screw in the pinion nut to the specified torque. Fit a new nut retaining ring, driving it home with a piece of tubing.

15 The steering gear must now be adjusted. To do this, make up two distance pieces to the dimensions shown in Fig.8.14. Using the tie-rod eye attaching bolts, bolt the slide, guide piece and distance pieces to the rack.

16 Insert the rack damper slipper and coil spring into their hole and screw in the setscrew until some resistance is felt.

17 Unscrew the setscrew between $\frac{1}{8}$ and $\frac{1}{4}$ of a turn and check that the rack will move freely throughout its complete travel.

18 Without disturbing the setting of the setscrew, fit the pressed steel locknut and tighten to the specified torque.

19 Tap a new end cap into the housing, fit the bellows and remove the temporary distance pieces and tie-rod eye bolts from the rack.

20 Fit the mountings and the pinion cap seal as described in Section 5, paragraphs 5 and 6.

21 Check the centering of the steering gear as described in Section 4, paragraph 12. If the pinion-to-rack tooth engagement is incorrect, the pinion will have to be withdrawn and moved as necessary to correct the setting.

22 Once the gear has been installed in the vehicle, carry out a test drive on a route having curves and corners. The gear should exhibit a well-defined self-centering action after steering lock has been applied. If it does not, the rack damper has been over-adjusted and should be reset.

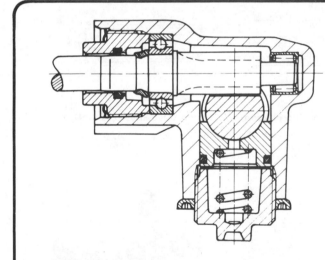

Fig. 8.11 Sectional view of rack damper (Sec 6)

Fig. 8.12 Prising out pinion nut locking ring (Sec 6)

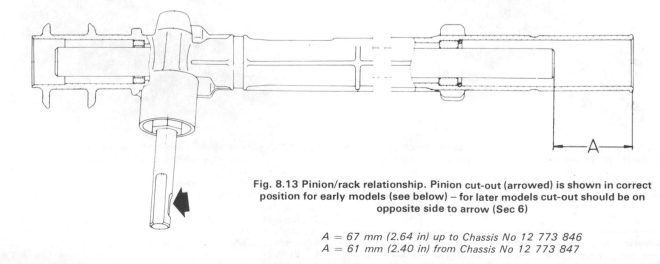

Fig. 8.13 Pinion/rack relationship. Pinion cut-out (arrowed) is shown in correct position for early models (see below) – for later models cut-out should be on opposite side to arrow (Sec 6)

A = 67 mm (2.64 in) up to Chassis No 12 773 846
A = 61 mm (2.40 in) from Chassis No 12 773 847

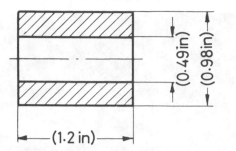

Fig. 8.14 Steering gear adjustment distance piece (Sec 6)

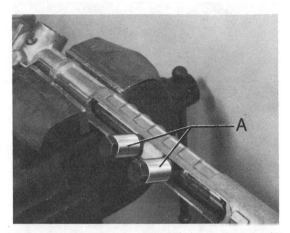

Fig. 8.15 Adjustment distance pieces (A) bolted to rack (Sec 6)

Fig. 8.16 Removing the horn button (Sec 7)

Fig. 8.17 Removing steering wheel with puller KM-210 (Sec 7)

7 Steering wheel – removal and refitting

1 Disconnect the battery negative lead.
2 Prise out the horn button from the centre of the steering wheel.
3 Set the steering wheel in the straight-ahead position and unscrew the retaining nut.
4 Remove the steering wheel using a small two-legged puller. Do not attempt to knock or thump the wheel off, or damage to the column may occur.
5 Refit by reversing the removal operations.
6 Check that the steering wheel is correctly aligned before tightening its retaining nut to the specified torque (photo).

8 Steering column – removal and refitting

1 Disconnect the battery earth lead. Extract the four screws and remove both halves of the steering column shroud.
2 Unclip the direction indicator and wiper switches by depressing the upper and lower locking tabs.
3 Pull out the wiring harness for the steering and ignition locks.
4 Set the steering wheel and the front roadwheels in the straight-ahead position.
5 Unscrew and remove the upper pinch-bolt from the steering flexible coupling.
6 Unscrew and remove the bolt that secures the base of the column to the bulkhead.
7 The bolts must now be extracted from the column upper mounting bracket. The left-hand bolt is of shear head type and must be centre-punched, drilled out and a bolt extractor used to remove it. A self-locking nut is used on the right-hand side (photo).
8 Withdraw the column assembly into the vehicle interior and then remove it from the vehicle. Remove the steering wheel (Section 7).
9 If a new column assembly is being installed, a plastic washer is located on the base of the shaft as an aid to centering the shaft in the

7.6 Tightening steering wheel nut

column tube.
10 Centre the steering gear as described in Section 4, paragraph 12.
11 Engage the plastic washer for centering the shaft in the column tube.
12 Offer the column into position and connect the coupling as described in Section 6, paragraphs 12 and 13.
13 Loosely connect the upper mounting using a new shear bolt.

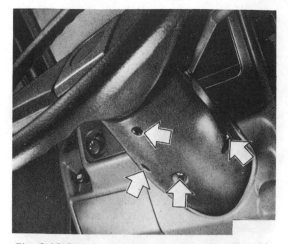

Fig. 8.18 Steering column shroud screws (Sec 8)

Fig. 8.20 Column base mounting bolt (Sec 8)

8.7 Steering column upper bracket

Fig. 8.19 Switch locking tabs (Sec 8)

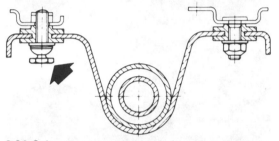

Fig. 8.21 Column upper mounting bolts – shear head arrowed (Sec 8)

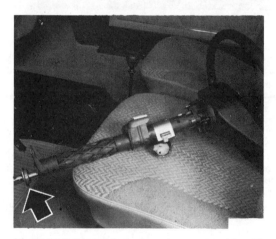

Fig. 8.22 Column/shaft centering washer (Sec 8)

14 Loosely screw in the column lower fixing bolt and the coupling pinch-bolt.
15 Tighten the lower fixing bolt to its specified torque. Tighten the shear head bolt until its head breaks off.
16 Pull up on the steering shaft until contact is made with the shaft bearing stop. Tighten the coupling pinch-bolt.
17 Remove the temporary plastic centering washer.
18 Refit the wiring harness and column switches, also the column upper shrouds.
19 Refit the steering wheel and reconnect the battery.

9 Steering column – overhaul

1 With the assembly removed from the vehicle as previously described, withdraw the steering wheel from the steering shaft (Section 7).
2 Remove the column switches (Section 8, paragraph 2).
3 Disconnect the wiring harness from the switches.
4 Prise out the safety plugs and remove the column switch housing by turning it to the left and pulling.
5 The double row ball-bearing can be pressed out of its housing if the two bearing fixing catches are first prised apart. Use a piece of tubing as a drift to remove the bearing.
6 Install the new bearing by reversing the removal operations. Note the bearing thrust washer (A) (Fig. 8.25).
7 Set the lock cylinder in 'I' position and depress the detent plunger using a thin rod. Remove the mechanical component of the switch.
8 Extract the two grub screws and withdraw the electrical component of the switch.

Fig. 8.23 Disconnecting switch wiring harness (Sec 9)

Fig. 8.24 Column switch housing plug (Sec 9)

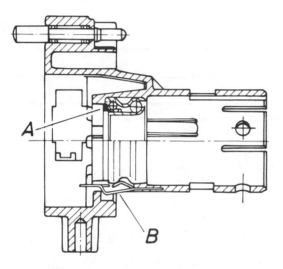

Fig. 8.25 Sectional view of switch housing (Sec 9)

A Thrust washer   B Contact springs

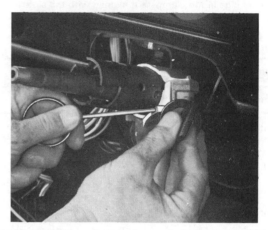

Fig. 8.26 Lock cylinder detent plunger being depressed (Sec 9)

9   Withdraw the steering shaft from the column tube.
10 To reassemble, first insert the shaft into the column tube and then engage the bottom of the shaft in the flexible coupling, making sure that the cut-out in the shaft aligns with the bolt hole in the clamp.
11 Fit the temporary plastic centering washer into the base of the column tube.
12 Install the lock cylinder and ignition lock.
13 Install the switch housing to the column tube, using new safety plugs.
14 Clip in the direction indicator and wiper switches and fix the wiring harness.
15 Fit the column shroud.
16 Fit the washer and spring on the shaft upper bearing.
17 Fit the steering wheel and tighten the nut to the specified torque using a new lockplate.
18 Pull the steering wheel/shaft upwards until the shaft upper bearing is contacted.
19 Retaining this position, tighten the coupling pinch-bolt.
20 Remove the temporary plastic centering washer.
21 Check the steering alignment as described in Section 4, paragraph 12.

10 Steering angles and wheel alignment – general

1   Accurate front wheel alignment is essential to good steering and for even tyre wear. Before considering the steering angles, check that the tyres are correctly inflated, that the front wheels are not buckled, the hub bearings are not worn or incorrectly adjusted and that the steering linkage is in good order, without slackness or wear at the joints.
2   Wheel alignment consists of four factors:
    Camber, is the angle at which the roadwheels are set from the vertical when viewed from the front or rear of the vehicle. Positive camber is the angle (in degrees) that the wheels are tilted outwards at the top from the vertical.
    Castor, is the angle between the steering axis and a vertical line when viewed from each side of the vehicle. Positive castor is indicated when the steering axis is inclined towards the rear of the vehicle at its upper end.
    Steering axis inclination, is the angle, when viewed from the front or rear of the vehicle, between the vertical and an imaginary line drawn between the upper and lower front suspension strut mountings.
    Toe, is the amount by which the distance between the front inside edges of the roadwheel rims differs from that between the rear inside edges. If the distance between the front edges is less than that at the rear, the wheels are said to toe-in. If the distance between the front inside edges is greater than that at the rear, the wheels toe-out.
3   Due to the need for precision gauges to measure the small angles of the steering and suspension settings, it is preferable that checking of camber and castor is left to a service station having the necessary equipment. Camber and castor are set during production of the vehicle, and any deviation from the specified angle will be due to accident damage or gross wear in the suspension mountings.
4   To check the front wheel alignment, first make sure that the lengths of both track rods are equal when the steering is in the straight-ahead position. The track rod lengths can be adjusted for length if necessary by releasing all the clamp pinch-bolts and turning the rods.

5   Obtain a tracking gauge. These are available in various forms from accessory stores, or one can be fabricated from a length of steel tubing suitably cranked to clear the sump and bellhousing and having a setscrew and locknut at one end.

6   With the gauge, measure the distance between the two wheel inner rims (at hub height) at the rear of the wheel. Push the vehicle forward to rotate the wheel through 180° (half a turn) and measure the distance between the wheel inner rims, again at hub height, at the front of the wheel. This last measurement should differ from the first by the appropriate toe-in/toe-out according to the Specifications. The vehicle must be on level ground.

7   Where the toe-in/toe-out is found to be incorrect, release the track rod clamp pinch-bolts and turn the track rods equally. Only turn them a quarter of a turn at a time before re-checking the alignment. Do not grip the threaded part of the track rod/balljoint during adjustment, but use an open-ended spanner on the flats provided. It is important not to allow the tie-rods to become unequal in length during adjustment, otherwise the alignment of the steering wheel will become incorrect and tyre scrubbing will occur on turns.

8   On completion, tighten the track rod clamps without disturbing their setting. Check that the balljoint is at the centre of its arc of travel and the openings in the clamps are aligned with the slots in the track rod and balljoint socket, also that the clamp pinch-bolts have their nuts at the top.

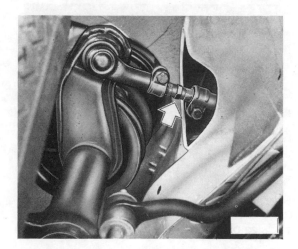

Fig. 8.27 Flats for spanner on outer tie-rod (Sec 10)

11 Fault diagnosis – steering

Symptom	Reason(s)
Lost motion at steering wheel	Wear in rack-and-pinion Wear in tie-rod end balljoints
Steering wander	Wear in gear or linkage Incorrect front wheel alignment Incorrectly adjusted or worn front hub bearings
Heavy or stiff steering	Incorrect front wheel alignment Seized balljoint Dry rack assembly Distorted shaft/column
Wheel wobble and vibration	Roadwheels out of balance Roadwheel buckled Incorrect front wheel alignment

Chapter 9 Braking system

For modifications, and information applicable to later models, see Supplement at end of manual

Contents

Specifications

System type
Dual circuit (diagonally split), 4-wheel hydraulic, discs front, drums rear. Handbrake mechanical to rear wheels. Vacuum servo assistance and pressure proportioning valve

Disc brakes

Disc diameter	236 mm (9.3 in)
Disc thickness	10.0 mm (0.39 n)
Disc minimum thickness after refinishing	9.0 mm (0.35 in)
Maximum disc run-out	0.1 mm (0.004 in)
Pad friction material minimum thickness	2.0 mm (0.08 in)

Drum brakes

Drum internal diameter:	
New	200 mm (7.87 in)
Maximum after refinishing	201 mm (7.91 in)
Drum width:	
Estate	45 mm (1.77 in)
All other models	28 mm (1.10 in)
Maximum out-of-round	0.1 mm (0.004 in)
Shoe friction material minimum thickness	1.5 mm (0.06 in)

Hydraulic system

Master cylinder bore:	
Estate	20.64 mm (0.8125 in)
All other models	19.05 mm (0.75 in)
Disc caliper piston diameter	48 mm (1.89 in)
Rear wheel cylinder bore:	
Estate	19.05 mm (0.75 in)
All other models	17.46 mm (0.6875 in)
Fluid type/specification	Hydraulic fluid to SAE J1703 (Duckhams Universal Brake and Clutch Fluid)

Servo

Type	Single diaphragm
Diameter	177.8 mm (7.0 in)

Torque wrench settings

	Nm	lbf ft
Caliper mounting bolts	95	70
Master cylinder mounting nuts	18	13
Servo mounting bolts	18	13
Rear brake backplate bolts	28	20
Proportioning valve and bracket bolts	20	15
Bleed screw	9	6
Master cylinder (ATE) stop screw	6	4
Brake pipeline unions	11	8
Rear brake cylinder mounting screws	9	6

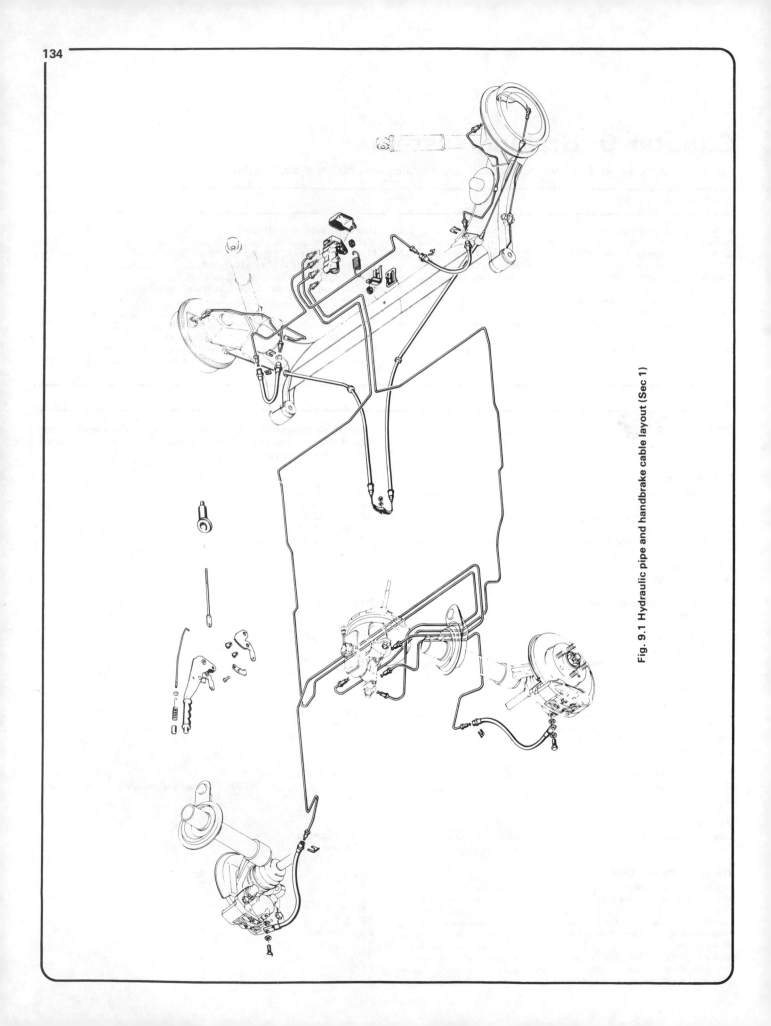

Fig. 9.1 Hydraulic pipe and handbrake cable layout (Sec 1)

1 Description

The braking system is of dual circuit (diagonal) hydraulic type having disc brakes at the front and drum brakes at the rear.

The handbrake is mechanical, operating on the rear wheels only, and is actuated by a floor-mounted lever.

A vacuum servo unit is fitted to all models. A hydraulic pressure proportioning valve is fitted to prevent rear wheel locking during heavy brake application.

The individual components of the braking system may be one of two makes – GMF or ATE. Both types are described in this Chapter.

2 Maintenance

1 Although a brake fluid warning lamp is connected to the master cylinder reservoir, it is still an extra safeguard to view the fluid level through the translucent container at the weekly check.

2 The level will drop very slowly indeed due to normal pad and lining wear, but any rapid drop and the need to top up at frequent intervals will be due to a leak somewhere in the hydraulic system, which should be investigated.

3 Regularly inspect the flexible and rigid pipelines for any sign of leakage and rectify immediately should any be observed.

4 Wear in the disc pads or rear drum shoe linings should be visually checked at the intervals specified in Routine Maintenance.

5 Renew the system fluid by bleeding at the specified intervals (see Routine Maintenance).

6 Adjust the rear brakes at the specified intervals as described in Section 7.

3 Disc pads – inspection and renewal

1 Raise the front of the vehicle and remove the roadwheels.

2 Inspect the thickness of the friction material on each pad. If any one is at or below the specified minimum, renew the pads as an axle set (four pads) in the following way.

3 Drive out the pad retaining pins by applying a punch to their inboard ends.

4 Remove the springs (photo).

5 Using a pair of pliers, withdraw the outboard pad (photo).

6 Remove the inboard pad. If it is very tight, move the pad sideways slightly to depress the caliper piston (photo).

7 In order to accommodate the new thicker pads, the caliper piston must be depressed fully into its cylinder using a flat bar of metal such as a tyre lever. The action of depressing the piston will cause the fluid in the reservoir to rise, so anticipate this by syphoning some off using an old (clean) battery hydrometer or similar.

8 Brush out the jaws of the caliper, taking care not to inhale the dust.

Fig. 9.2 Removing pad retaining pins (Sec 3)

3.4 Disc pad spring

3.5 Outboard disc pad partially withdrawn

3.6 Removing inboard disc pad

9 Insert the pads, making sure that the lining side is against the disc.
10 Locate the spreader springs and drive in the retaining pins (photo).
11 Repeat the operations on the opposite brake.
12 Refit the roadwheels and lower the vehicle.
13 Apply the footbrake hard several times to position the pads against the discs.
14 Top up the fluid reservoir to the correct level.

4 Caliper (ATE type) – removal, overhaul and refitting

1 Raise the front of the vehicle and remove the roadwheel.
2 Unscrew and remove the caliper fluid union bolt. Plug the union with two suitable grommets or allow the fluid to drain into a container.
3 Unscrew the two caliper mounting bolts and withdraw the caliper.
4 Brush away external dirt and mud and remove the disc pads as described in Section 3, then secure the caliper in the jaws of a vice.
5 Separate the caliper body from its bracket by sliding it off its splines.
6 Using a screwdriver, prise off the retaining ring from the dust excluder.
7 Remove the dust excluder.
8 Place a thin piece of wood or hardboard on the end of the piston and apply air pressure to the fluid pipe connection on the caliper body. Only low air pressure will be required to eject the piston, such as is generated by a tyre foot pump.

9 Once the piston has been removed, pick out the seal from its groove in the cylinder, using a plastic or wooden instrument.
10 Inspect the surfaces of the piston and cylinder bore for scoring or evidence of metal-to-metal rubbing. If evident, renew the caliper complete.
11 If these components are in good condition, discard the rubber seal and dust excluder and obtain a repair kit which will contain all the necessary replaceable items.

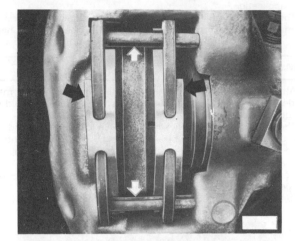

Fig. 9.3 Disc pad springs correctly located (Sec 3)

3.10 Installing disc pad retaining pin

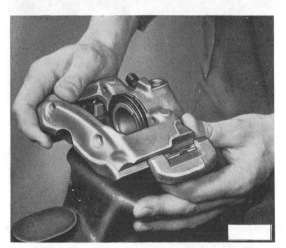

Fig. 9.4 Separating ATE caliper body from bracket (Sec 4)

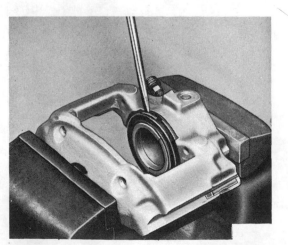

Fig. 9.5 Removing dust excluder retaining ring (Sec 4)

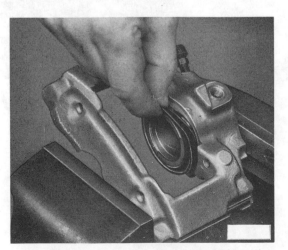

Fig. 9.6 Removing caliper dust excluder (Sec 4)

Fig. 9.7 Exploded view of ATE type caliper brake (Sec 4)

1 Bracket
2 Mounting bolt
3 Caliper guide spring
4 Bleed nipple
5 Caliper body
6 Disc pad
7 Pad spreader spring
8 Pad retaining pin
9 Piston seal
10 Piston
11 Dust excluder
12 Dust excluder retaining ring
13 Dust cap
14 Split pin
15 Castellated nut
16 Thrust washer
17 Hub
18 Disc
19 Wheel stud
20 Disc splash shield

12 Clean the piston and cylinder bore with brake hydraulic fluid or methylated spirit – nothing else!
13 Commence reassembly by fitting the seal into the cylinder groove.
14 Locate the dust excluder in its groove in the piston. Dip the piston in clean brake fluid, or apply rubber grease to its external surface, and insert it squarely into the cylinder. Check that the piston step is positioned as shown (Fig. 9.9).
15 When the piston has been partially depressed, engage the dust excluder with the rim of the cylinder and fit the retaining clip.
16 Depress the piston fully into its cylinder bore.
17 Secure the caliper bracket in a vice and install the guide springs.

18 Slide the caliper body into the bracket splines until the body and bracket are flush as shown (Fig. 9.13).
19 Refit the caliper to the hub carrier, tighten the bolts to the specified torque and fit the disc pads as described in Section 3.
20 Connect the fluid hose, using new seals at the union.
21 Bleed the system as described in Section 17.
22 Refit the roadwheel and lower the car to the ground. Depress the brake pedal several times to bring the pads up to the disc, then top up the master cylinder if necesssary.

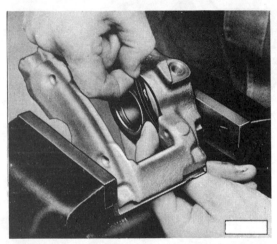

Fig. 9.8 Fitting dust excluder to piston groove (Sec 4)

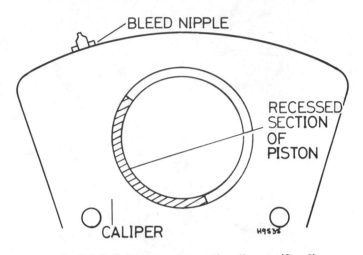

Fig. 9.9 Caliper piston step setting diagram (Sec 4)

Fig. 9.10 Engaging dust excluder with cylinder body (Sec 4)

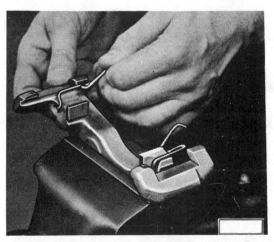

Fig. 9.11 Fitting caliper bracket guide springs (Sec 4)

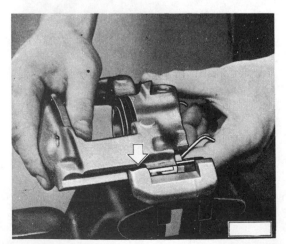

Fig. 9.12 Connecting caliper body and bracket (Sec 4)

Fig. 9.13 Flush connection of caliper body and bracket (Sec 4)

5 Caliper (GMF type) – removal, overhaul and refitting

1   With the front of the vehicle raised and supported on stands, prise off the mounting bolt caps. Do not unscrew the two hexagon-headed bolts, as these connect the caliper body and bracket (photo).

2   Disconnect the fluid line from the caliper and either plug it with two rubber grommets or allow the fluid to drain into a container.

3   Using an Allen key type wrench, unscrew the two socket-headed mounting bolts (photo).

4   Remove the caliper from the vehicle.

5   Brush away external dust and remove the disc pads as described in Section 3.

6   Using a chisel, release the sliding sleeve inner dust caps from the caliper housing.

7   Prise off the piston dust excluder.

8   Apply pressure to the outboard ends of the sliding sleeves until their dust caps can be disengaged from the sleeve grooves and removed.

9   Press the sliding sleeves from the caliper housing.

10 Carry out the operations described in Section 4, paragraphs 8 to 13.

11 When the piston has been partially inserted, engage the new dust excluder with the groove in the piston.

12 Renew the sealing rings on the sliding sleeves, applying the special grease supplied in the repair kit to the sealing ring grooves. Make sure that the sealing ring is located in the centre groove.

13 Install the sliding sleeves so that the dust cap groove is towards the caliper bracket. Do not push the sleeves fully in at this stage.

14 Install the new dust caps for the sliding sleeves onto their caliper housing collars. Use a piece of tubing to drive them fully home.

Fig. 9.14 Prising off caliper mounting bolt cap (GMF) (Sec 5)

5.1 Removing caliper mounting bolt cap (GMF)

5.3 Socket-headed caliper mounting bolt (GMF)

Fig. 9.15 Unscrewing caliper mounting bolt (GMF) (Sec 5)

Fig. 9.16 Removing inner dust caps from sliding sleeves (GMF) (Sec 5)

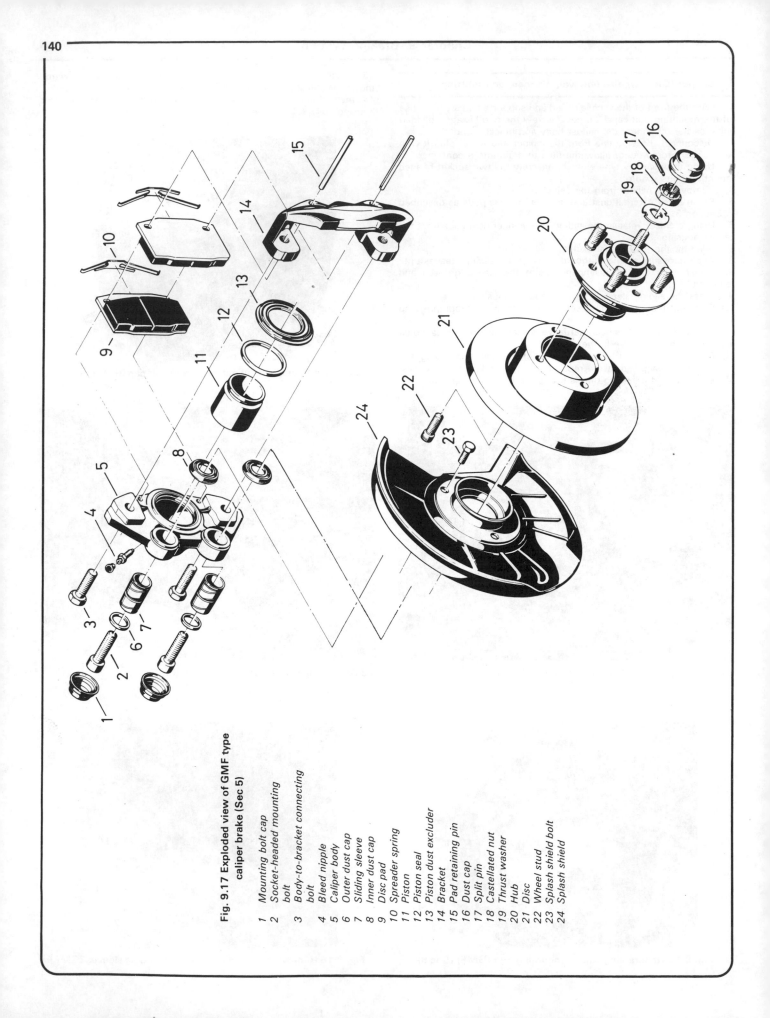

Fig. 9.17 Exploded view of GMF type caliper brake (Sec 5)

1 Mounting bolt cap
2 Socket-headed mounting bolt
3 Body-to-bracket connecting bolt
4 Bleed nipple
5 Caliper body
6 Outer dust cap
7 Sliding sleeve
8 Inner dust cap
9 Disc pad
10 Spreader spring
11 Piston
12 Piston seal
13 Piston dust excluder
14 Bracket
15 Pad retaining pin
16 Dust cap
17 Split pin
18 Castellated nut
19 Thrust washer
20 Hub
21 Disc
22 Wheel stud
23 Splash shield bolt
24 Splash shield

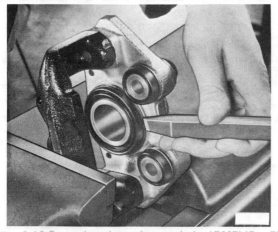
Fig. 9.18 Removing piston dust excluder (GMF) (Sec 5)

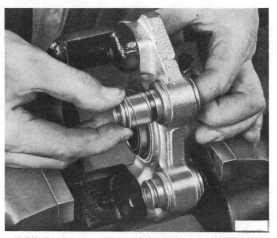
Fig. 9.19 Removing caliper sliding sleeves (GMF) (Sec 5)

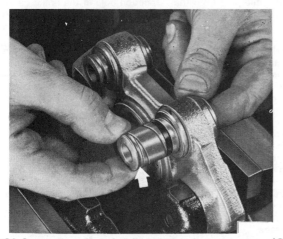
Fig. 9.20 Correct location of sliding sleeve dust cap groove (GMF) (Sec 5)

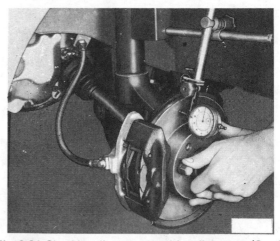
Fig. 9.21 Checking disc run-out with a dial gauge (Sec 6)

15 Depress the piston fully and secure the dust excluder to the housing, driving it fully home with a piece of suitable tubing.
16 Refit the caliper and screw in and tighten the socket-headed mounting bolts
17 Reconnect the fluid hose using new seals.
18 Refit the disc pads as described in Section 3.
19 Bleed the hydraulic system as described in Section 17.
20 Fit the roadwheels and lower the vehicle.

6 Brake disc – inspection, removal and refitting

1   Raise the front of the vehicle and remove the roadwheel.
2   Inspect the braking surface of the disc for deep grooving or tiny cracks. If these conditions are evident, the disc will have to be renewed or refinished. Any refinishing of both faces of the disc must not reduce the thickness of the disc below the minimum specified. Light, shallow scoring is a normal condition for brake discs.
3   If it is thought that the brake disc is distorted, check it for run-out using a dial gauge or using feeler blades between the disc and a fixed point as the disc is rotated.
4   If the run-out exceeds the specified limits, renew the disc.
5   To remove a brake disc for renewal of refinishing, first withdraw the pads as described in Section 3.
6   Extract the small retaining screw and then tilt the disc and withdraw it from the hub (photos).
7   It is recommended that both brake discs are refinished or renewed at the same time in order to maintain even braking.
8   Refitting is a reversal of removal.

6.6A Disc retaining screw

6.6B Removing disc from hub

7.4 Rear brake hexagon adjuster (arrowed)

7   Rear brakes – adjustment

1   Each rear brake shoe is individually adjusted by means of an eccentric cam.
2   Raise the rear of the vehicle and support it securely. Chock the front wheels.
3   Release the handbrake fully. Apply the brake hard a couple of times to centralise the shoes.
4   Turn one hexagon adjuster on the brake backplate while turning the roadwheel until the wheel locks, then back it off until the wheel rotates freely without binding (photo).
5   Repeat the adjustment on the second adjuster and then on the two adjusters on the opposite brake.
6   Lower the vehicle and apply the handbrake.
7   In order to combat corrosion occurring in the adjusters, apply some lubricant round the hexagon head periodically and apply a little grease to prevent water penetrating.

8   Rear brake shoes – inspection and renewal

1   The state of wear of the rear shoe linings can be observed by removing the plug from the inspection hole in the brake backplate.
2   Use a torch and mirror to check that the friction material has not worn down to less than the specified minimum. If it has then the shoes must be renewed in the following way.
3   Raise the rear of the vehicle and remove the rear roadwheels.
4   Extract the drum securing screw and remove the drum. If the drum is tight on the hub, tap it off with a plastic hammer. If the drum is grooved due to wear, the cam adjusters may have to be backed right off before the drum can be pulled off and the shoes cleared from the grooves. Sketch the location of the shoes and which way round the linings are fitted with regard to leading and trailing ends, before dismantling them (photos).
5   Disconnect the upper shoe return spring using a pair of pliers.
6   The shoe steady springs may be one of three types: A flat metal spring out of which the shoe can be slid, or a wire type spring clip, the ends of which should be compressed to release it from the backplate. The third type is a steady pin and coil spring which is removed by depressing the spring cap and turning it through 90°.
7   Pull the shoes apart until they can be released from the bottom anchorage.
8   Detach the shoe lower return spring and remove the strut from between the shoes.
9   Disconnect the end of the handbrake cable from the lever on the brake shoe and withdraw the shoes (photo). Do not depress the brake pedal while the shoes are off.
10   Unusual these days is the fact that friction linings are available for fitting to the original shoes. These linings are 5.0 mm (0.197 in) thick, as against 5.6 mm (0.220 in) thick for linings which must be ground

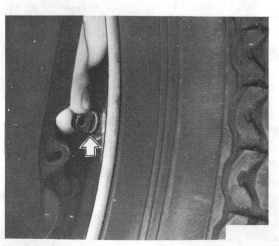

Fig. 9.22 Removing rear drum inspection plug (Sec 8)

8.4A Brake drum securing screw

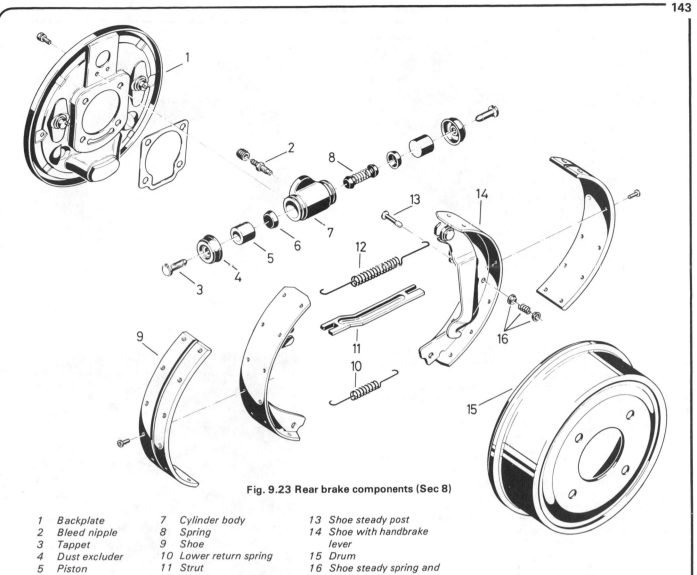

Fig. 9.23 Rear brake components (Sec 8)

1 Backplate	7 Cylinder body	13 Shoe steady post
2 Bleed nipple	8 Spring	14 Shoe with handbrake
3 Tappet	9 Shoe	lever
4 Dust excluder	10 Lower return spring	15 Drum
5 Piston	11 Strut	16 Shoe steady spring and
6 Seal	12 Upper return spring	retainers

8.4B Removing the brake drum

Fig. 9.24 Removing brake shoe from blade type steady spring (Sec 8)

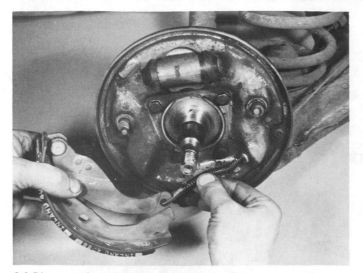

8.9 Disconnecting handbrake cable from shoe lever

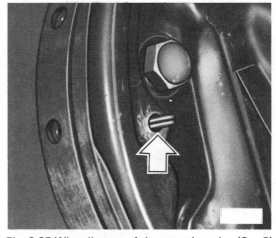

8.15 Rear brake shoes ready for refitting

to the drum contour after riveting. The old rivets can be drilled and punched out and new rivets used to fit the new linings, starting at the centre holes and working towards each end.

11 Having said all this, it is still recommended that new or factory relined shoes are used as replacements, rather than attempting to reline the shoes yourself.

12 Before installing the new shoes, brush away all dirt and dust, taking care not to inhale it as it contains asbestos which is injurious to health.

13 Any signs of oil contamination on the rear brake shoes will be due to a leaking hydraulic wheel cylinder (Section 9) or to a faulty hub oil seal (Chapter 11). Remedy the leak immediately, and renew the shoes.

14 Apply a little high melting point grease to the adjuster cams and the shoe contact high points on the brake backplate.

15 Lay the shoes out on the bench, making sure that they are correctly located with regard to handbrake lever and shoe lining leading and trailing ends (photo).

16 Fit the lower return spring.

17 Pull the shoes apart and engage their lower ends in the anchorage, then attach the handbrake cable.

18 Fit the strut and the shoe return upper spring.

19 Fit new shoe steady spring clips if of wire type.

20 Refit the brake drum.

21 Adjust the shoes as described in Section 7.

22 Refit the roadwheel.

23 Repeat the operations on the opposite brake as the shoes must be renewed as axle sets (four shoes). Adjust the handbrake on completion if necessary (Section 19).

9 Rear brake wheel cylinder – removal, overhaul and refitting

1   Raise the rear of the vehicle and remove the roadwheel.

2   Extract the securing screw and pull of the brake drum. Back off the brake adjusters if necessary.

3   Using a pair of pliers, disconnect the shoe upper return spring and push the upper ends of the shoes apart until they clear the wheel cylinder.

4   Disconnect the fluid line from the wheel cylinder and cap the end of the pipe as soon as the union is unscrewed to prevent loss of fluid. A bleed nipple dust cap is useful for this job.

5   Unscrew the mounting bolts and withdraw the cylinder from the backplate.

6   Clean away external dirt and pull off the rubber dust excluders from the cylinder body.

7   The pistons will normally be ejected by pressure of the coil spring but if they are not, tap the end of the cylinder on a piece of hardwood or apply low air pressure from a tyre foot pump at the pipeline connection.

8   Inspect the surfaces of the piston and the cylinder bore for scoring

Fig. 9.25 Wire clip type of shoe steady spring (Sec 8)

or metal-to-metal rubbed areas. If these are evident, renew the wheel cylinder complete.

9   If these components are in good order, discard the seals and dust excluders and obtain a repair kit which will contain all the renewable items.

10 Fit the piston seals (using the fingers only to manipulate them into position) so that the spring is between them. Dip the pistons in clean hydraulic fluid and insert them into the cylinder.

11 Fit the dust excluders.

12 Refit the wheel cylinder to the backplate and connect the pipeline.

13 Engage the brake shoes with the pistons and fit the shoe return spring.

14 Fit the brake drum and adjust the shoes.

15 Bleed the hydraulic system as described in Section 17.

16 Refit the roadwheel and lower the vehicle.

10 Rear brake backplate – removal and refitting

1   Raise the rear of the vehicle and remove the roadwheel and the brake drum.

2   Remove the brake shoes as described in Section 8.

3   Using a screwdriver, prise up the lockplate which secures the handbrake cable in the plastic sleeve in the backplate.

4   Tap off the hub dust cap.

5   Extract the split pin and unscrew and remove the castellated nut and thrust washer.

Fig. 9.26 Removing handbrake cable grommet lockplate (Sec 10)

Fig. 9.27 Removing rear hub (Sec 10)

Fig. 9.28 Unscrewing backplate mounting bolts (Sec 10)

12.1 Removing the reservoir cap

6 Withdraw the hub from the axle shaft.
7 Disconnect the pipeline from the wheel cylinder by unscrewing the union. Cap the end of the pipe to prevent loss of fluid.
8 Unbolt and remove the wheel cylinder.
9 Unscrew the backplate mounting bolts and remove the plate.
10 Refitting is a reversal of removal, but observe the following points.
11 Apply a little jointing compound between the backplate and the axle flange before bolting up.
12 Adjust the hub bearings as described in Chapter 11.
13 Adjust the brake shoes (Section 7).
14 Bleed the hydraulic system (Section 17).

11 Brake drum – inspection and renovation

1 Whenever the rear drums are removed, brush away internal dust, taking care not to inhale it, and inspect the lining rubbing surface. If the shoes have worn grooves in the metal, then it may be possible to re-grind the inside provided the maximum internal diameter is not exceeded (refer to Specifications). Light grooving is normal and requires no attention.
2 If the drum is suspected of being out-of-round, it should be renewed.

12 Master cylinder – removal and refitting

1 Unscrew the reservoir cap and place it to one side complete with float and warning switch (photo).

Fig. 9.29 Disconnecting master cylinder pipe unions (Sec 12)

2 Disconnect the pipelines from the master cylinder by unscrewing the unions. Cap the ends of the pipes to prevent the entry of dirt. Take care not to spill hydraulic fluid on the car bodywork.
3 Unscrew the mounting nuts and withdraw the master cylinder from the vacuum servo unit.

Fig. 9.30 Withdrawing master cylinder from servo unit (Sec 12)

Fig. 9.31 Prising fluid reservoir from master cylinder (Sec 12)

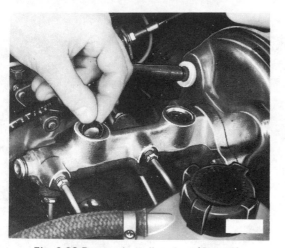

Fig. 9.32 Reservoir sealing rings (Sec 12)

Fig. 9.33 Extracting master cylinder circlip (GMF) (Sec 13)

4   Refitting is a reversal of removal. If a new cylinder is being installed, the reservoir will have to be prised off the original unit and fitted to the new one. Take care when prising off the reservoir, as it is retained by concealed circlips. Use new sealing rings at the reservoir pipe studs and prime the cylinder as described in Section 13, paragraph 15.
5   Bleed the hydraulic system as described in Section 17.

13 Master cylinder (GMF type) – overhaul

1   With the unit removed from the vehicle, clean away external dirt.
2   Insert a rod into the end of the cylinder and depress the piston until it can be held depressed by inserting a smooth pin or rod 3.0 mm (0.118 in) in diameter though the primary outlet.
3   Extract the circlip from the end of the cylinder using two screwdrivers. Discard the circlip.
4   Remove the primary piston after first having pulled out the temporary retaining pin.
5   Remove the secondary piston by tapping the end of the cylinder on a piece of hardwood.
6   Dismantle the primary piston. This can be done by compressing the spring with a cap from an aerosol or similar in which a hole has been drilled. As soon as the circlip appears, prise it off with two screwdrivers and discard it.
7   Examine the surfaces of the pistons and the cylinder bore for scoring or metal-to-metal rubbed areas. If evident, renew the master cylinder complete.
8   If the components are in good order, clean them in hydraulic fluid or methylated spirit – nothing else!
9   Obtain a repair kit which will contain all the necessary replaceable items.

Fig. 9.34 Removing master cylinder primary piston circlip (GMF) (Sec 13)

10 Install the new seals to the pistons, manipulating them into position with the fingers only.
11 Reassemble the primary piston using a new circlip. The circlip can be fully installed into its groove in the piston by tapping it down with a piece of tubing.
12 Dip the pistons in clean hydraulic fluid and fit the secondary piston, followed by the primary piston, into the cylinder.

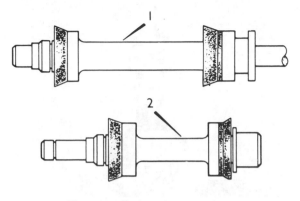

Master cylinder piston seals

1 Primary piston 　　　　 2 Secondary piston

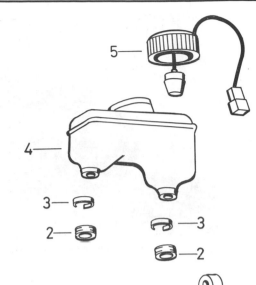

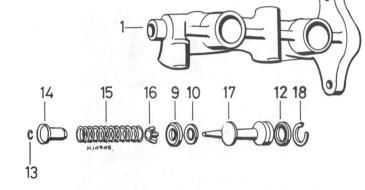

Fig. 9.35 Exploded view of GMF type master cylinder (Sec 13)

1 Body	5 Cap with warning	10 Shim	15 Primary piston spring
2 Reservoir sealing rings	switch	11 Secondary piston	16 Spring retainer
3 Circlips	7 Spring	12 Primary seals	17 Primary piston
4 Reservoir	8 Spring retainer	13 Circlip	18 Circlip
	9 Secondary piston seals	14 Spring sleeve	

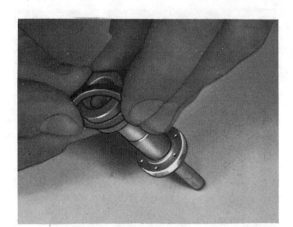

Fig. 9.36 Fitting a piston seal (Sec 13)

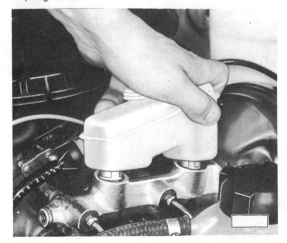

Fig. 9.37 Fitting master cylinder fluid reservoir (Sec 13)

13 Depress and hold the primary piston as described for dismantling while a new circlip is fitted.

14 Fit new rubber sealing rings and press the fluid reservoir into position on the cylinder body.

15 Pour some clean fluid into the reservoir and prime the master cylinder before installation by depressing the primary piston several times with a rod. A great deal of the fluid will of course be ejected from the open ports of the cylinder.

14 Master cylinder (ATE type) – overhaul

1 With the unit removed from the vehicle, clean away external dirt.

2 Prise the fluid reservoir from the cylinder body.

3 Extract the circlip from the end of the cylinder housing.

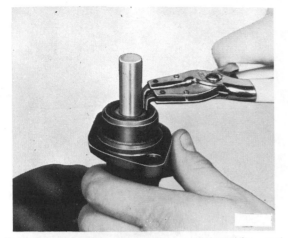

Fig. 9.38 Extracting cylinder body circlip (ATE) (Sec 14)

Fig. 9.39 Removing master cylinder primary piston (ATE) (Sec 14)

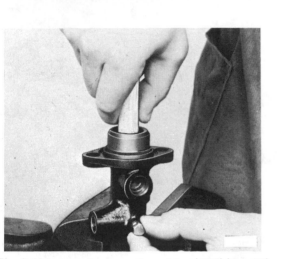

Fig. 9.40 Depressing secondary piston (ATE) (Sec 14)

Fig. 9.41 Removing secondary piston (ATE) (Sec 14)

4   Withdraw the primary piston.

5   Insert a rod and depress the secondary piston so that the stop screw can be removed from the cylinder body.

6   Withdraw the secondary piston by tapping the end of the cylinder on a block of hardwood.

7   Carry out the operations described in Section 13, paragraphs 7 to 10.

8   Reassembly is a reversal of dismantling, then carry out the operations described in Section 13, paragraphs 14 and 15.

15 Pressure proportioning valve – removal, refitting and adjustment

1   One of two types of valve may be fitted, depending upon whether the vehicle is equipped with automatic level control (Chapter 11), and upon the version (Hatchback, Estate etc).

Pressure-dependent (with ride height control)

2   Unscrew the unions and disconnect the brake lines from the valve. Cap the ends of the pipes to prevent loss of fluid. The unions are of different sizes so there should not be any confusion when refitting.

3   Unscrew the mounting bolts and remove the valve from the vehicle.

Load-dependent (without ride height control)

4   Release the bracket for the tension spring on the rear axle, move the bracket towards the rear of the vehicle and then detach the spring from the valve (photo).

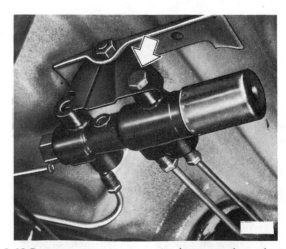

Fig. 9.42 Pressure proportioning valve (pressure-dependent type) showing (arrowed) mounting bolt (Sec 15)

5   Disconnect the brake lines from the valve and plug the ends of the pipes to prevent fluid loss.

6   Unscrew the mounting bolts and remove the valve from the vehicle. Unbolt and remove the impact shield.

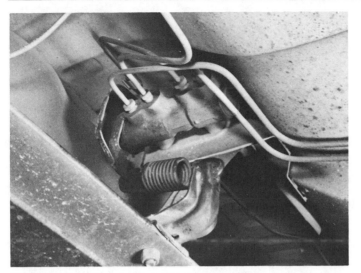

15.4 Load-dependent pressure proportioning valve

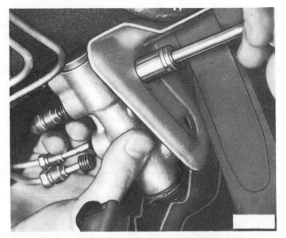

Fig. 9.43 Dismounting load-dependent type pressure proportioning valve (Sec 15)

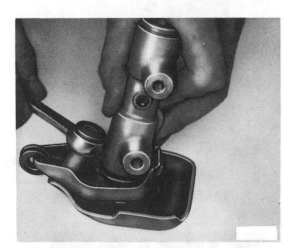

Fig. 9.44 Unbolting impact shield from pressure valve (Sec 15)

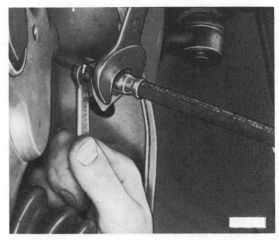

Fig. 9.45 Disconnecting a brake front hose (Sec 16)

Both types

7   Do not attempt to dismantle either type of valve.

8   Refitting is a reversal of removal, but with the load-dependent type, connect the spring in the following way.

9   Connect the spring to the bracket and to the valve, then push the valve lever forward against its stop.

10 Move the position of the bracket on the rear axle until the spring is neither loose nor under tension. Tighten the bracket bolts without disturbing the spring setting.

11 On all types, bleed the hydraulic system as described in Section 17.

16 Flexible hoses and rigid pipelines – inspection and renewal

1   Periodically, inspect the condition of the flexible brake hoses. If they appear swollen, chafed or when bent double with the fingers tiny cracks are visible, then they must be renewed.

2   Always uncouple the rigid pipe from the flexible hose first, then release the end of the flexible hose from the support bracket. Now unscrew the flexible hose from the caliper or connector. If this method is followed, no kinking of the hoses will occur (photo).

3   When installing the hose, always use a new sealing washer.

4   When installation is complete, check that the flexible hose does not rub against the tyre or other adjacent components. Its attitude may be altered to overcome this by pulling out the clip at the support bracket and twisting the hose in the required direction by not more than one quarter turn.

5   Bleed the hydraulic system (Section 17).

6   At regular intervals wipe the steel brake pipes clean and examine them for signs of rust or denting caused by flying stones.

16.2 Rear brake hose connection showing bracket and clip

7 Examine the fit of the pipes in their insulated securing clips and bend the tongues of the clips if necessary to ensure a positive fit.

8 Check that the pipes are not touching any adjacent components or rubbing against any part of the vehicle. Where this is observed, bend the pipe gently away to clear.

9 Any section of pipe which is rusty or chafed should be renewed. Brake pipes are available to the correct length and fitted with end unions from most dealers and can be made to pattern by many accessory suppliers. When installing the new pipes use the old pipes as a guide to bending and do not make any bends sharper than is necessary.

10 The system will of course have to be bled when the circuit has been reconnected.

17 Hydraulic system – bleeding

1 The two independent hydraulic circuits are as follows:

   (a) Front right-hand caliper and left rear wheel cylinder
   (b) Front left-hand caliper and right rear wheel cylinder

2 If the master cylinder or the pressure regulating valve has been disconnected and reconnected then the complete system (both circuits) must be bled.

3 If a component of only one circuit has been disturbed then only the particular circuit need be bled.

4 Due to the design of the hydraulic system and pipeline layout, satisfactory bleeding can only be carried out using a pressure bleeding kit. These are available from motor accessory shops and are usually operated by air pressure from the spare tyre.

5 By connecting a pressurised container to the master cylinder fluid reservoir, bleeding is then carried out by simply opening each bleed nipple in turn and allowing the fluid to run out, rather like turning on a tap, until no air is visible in the fluid.

6 Using this system, the large reserve of hydraulic fluid provides a safeguard against air being drawn into the master cylinder during the bleeding operation.

7 This method is particularly effective when bleeding 'difficult' systems and when bleeding the entire system at time of routine fluid renewal.

8 On vehicles equipped with load-dependent proportioning valves, disconnect the tension spring and retain the lever in its fully forward position with a piece of wire before commencing bleeding.

9 Bleed the front brakes first followed by the rear ones.

10 Discard fluid bled from the system.

11 Fresh fluid used at bleeding or for topping up should always be stored in an airtight container and remain unshaken for 24 hours before use.

12 During pressure bleeding it is permissible to depress the brake pedal slowly two or three times as an aid to expelling any trapped air.

13 When completed, recheck the fluid level in the master cylinder, top up if necessary and refit the cap. Check the 'feel' of the brake pedal which should be firm and free from any 'sponginess' which would indicate air still present in the system.

14 On vehicles so equipped, reconnect the tension spring of the proportioning valve and adjust if necessary as described in Section 15.

18 Vacuum servo unit – removal and refitting

Left-hand drive vehicles

1 Refer to Section 12 and remove the master cylinder.

2 Disconnect the servo unit vacuum hose either from the servo unit or from the intake manifold according to engine type.

3 Disconnect the brake pedal return spring.

4 Remove the clip from the brake pedal clevis pin and withdraw the pin.

5 Unscrew and remove the brake pedal support nuts.

6 Unscrew the servo bracket from the engine compartment rear bulkhead.

7 Withdraw the servo unit from the vehicle.

8 The servo unit base and bracket assembly should be unbolted and removed ready for installation to the new unit.

9 Repair or dismantling of the servo unit should not be attempted by the home mechanic.

10 Before fitting the new servo, attach the base and bracket to it and screw the clevis fork and locknut onto the pushrod.

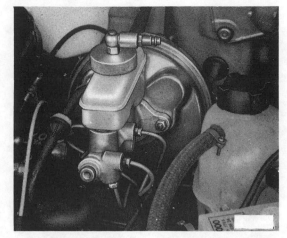

Fig. 9.46 Pressure bleeder connected (Sec 17)

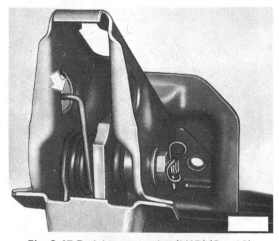

Fig. 9.47 Pedal return spring (LHD) (Sec 18)

Fig. 9.48 Brake pedal support nuts (Sec 18)

11 Bolt the servo into position and reconnect the brake pedal components.

12 Refit the master cylinder and connect the servo vacuum hose (photo).

13 With the engine off, pump the brake foot pedal five times and immediately measure the pedal free travel at the pedal pad. This should be between 6.0 and 9.0 mm (0.24 and 0.35 in). If it is not,

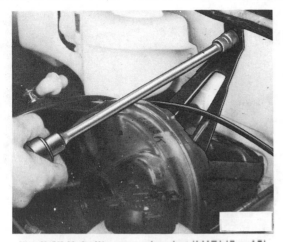

Fig. 9.49 Unbolting servo bracket (LHD) (Sec 18)

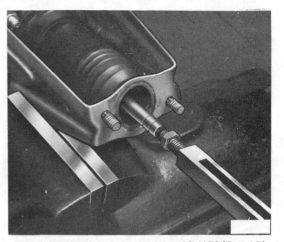

Fig. 9.50 Servo base and pushrod (LHD) (Sec 18)

Fig. 9.51 Pedal travel diagram (Sec 18)

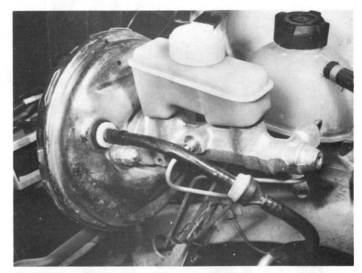

18.12 Servo vacuum hose and non-return valve

rotate the pushrod and when adjustment is complete, tighten the pushrod lock nut.

14 Bleed the complete hydraulic system (refer to Section 17).

Right-hand drive vehicles

15 Due to the fact that the vehicle was originally designed for left-hand drive steering, on right-hand drive versions, the brake pedal is connected to the vacuum servo unit by a remote control cable and bellcrank arrangement (refer to Section 22).

16 To remove the servo unit, disconnect the vacuum pipe and remove the master cylinder (Section 12).

17 Unbolt the booster from its cast mounting bracket and withdraw it from the pushrod (photo).

18 Refitting is a reversal of removal. On completion, check the brake pedal pad movement as described in paragraph 13, but on right-hand drive versions, any adjustment is made at the cable anchorage by altering the position of the locknuts (photo) and at the pedal pushrod.

All models

19 If the vacuum pipe non-return valve is ever removed, make sure that it is installed with its directional arrow pointing towards the intake manifold.

---

19 Handbrake – adjustment

1 The handbrake will normally be kept in correct adjustment by the routine adjustment of the rear shoes. However, due to cable stretch over a period of time, the travel of the handbrake lever may become excessive and the following operations should be carried out.

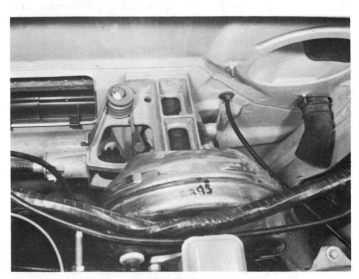

18.17 Vacuum servo and bracket (RHD)

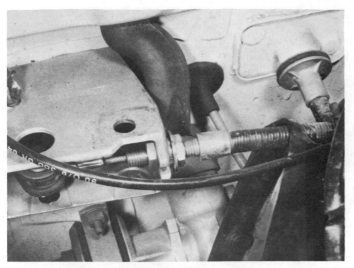

18.18 Footbrake remote control cable at bellcrank bracket

19.4 Handbrake equaliser

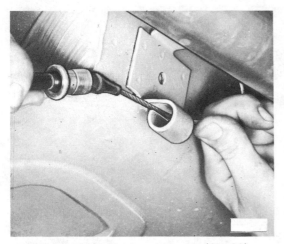

Fig. 9.52 Handbrake cable guide (Sec 20)

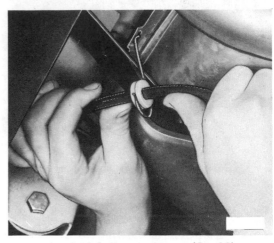

Fig. 9.53 Cable wire hanger (Sec 20)

2   From the fully off position, pull the handbrake lever onto the third notch of its ratchet.

3   Raise the rear of the vehicle so that the roadwheels are free to rotate.

4   Adjust the position of the self-locking nut on the threaded rod at the cable equaliser (photo) until both rear wheels when turned, emit a slight rubbing sound from the brake linings.

5   It is very important that the cable is always free to slide in the cable equaliser so keep its groove well greased.

6   Lower the vehicle and apply the handbrake fully.

20 Handbrake cable – renewal

1   To renew an excessively stretched, frayed or broken cable, raise the vehicle and unscrew the nut at the cable equaliser until the cable can be slipped out of the equaliser groove.

2   Slip the cable out of the guides on the body floor pan.

3   Slide the cable plastic grommets out of the wire hangers on the fuel tank.

4   Slide the cable out of the rear axle guides.

5   Remove the rear roadwheels and the brake drums.

6   Prise the cable lock out of the plastic sleeve at the brake backplate.

7   Disconnect the end of the cables from the shoe levers and withdraw the cable through the hole in the backplate.

8   Refitting is a reversal of removal. Adjust the cable as described in Section 19, adjusting the brake shoes first if necessary (Section 7).

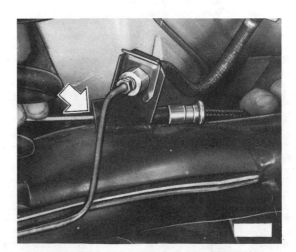

Fig. 9.54 Cable rear axle guides (Sec 20)

Fig. 9.55 Prising off handbrake cable grommet lockplate (Sec 20)

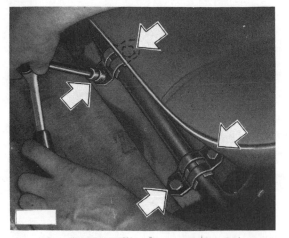

Fig. 9.56 Unbolting front seat (Sec 21)

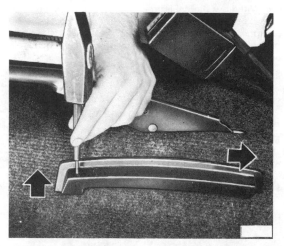

Fig. 9.57 Removing the seat slides (Sec 21)

Fig. 9.58 Handbrake switch fixing bolt (Sec 21)

21 Handbrake control lever – removal and refitting

1   Raise the vehicle and fully release the handbrake.
2   Remove the nut from the threaded rod at the equaliser.
3   Fold back the carpet under the driver's seat and unbolt the seat clamps from the floor. Remove the seat from the vehicle.
4   Remove the seat rail slides by knocking out the fixing pins with a punch.
5   Detach the handbrake warning switch by removing its fixing bolt.
6   Unbolt the handbrake control lever by passing a socket wrench through the opening provided in the carpet.
7   The handbrake lever can be dismantled to renew a worn ratchet pawl or segment.
8   Refitting is a reversal of removal, but use self-tapping screws to attach the seat slides.
9   Adjust the handbrake cable as described in Section 19.

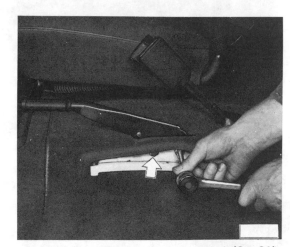

Fig. 9.59 Removing handbrake lever bolt (Sec 21)

22 Brake pedal – removal and refitting

Left-hand drive

1   As previously described, this is directly coupled to the servo unit on the left-hand side of the engine compartment.
2   Working under the instrument panel, pull out the clevis pin retaining clip and disconnect the pedal return spring.
3   Pull the connectors from the stop-lamp switch and pull the clevis pin out of the pedal arm.

4   Unbolt the pedal support from the bulkhead. Some nuts are accessible from within the engine compartment.
5   The pedal arm may be detached from the support for renewal of individual components.
6   Reassembly and refitting are reversals of removal and dismantling, but apply grease to the pivot bushes and note the method of attachment of the return spring.
7   Check pedal movement as described as Section 18, paragraph 13.

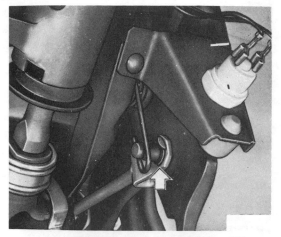

Fig. 9.60 Brake pedal pivot (LHD) (Sec 22)

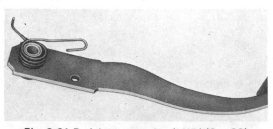

Fig. 9.61 Pedal return spring (LHD) (Sec 22)

Right-hand drive

8   As previously explained in Section 18, the brake pedal on these models incorporates a remote control cable linkage which complicates removal and refitting compared with left-hand drive vehicles.

9   Working at the engine compartment rear bulkhead, remove the rubber cover from the bellcrank mounting bracket (photo).

10   Working at the servo unit, release the remote control cable linkage return spring and then disconnect the end of the cable from the bellcrank. Withdraw the cable from the case servo support bracket.

11   Working at the bellcrank mounting bracket, release the two cable lock nuts (photo).

12   Working within the vehicle under the instrument panel, release the

22.9 Footbrake remote control bellcrank bracket cover (arrowed)

22.11 View inside bellcrank mounting bracket

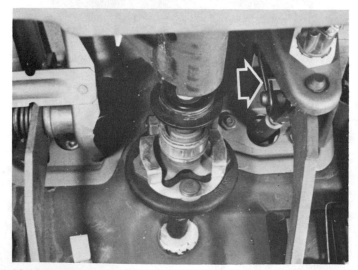

22.12 Footbrake pedal return spring (arrowed)

22.15 Footbrake stoplamp switch

pedal return spring, pull out the retaining clip and clevis pin and disconnect the pushrod from the pedal arm (photo).
13 Once more turning your attention to the engine compartment bulkhead, remove the bellcrank mounting bracket.
14 The cable, bellcrank and pushrod may now be detached from the bracket for renewal of individual components.
15 The brake pedal and support bracket can be removed after

unscrewing the mounting bolts and nuts, and disconnecting the stop-lamp switch (photo).
16 The pedal can be dismantled from the bracket if the clip and pivot shaft are first withdrawn.
17 Refitting is a reversal of removal and dismantling but apply pressure to the pivot bushes and on completion, check the pedal movement as described in Section 18, paragraph 18.

23 Fault diagnosis – braking system

Before diagnosing faults from the following chart, check that any braking irregularities are not caused by:
Uneven and incorrect tyre pressures
Wear in the steering mechanism
Defects in the suspension and dampers
Misalignment of the bodyframe

Symptom	Reason(s)
Pedal travels a long way before the brakes operate	Incorrect pedal adjustment Brake shoes set too far from the drums
Stopping ability poor, even though pedal pressure is firm	Linings, discs or drums badly worn or scored One or more wheel hydraulic cylinders seized, resulting in some brake shoes not pressing against the drums (or pads against disc) Brake linings contaminated with oil Wrong type of linings fitted (too hard) Brake shoes wrongly assembled Servo unit not functioning
Car veers to one side when the brakes are applied	Brake pads or linings on one side are contaminated with oil Hydraulic wheel cylinder on one side partially or fully seized A mixture of lining materials fitted between sides Brake discs not matched Unequal wear between sides caused by partially seized wheel cylinders
Pedal feels spongy when the brakes are applied	Air is present in the hydraulic system
Pedal feels springy when the brakes are applied	Brake linings not bedded into the drums (after fitting new ones) Master cylinder or brake backplate mounting bolts loose Severe wear in brake drums causing distortion when brakes are applied Discs out of true
Pedal travels right down with little or no resistance and brakes are virtually non-operative	Leak in hydraulic system resulting in lack of pressure for operating wheel cylinders If no signs of leakage are apparent the master cylinder internal seals are failing to sustain pressure
Binding, juddering, overheating	One or a combination of reasons given above Shoes installed incorrectly with reference to leading and trailing ends Broken shoe return spring Disc out-of-round Drum distorted Incorrect pedal adjustment
Lack of servo assistance	Vacuum hose disconnected or leaking Non-return valve defective or incorrectly fitted Servo internal defect

Chapter 10 Electrical system

For modifications, and information applicable to later models, see Supplement at end of manual

Contents

Specifications

General

System type	12 volt, negative earth
Battery capacity	36 Ah

Alternator

	Bosch	Delco-Remy
Make		
Type	K1-14V 45A 20	–
Nominal voltage	14	14
Maximum current (amps)	45	45
Minimum permissible brush length	14 mm (0.55 in)	10 mm (0.39 in)

Starter motor

	Bosch	Delco-Remy
Make	DF 0.7 kW	–
Type		
Code number	0 001 157 024	3 470 143
Minimum diameter of commutator	31.2 mm (1.23 in)	37.0 mm (1.46 in)
Minimum permissible brush length	11.5 mm (0.45 in)	7.0 mm (0.28 in)

Wiper blades .... Champion C-4101 (all models)

Lamp bulb data

	Wattage
Headlight (halogen)	60/55
Headlight (standard)	45/40
Foglight (front)	55
Spotlight	55
Direction indicators, front and rear	21
Fog rear warning light	21
Reversing light	21
Brake and tail light	21/5
Rear number plate light	10
Interior courtesy light	10
Boot light	10

	Wattage
Engine compartment light	10
Glove compartment light	5
Parking light	4
Charge indicator	3
Instrument lights	1.2
High beam indicator	1.2
Oil pressure warning indicator	1.2
Direction signal indicator	1.2
Warning light indicator	1.2
Parking brake indicator	1.2
Cigarette lighter and ashtray lights	1.2
Heated rear window indicator	1.2

Fuses

Position:	**Amps**	**Circuits**
1	7.5	Left side parking and tail light
2	7.5	Right side parking and tail light, instrument lights, engine compartment, rear foglight
3	—	Spare
4	15	Courtesy lights, luggage/load compartment light, hazard warning flasher system, clock, radio
5	30	Windshield wipers, horn
6	20	Reversing light, cigarette lighter, carburettor pre-heater, instruments
7	10	Direction indicator lights, brake lights
8	25	Heated rear window, driver's heated seat
9	20	Heater fan motor
10	20	Cooling fan motor
11	—	Spare
12	15	Front foglights
13	15	Spotlights

Torque wrench settings

	lbf ft	**Nm**
Alternator pulley nut:		
Bosch	29	40
Delco-Remy	51	70
Reversing light switch	15	20
Starter (1297cc engine)	18	25
Oil pressure switch (1297cc engine)	22	30

1 General description

The major components of the 12 volt negative earth system comprise a 12 volt battery, an alternator (driven from the crankshaft pulley), and a starter motor.

The battery supplies a steady amount of current for the ignition, lighting and other electrical circuits and provides a reserve of power when the current consumed by the electrical equipment exceeds that being produced by the alternator.

The alternator has its own regulator which ensures a high output if the battery is in a low state of charge and the demand from the electrical equipment is high, and a low output if the battery is fully charged and there is little demand from the electrical equipment.

When fitting electrical accessories to cars with a negative earth system it is important, if they contain silicon diodes or transistors, that they are connected correctly, otherwise serious damage may result to the components concerned. Items such as radios, tape players, electronic ignition systems, electronic tachometer, automatic dipping etc, should all be checked for correct polarity.

It is important that the battery positive lead is always disconnected if the battery is to be boost charged. Also, if body repairs are to be carried out using electrical welding equipment, the alternator must be disconnected otherwise serious damage can be caused.

2 Battery – maintenance and inspection

1 Normal weekly battery maintenance consists of checking the electrolyte level of each cell to ensure that the separators are covered by 0.2 in (5 mm) of electrolyte. If the level has fallen, top up the battery using purified (distilled) water only. Do not overfill. If the battery is overfilled or any electrolyte spilled, immediately wipe away the excess as the electrolyte, which is dilute sulphuric acid, attacks and corrodes most metals it comes into contact with very quickly.

2 As well as keeping the terminals clean and covered with a light film of petroleum jelly, the top of the battery, and especially the top of the cells, should be kept clean and dry. This helps prevent corrosion and ensures that the battery does not become partially discharged by leakage through dampness and dirt.

3 Every three months remove the battery and inspect the support tray, the battery clamp and the battery terminals for corrosion. This has the appearance of white fluffy deposits and if it exists it should be cleaned off using warm water to which a little ammonia or washing soda has been added. Treat the battery terminals with petroleum jelly and other metalwork with an anti-rust, anti-acid paint.

4 If topping up the battery become excessive and there has been no leakage of electrolyte then it is likely that the battery is being overcharged and it will have to be checked by an auto-electrician. An elderly battery, may need more frequent topping up than a new one because it will take a bigger charge. There is no need to worry about this provided that it gives good service.

5 With the battery on the bench at the three monthly interval check, measure the specific gravity of the electrolyte with a hydrometer to determine the state of charge and condition of the electrolyte. There should be very little variation between individual cells and, if a variation in excess of 0.025 exists it will be due to either:

(a) Loss of electrolyte from the battery at some time caused by spillage or a leak, resulting in a drop in the specific gravity of the electrolyte when the deficiency was made up with purified water instead of fresh electrolyte, or,

2.7 Maintenance-free type battery

2.9 Battery condition indicator

(b) *An internal short circuit caused by buckling of the plates or similar malady pointing to the likelihood of total battery failure in the near future*

6   The specific gravity of the electrolyte for fully charged and fully discharged conditions at different temperatures of the electrolyte is given below.

Fully discharged	Electrolyte temperature	Fully charged
1.098	38°C (100°F)	1.268
1.102	32°C (90°F)	1.272
1.106	27°C (80°F)	1.276
1.110	21°C (70°F)	1.280
1.114	16°C (60°F)	1.284
1.118	10°C (50°F)	1.288
1.122	4°C (40°F)	1.292
1.126	-1.5°C (30°F)	1.296

7   On later models a sealed type, maintenance-free battery may be fitted (photo).
8   Apart from keeping the terminals clean and the leads secure, nothing else is required.
9   A battery condition indicator is built into the top surface of the battery casing (photo). Refer to Chapter 13, Section 16.

3   Battery – removal and refitting

1   The battery is located on a support plate fitted to the left-hand wing valance in the engine compartment. Disconnect the negative and then the positive leads from the battery terminals after slackening the securing nuts and bolts.
2   Release the battery clamp plate and carefully lift the battery from the support plate. Hold it vertically to ensure that none of the electrolyte is spilled.
3   Refitting is a direct reversal of this procedure. Reconnect the negative lead before the positive lead and smear the terminals with petroleum jelly to prevent corrosion; never use ordinary grease. Do not overtighten the terminal securing bolts, nor hammer the fittings on. The terminals are made of lead and are easily damaged.

4   Battery – electrolyte replenishment

If as a result of tests described in Section 2, acid is ever required to be added to a battery, leave this job to your auto electrician or battery specialist.

5   Battery – charging

1   In winter time when heavy demand is placed on the battery, such as when starting from cold and when much electrical equipment is continually in use, it is a good idea to occasionally have the battery fully charged from an external source at the rate of 3.5 to 4 amps.
2   Continue to charge the battery at this rate until no further rise in specific gravity is noted over a four hour period.
3   Alternatively, a trickle charger charging at a rate of 1.5 amps can safely be used overnight.
4   Specially rapid 'boost' charges which are claimed to rstore the power of the battery in one to two hours should be avoided as they can cause serious damage to the battery plates through overheating.
5   While charging the battery note that the temperature of the electrolyte should never exceed 38°C (100°F) and remember that the gas produced in the cells contains hydrogen which is flammable and explosive, so do not smoke or bring naked lights near the top of the battery.

6   Alternator – special precautions

1   If there are indications that the charging system is malfunctioning in any way, care must be taken when diagnosing faults otherwise damage of a serious and expensive nature may occur to parts which are in fact quite serviceable. The following basic requirements must be observed at all times, therefore, if damage is to be prevented.
2   All alternator systems use a negative earth. Even the simple mistake of connecting the battery the wrong way round could burn out the alternator diodes quickly.
3   Before disconnecting any wires in the system the engine and ignition circuits should be switched off. This will minimise the risk of short-circuits in the system.
4   The engine must never be run with the alternator output wire (red wire on the positive terminal) disconnected.
5   Always disconnect the battery positive lead from the car's electrical system if an outside charging source is being used.
6   Do not use test wire connections that could move accidentally and short-circuit against nearby terminals. Short-circuits may not only blow fuses – they can also burn out diodes and transistors.
7   Always disconnect the battery cables and alternator output wires before any electric arc-welding work is done on the car body.

7   Alternator – general description

Cars covered by this manual are fitted with either a Bosch or a Delco-Remy alternator; the two types are similar in construction and in output. The alternator generates alternating current (ac) which is rectified by diodes into direct current (dc) as this is the current needed for charging the battery.
The main advantage of the alternator lies in its ability to provide a high charge at relatively low engine speed. Driving slowly in heavy traffic with a dynamo invariably means no charge is reaching the battery. In similar conditions even with the heater, wiper, lights and perhaps other electrical equipment on, the alternator will ensure that a charge reaches the battery.
The alternator is of the rotating field, ventilated design and comprises principally a laminated stator on which is wound the output winding, a rotor carrying the field winding, and a diode rectifier. A

voltage regulator is incorporated in the Delco-Remy alternator but on the Bosch machine it is separately mounted at the rear. The alternator generates its current in the stator windings and the rotor carries the field. The field brushes therefore are only required to carry a light current and as they run on simple slip rings they have a relatively long life. This design makes the alternator a reliable machine requiring little servicing.

The rotor is belt-driven from the crankshaft pulley through a pulley keyed to the rotor shaft. A fan adjacent to the pulley draws cooling air through the unit. Rotation is clockwise when viewed from the drive end.

8 Alternator – removal and refitting

1 Disconnect the battery leads.
2 Note the terminal connections at the rear of the alternator and disconnect the plug, multi-pin connector or terminals as appropriate.
3 Undo and remove the alternator adjustment arm bolt, slacken the lower pivot bolt and swing the alternator in towards the engine. Lift the drivebolt off the alternator pulley.
4 Remove the lower pivot bolt and lift the alternator away from the engine. Take care not to drop or knock the alternator as this can cause irreparable damage.
5 Refitting the alternator is the reverse of the removal sequence.

Tension the drivebelt as described in Chapter 2 (photo).

9 Alternator – fault diagnosis

Due to the specialist knowledge and equipment required to test or service an alternator it is recommended that if the performance is suspect the car be taken to an automobile electrician who will have the facilities for such work. Because of this recommendation, information is limited to the inspection and renewal of the brushes. Should the alternator not charge or the system be suspect the following points may be checked before seeking further assistance:

(a) *Check the drivebelt tension as described in Chapter 2*
(b) *Check condition of battery and its connections (see Section 2)*
(c) *Inspect all electrical cables and connections for condition and security*

10 Alternator brushes (Delco-Remy) – inspection, removal and refitting

1 Remove the alternator from the engine, as described in Section 8.
2 Scribe a line across the stator casing and front end cover to ensure correct location when reassembling.

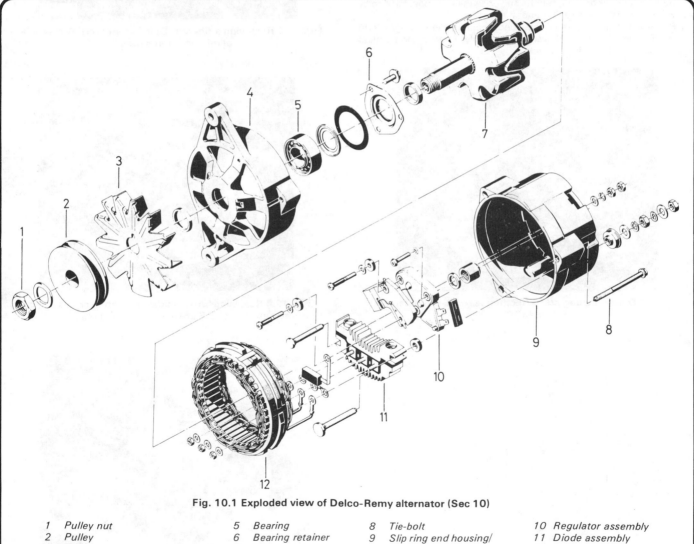

Fig. 10.1 Exploded view of Delco-Remy alternator (Sec 10)

1 Pulley nut	5 Bearing	8 Tie-bolt	10 Regulator assembly
2 Pulley	6 Bearing retainer	9 Slip ring end housing/	11 Diode assembly
3 Fan	7 Rotor	bracket	12 Stator
4 Drive end housing/bracket			

8.5 Checking the drivebelt tension (ohc engine)

5   Undo the two screws retaining the brush holder and voltage regulator to the end casing and remove the brush holder assembly. Note insulation washers.

6   Check that the brushes move freely in the guides and that the length is within the limit given in the Specifications. If any doubt exists regarding the condition of the brushes the best policy is to renew them.

3   Remove the three through-bolts and prise the front cover and rotor away from the rear end casing and stator.

4   Remove the three nuts and washers securing the stator leads to the rectifier and lift away the stator assembly, remove the terminal screw and lift out the diode bracket.

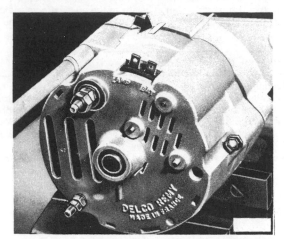

Fig. 10.2 Removing a tie-bolt (Delco alternator). Arrow shows alignment marks (Sec 10)

Fig. 10.3 Disconnecting stator/rectifier leads (Delco alternator) (Sec 10)

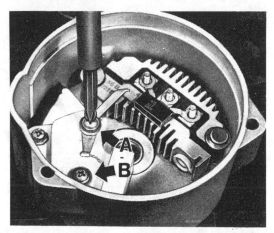

Fig. 10.4 Releasing brush holder/regulator screws (Delco alternator). A and B are insulating washers (Sec 10)

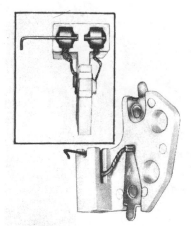

Fig. 10.5 Method of holding brushes in retracted position (Delco alternator) (Sec 10)

Fig. 10.6 Housing installed showing (arrowed) brush retaining wire (Delco alternator) (Sec 10)

7   To fit new brushes, unsolder the old brush leads from the brushholder and solder on the new leads in exactly the same place.

8   Check that the new brushes move freely in the guides.

9   Before refitting the brushholder assembly retain the brushes in the retracted position using a piece of stiff wire as shown in Fig. 10.5.

10   Refit the brushholder so that the wire protrudes through the slot in the end casing as shown (Fig. 10.6).

11   Refit the diode bracket and stator to the casing, making sure the stator leads are in their correct positions.

12   Assemble the front casing and rotor to the stator casing ensuring that the scribe marks are aligned. Insert the three through bolts and tighten.

13   Now carefully pull the piece of wire out of the end casing slot so that the brushes drop onto the rotor slip ring.

14   The alternator can now be refitted to the car and tested.

---

11 Alternator brushes (Bosch) – inspection, removal and refitting

1   Undo and remove the two screws, spring and plain washers that secure the brush box to the rear of the brush end housing. Lift away the brush box and voltage regulator.

2   Check that the carbon brushes are able to slide smoothly in their guides without any sign of binding.

3   Measure the length of brushes. If they have worn below the specified limit, they must be renewed.

4   Hold the brush wire with a pair of engineer's pliers and unsolder it from the brush box. Lift away the two brushes.

5   Insert the new brushes and check to make sure that they are free to move in their guides. If they bind, lightly polish with a very fine file.

6   Solder the brush wire ends to the brush box taking care that solder is not allowed to pass to the stranded wire.

7   Whenever new brushes are fitted new springs should also be fitted.

8   Refitting the brush box is the reverse sequence to removal.

Fig. 10.7 Brush holder/regulator screws (Bosch alternator) (Sec 11)

Fig. 10.8 Exploded view of Bosch alternator (Sec 11)

1   *Pulley nut*
2   *Pulley*
3   *Fan*
4   *Drive end bracket*
5   *Bearing*
6   *Bearing retainer*
7   *Tie-bolts*
8   *Brush holder/regulator*
9   *Slip ring end housing/ bracket*
10   *Collector ring endplate*
11   *Stator*
12   *Bearing*
13   *Rotor*

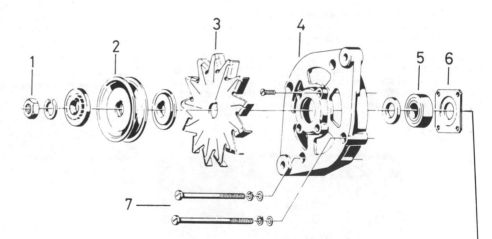

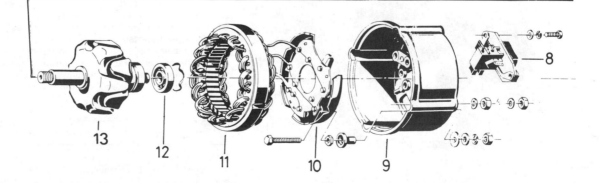

12 Starter motor – general description

The starter motor is mounted on the back of the engine and is of either Bosch or Delco-Remy manufacture. Both makes are of the pre-engaged type, ie the drive pinion is brought into mesh with the starter ring gear on the flywheel before the main current is applied.

When the starter switch is operated, current flows from the battery to the solenoid which is mounted on the starter body. The plunger in the solenoid moves inwards, so causing a centrally pivoted lever to push the drive pinion into mesh with the starter ring gear. When the solenoid plunger reaches the end of its travel, it closes an internal contact and full starting current flows to the starter field coils. The armature is then able to rotate the crankshaft, so starting the engine.

A special freewheel clutch is fitted to the starter drive pinion so that as soon as the engine fires and starts to operate on its own it does not drive the starter motor.

When the starter switch is released, the solenoid is de-energised and a spring moves the plunger back to its rest position. This operates the pivoted lever to withdraw the drive pinion from engagement with the starter ring.

The construction of the two makes of starter motor is quite similar and the removal, refitting, dismantling, inspection and reassembly procedures detailed here will serve for both motors. Significant differences will be noted.

13 Starter motor – in-situ testing

1 If the starter motor fails to turn the engine when the switch is operated there are five possible causes:

(a) *The battery is faulty*
(b) *The electrical connections between the switch, solenoid, battery and starter motor are somewhere failing to pass the necessary current from the battery through the starter to earth*
(c) *The solenoid switch is faulty*
(d) *The starter motor is electrically defective*
(e) *The starter motor pinion and/or flywheel ring gear is badly worn and in need of replacement*

2 To check the battery, switch on the headlights. If they dim after a few seconds the battery is in a discharged state. If the lights glow brightly, operate the starter switch and see what happens to the lights. If they dim then you know that power is reaching the starter motor but failing to turn it. If the starter turns slowly when switched on, proceed to the next check.

14.3 Removing the starter motor

3 If, when the starter switch is operated the lights stay bright, then insufficient power is reaching the motor. Remove the battery connections, starter/solenoid power connections and the engine earth strap and thoroughly clean them and refit them. Smear petroleum jelly around the battery connections to prevent corrosion. Corroded connections are the most frequent cause of electric system malfunctions.

4 When the above checks and cleaning tasks have been carried out but without success, you will possibly have heard a clicking noise each time the starter switch was operated. This was the solenoid switch operating, but it does not necessarily follow that the main contacts were closing properly (if no clicking has been heard from the solenoid, it is certainly defective). The solenoid contact can be checked by putting a voltmeter or bulb across the main cable connection on the starter side of the solenoid and earth. When the switch is operated, there should be a reading or lighted bulb. If there is no reading or lighted bulb, the solenoid unit is faulty and should be renewed.

5 If the starter motor operates but doesn't turn the engine over then it is most probable that the starter pinion and/or flywheel ring gear are badly worn, in which case the starter motor will normally be noisy in operation.

6 Finally, if it is established that the solenoid is not faulty and 12 volts are getting to the starter, then the motor is faulty and should be removed for inspection.

14 Starter motor – removal and refitting

1 With the engine installed in the car it is easier to get to the starter motor from underneath as it is located low on the left rear side of the engine. If you prefer not to work under the car then it will be almost essential to remove the exhaust downpipe and manifold on the 1196cc engine and at least the air cleaner on the 1297cc engine to gain access to the starter.

2 Start by disconnecting the battery earth lead and then disconnect the solenoid and starter electrical leads. Take note of their respective locations to ensure correct reassembly.

3 Unscrew and remove the starter motor unit retaining bolts and withdraw the unit from the clutch housing (photo).

4 Refitting the starter motor assembly is a direct reversal of the removal procedure. Note that on the 1297cc engine the retaining bolts must be tightened to the specified torque.

15 Starter motor renovation – general

1 Such is the inherent reliability and strength of the starter motors fitted, it is very unlikely that a motor will need dismantling until it is totally worn out and in need of replacement as a whole.

2 If, however, the motor is only a couple of years old or so and a pinion carriage, solenoid system or brush fault is suspected then remove the motor from the engine and dismantle as described in the following Sections.

16 Starter solenoid – removal and refitting

1 The Delco-Remy solenoid is retained by two setscrews to the pinion carriage operating mechanism casing. Remove the two setscrews, retrieve the lockwashers and remove the electrical power connection to the motor. Extract the solenoid from the end casing.

2 The Bosch starter/solenoid assembly differs from the Delco-Remy unit described above. The solenoid is retained by two screws to the end casing and is extracted after unhooking the solenoid switch shaft from the pinion carriage actuating arm mounted in the end casing.

3 Refitting of the solenoid is the reversal of removal.

17 Starter motor brushes – inspection and renewal

Bosch

1 With the starter removed from the engine and on a clean bench, begin by removing the armature end cap which is secured by two small screws on the front end of the motor. Remove the armature

Fig. 10.9 Removing armature end cap (Bosch starter motor) (Sec 17)

Fig. 10.10 Armature retaining clip (Bosch) (Sec 17)

Fig. 10.11 Removing tie-bolt (Bosch starter motor) (Sec 17)

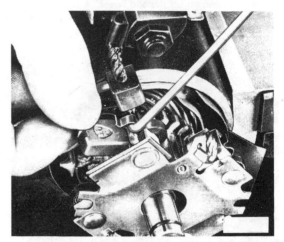

Fig. 10.12 Withdrawing the brushes (Bosch starter motor) (Sec 17)

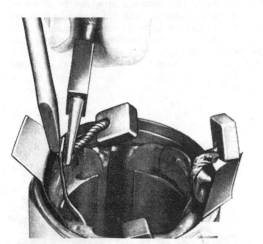

Fig. 10.13 Soldering starter motor brush leads (Bosch) (Sec 17)

Fig. 10.14 Attaching negative brush holder leads (Bosch starter motor) (Sec 17)

retaining clip, washers and the rubber sealing ring which were exposed. Undo and remove the two long bolts which hold the motor assembly together. The front end cover can now be removed to reveal the brushes and mounting plate.

2   Take the brushes from the holder and slip the holder off the armature shaft. Retrieve the spacer washers between the brush plate and the armature block.

3   Inspect the brushes; if they are worn down to less than the minimum length given in Specifications, they should be renewed. Replacement brushes to the latest standard have no shunt wire and to fit this type first crush the old brush in a vice, or with a hammer, to remove all the carbon from the shunt wire and scrape the wire to clean it ready for soldering. Insert the wire in the hole in the new brush and spread the end out to fill the countersunk hole in the brush. Hold the wire close under the brush with a pair of pliers to locate the wire

properly for soldering and to prevent solder from penetrating the wire further than necessary as this would reduce its flexibility. A 12 to 15 watt pencil soldering iron is adequate for this job. After soldering the wire in place remove any excess solder with a file and check that the brush is an easy fit in the brush holder.

4   Wipe the starter motor armature and commutator clean with a non-fluffy rag wetted with petrol.

5   Reassemble the brushes into the holder and refit the holder over the armature shaft, remembering to fit the two washers between the holder and armature.

6   Refit the motor end cover and secure with two long bolts.

7   Refit the armature shaft end cap after fitting the rubber sealing ring, washer and shaft clip.

Delco-Remy

8   With the motor removed from the engine and on a clean bench, begin by undoing and removing the two long bolts which hold the motor assembly together. Punch mark the relative positions of the end cover and the yoke to ensure correct relocation on assembly.

9   Undo the two small screws which secure the end cover to the brush holder plate and lift off the end cover.

10 Lift the brush springs to remove the positive brushes and then remove the brush holder plate from the motor.

11 If the brushes are worn to less than the minimum length given in the Specifications, they should be renewed; always replace all four.

12 When soldering new positive brushes, hold the connecting wires in a pair of pliers to prevent the solder from running into the wire strands and reducing its flexibility. Use a 12 to 15 watt pencil soldering iron.

13 Clean the motor armature and commutator with a non-fluffy rag moistened with petrol.

14 Position the brushes in the brush holder plate and place this assembly over the commutator.

15 Relocate the end cover, aligning the relevant marks, and refit the brush holder securing screws and the two long tie-bolts.

18 Starter motor – dismantling and reassembly

1   The complete overhaul of a starter motor is beyond the resources of the average home mechanic as special tools and equipment for testing are necessary but if the appropriate spares can be obtained repairs can be made by renewing parts. With the starter on the bench proceed as follows.

Bosch starter motors

2   Undo the two screws and remove the bearing cap from the commutator cover.

3   Prise the clip off the end of the armature and, after carefully noting the sequence of assembly, remove the washers and rubber sealing ring from the armature.

4   Mark the commutator cover relative to the starter casing and then remove the two long bolts which hold the assembly together. Remove the commutator cover.

5   Lift the brush springs to remove the positive brushes and then remove the brushplate from the assembly. Note and remove any shims that may be fitted.

6   Disconnect the field winding lead from the solenoid terminal and then undo the two retaining screws to release the solenoid from the assembly. As the solenoid is removed unhook the end fitting from the engaging lever.

7   Unscrew and remove the engaging lever pivot and then remove the end frame from the field and casing assembly. As this is done remove the rubber plug and the engaging lever. Slide the armature out of the casing.

8   If it is required to remove the pinion or the clutch from the armature, press the retaining ring back on the shaft to enable the snap-ring to be removed. Then slide the components off the shaft.

9   With the starter motor dismantled the various components can be cleaned and inspected for general wear and/or signs of damage. Use a petrol damped cloth for cleaning but avoid wetting electrical components. Dry thoroughly with a fluff-free cloth.

10 Renew worn or damaged carbon brushes as explained in Section 17.

Fig. 10.15 Unscrew the tie-bolts (A) and the brush holder screws (B) – Delco-Remy starter (Sec 17)

Fig. 10.16 Remove the brush holder (Delco-Remy starter) (Sec 17)

Fig. 10.17 Disconnecting field winding lead from solenoid terminal (Bosch starter) (Sec 18)

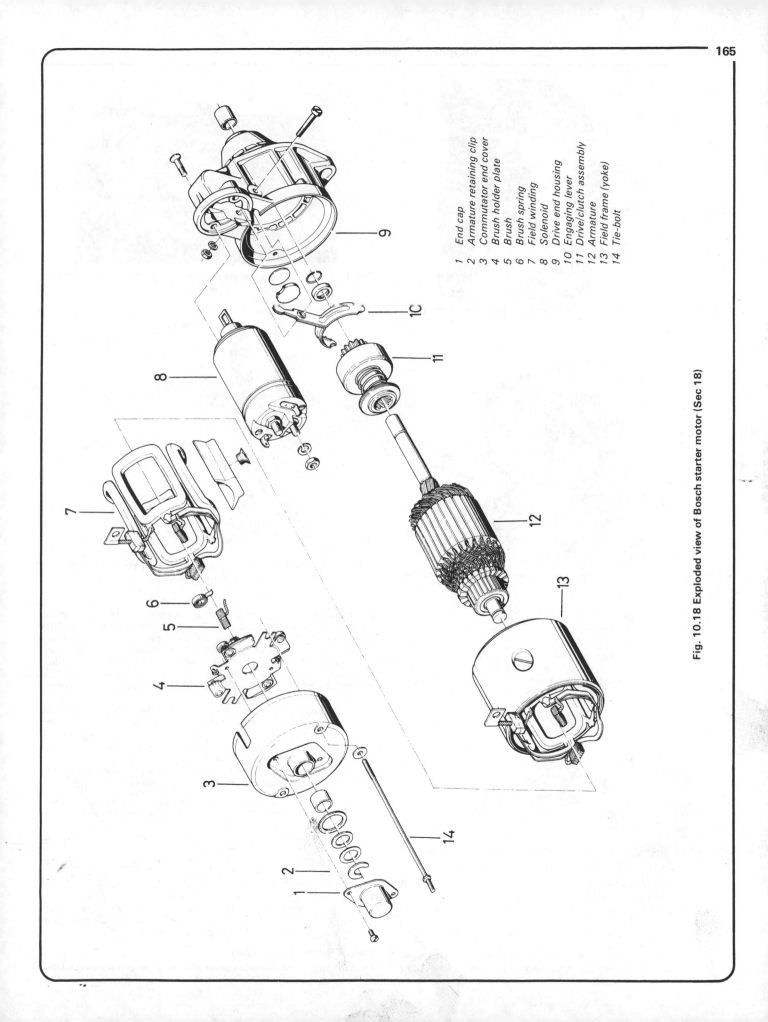

1 End cap
2 Armature retaining clip
3 Commutator end cover
4 Brush holder plate
5 Brush
6 Brush spring
7 Field winding
8 Solenoid
9 Drive end housing
10 Engaging lever
11 Drive/clutch assembly
12 Armature
13 Field frame (yoke)
14 Tie-bolt

Fig. 10.18 Exploded view of Bosch starter motor (Sec 18)

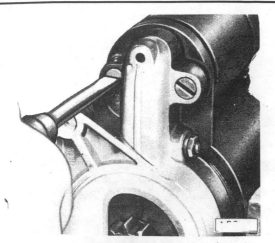

Fig. 10.19 Removing solenoid retaining screws (Bosch starter)
(Sec 18)

Fig. 10.20 Releasing solenoid from engaging lever (Bosch starter)
(Sec 18)

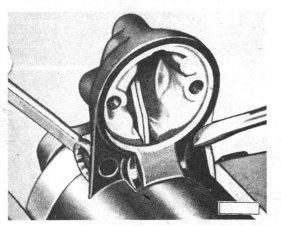

Fig. 10.21 Releasing solenoid engaging lever pivot (Bosch starter)
(Sec 18)

Fig. 10.22 Driving snap-ring stop collar down armature shaft
(Bosch starter) (Sec 18)

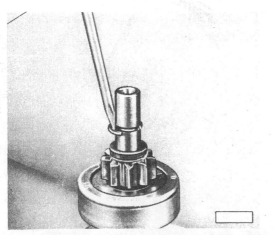

Fig. 10.23 Prising snap-ring from armature shaft (Bosch starter)
(Sec 18)

11 If the starter motor has shown a tendency to jam or a reluctance to disengage then the starter pinion is almost certainly the culprit. Dirt accumulation on the shaft or on the pinion could cause this. After cleaning off any such dirt, check that the pinion can move freely in a spiral movement along the shaft. If it still tends to bind or stick, or if it is defective in any way, renew the pinion.

12 A badly worn or burnt commutator will need skimming on a lathe, but if it is only dirty or lightly marked, clean it up with a piece of fine grade glass paper wrapped round. If the commutator has to be skimmed have the job done by a specialist but make sure that the minimum diameter, as listed in the Specifications, is maintained. After skimming, the separators should be undercut using a piece of old hacksaw blade ground down to the same thickness as the separators. Undercut to a depth of about 0.02 to 0.03 in (0.5 to 0.8 mm) and then clean up with fine grade glass cloth. Do not use emery on the commutator as abrasive particles could get embedded in the copper and cause rapid brush wear.

13 An armature with a bent shaft or other signs of damage must be renewed. Electrical checks should be undertaken by an auto-electrician with special equipment. Although simple continuity checks are possible with a lamp and low power source, more extensive checking is needed which is beyond the scope of the home mechanic.

14 Reassembly of the starter motor is a straightforward reversal of the dismantling sequence, but the following points should be noted:

   (a) After assembling the clutch and pinion to the armature shaft, fit the retaining ring using a new snap-ring and then reposition the retainer
   (b) Make sure that all shims and washers are fitted in the correct order
   (c) Align the locating key and slot when assembling the case to the end frame
   (d) Make sure that the carbon brushes slide freely in their boxes
   (e) Lightly oil all sliding parts including the armature spiral spline, the engaging lever sliding surfaces, the clutch bearing surfaces and armature bearings. Of course, no oil must contaminate the commutator or brushes

Delco-Remy starter motors

15 Mark the commutator end cover and the drive end housing relative to the yoke to ensure correct reassembly, and then disconnect the field

18.16 Removing tie-bolt (Delco starter)

18.17 Removing end cover (Delco starter)

18.18 Remove the positive brushes and withdraw the brush holder plate

18.19A Removing starter solenoid and spring (Delco starter)

18.19B Actuating lever spindle clip (Delco starter)

18.19C Removing actuating lever spindle (Delco starter)

18.19D Separating bearing housing (Delco starter)

18.19E Components of Delco starter motor

winding connection from the lower stud on the solenoid.

16 Undo and remove the two long bolts which hold the motor assembly together (photo). Punch mark the relative positions of the end cover and the yoke to ensure correct relocation on assembly.

17 Undo the two small screws which secure the end cover to the brush holder plate and lift off the end cover (photo).

18 Lift the brush springs to remove the positive brushes and then remove the brush holder plate from the motor (photo).

19 Undo the two retaining screws and remove the solenoid and its spring from the drive end housing (photo). Extract the clip from the actuating arm spindle (photo) and tap the spindle out of the housing (photo). This will allow the armature and the actuating arm to be removed together (photo). The actuating arm can then be removed from the armature assembly (photo).

20 With the exception of the above, the remainder of the dismantling and reassembly procedures for this starter are the same as those described in paragraphs 8 to 14, to which reference should now be made. When the solenoid has been refitted to the drive end housing,

use a little plastic sealing compound to seal the slot in the housing to prevent water entering. Then continue the reassembly as described.

19 Windscreen wiper – fault diagnosis

1 If the wipers fail to operate first check the fuse, see Section 26, and if this is satisfactory then check that current is reaching the motor. This can be done by switching the ignition and wiper switches on and checking with a 12 volt lamp and leads that power is available at the connector plug on the wiper motor.

2 If there is no power at the motor connector plug the cause must be traced back through the supply circuit. If there is a current supply at the plug, reconnect and with the switches on give a wiper arm a push in the direction of operation. Sometimes a high mechanical load or excessive friction may prevent normal working. Switch off immediately if nothing happens though, or further damage might be caused. If the wipers do run after this test the reason for the jamming

must be found. It will probably be due to wear in either the wiper mechanism linkage or in the motor gearbox.

3   If the wipers run too slowly it will be due to something restricting the free operation of the linkage mechanism or a fault in the motor. In such cases check the current consumption by connecting an ammeter in the supply circuit. If it exceeds, say, three amps this would indicate that something is affecting free movement, but if it is less then the commutator and brush gear in the motor are suspect. The shafts to which the wiper arms are attached run in long bushes and often suffer from lack of lubrication. An occasional application of a few drops of light oil helps to prevent partial or total seizure.

4   If wear is obviously causing malfunction or there is a fault in the motor, then it is best to remove the motor assembly or linkage for further examination and repairs or renewal.

20 Windscreen wiper assembly components – removal and refitting

Wiper blades

1   To remove the wiper blade, depress the catch on the wiper blade U-shaped retainer and slide the blade assembly from the arm (photos).
2   Removing the blade from a rear window wiper is a little more complicated on estate cars due to the additional articulating link on the wiper arm. Prise off the blade pivot cover at the end of the wiper arm and remove the blade retaining clip. Disconnect the blade pivot from the arm and then unscrew and remove the screw securing the blade assembly to the link to free the blade assembly (photos).
3   Refit the blade(s) by reversing the removal procedure.

Wiper arms

4   The windscreen wiper arm assembly can be removed from the drive spindle by first lifting the arm as far as possible off the windscreen and then pulling firmly on the base of the arm to take it off the spindle. It may be necessary to prise open the small spring retaining clip to allow the arm to be slid up the shaft splines (photo).
5   On the tailgate wiper, lift the hinged cap at the bottom of the arm and then remove the retaining nut. It will probably be found that the

arm assembly is too tight on the drive spindle for it to be removed without the aid of a small universal puller. Undo the screw to free the link (photos).
6   Refit the arms in the reverse order, but ensure that the wipers are in the same position as when they were removed and operate the wipers on completion to ensure that the blades cover the correct arcs and do not foul the surrounds.

Windscreen wiper motor

7   Disconnect the battery earth lead and then undo and remove the nut securing the mechanism drive arm to the motor drive spindle (photo).
8   Undo and remove the four, or three on some models, nuts or bolts securing the motor mounting plate to the car and remove the plate complete with motor. Be careful not to lose the metal and rubber washers (photo).
9   Unplug the electrical multi-connector block to enable the motor assembly to be removed from the car (photo).
10 For the tailgate wiper the procedure is broadly similar, but first unclip the tailgate lining panel by carefully prising up the clips around its edge. With a small screwdriver located at the inboard edge prise up the plastic block carrying the three plunger contacts located in the edge of the tailgate. Take note of the connections on the plungers and disconnect the outer two. The middle one is earth and this can be left secured to the tailgate (photo).
11 Undo the bolt joining the two parts of the link between the motor assembly and the wiper drive shaft assembly. Undo and remove the bolts securing the motor mounting plate to the tailgate and remove the motor assembly from the car (photos).
12 Refitting the wiper motor is the reverse of the removal procedure for all types.

Wiper operating linkage

13 Apart from occasionally lubricating the pivots the linkage rarely needs attention. To remove the mechanism, disconnect the drive at the motor driveshaft or, for the tailgate wiper, at the horizontal link joint and then remove the wiper arm(s) as already described.

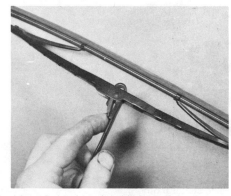
20.1A Releasing wiper blade retaining tab

20.1B Removing wiper blade from arm

20.2A Rear wiper arm pivot cover (Estate)

20.2B Rear wiper arm pivot circlip (Estate)

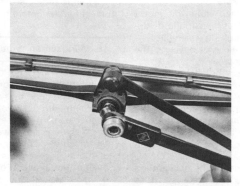
20.2C Removing rear wiper arm from pivot (Estate)

20.2D Removing rear wiper arm link screw (Estate)

20.4 Removing windscreen wiper arm

20.5A Removing rear wiper arm nut (Hatchback)

20.5B Removing rear wiper arm (Hatchback)

20.5C Removing rear wiper arm link screw (Hatchback)

20.7 Removing wiper crankarm nut

20.8 Unscrewing wiper motor mounting plate

20.9 Removing wiper motor

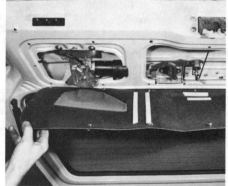

20.10 Tailgate wiper arrangement

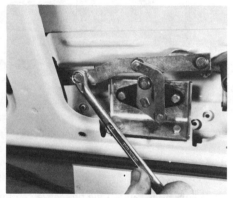

20.11A Removing tailgate wiper link bolt

20.11B Removing tailgate wiper mounting plate

20.11C Tailgate wiper motor

20.14 Removing windscreen wiper drive spindle ring nut

20.15A Wiper drive spindle removed

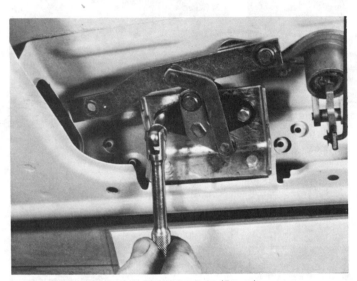

20.15B Unscrewing spindle mounting bolts (Estate)

20.15C Removing rear wiper spindle and linkage (Estate)

14 Where fitted remove the protective cap from the drive spindle to reveal the retaining nut. Undo the nut and, on front wipers, repeat on the other spindle. After removing the nut(s) remove the mounting washers, carefully noting how they are fitted (photo).

15 With the spindle nuts removed the linkage mechanism can then be manoeuvred out of its location but on the rear wiper of estate cars it will first be necessary to remove the two securing bolts in the spindle bush flange (photos).

16 Refit the mechanism in the reverse order to that for removal. On completion check the sweep of the wiper blades and adjust their position on the splines of the drive spindle if necessary.

21 Windscreen wiper motor – renovation

1 It is unlikely that individual spare parts will be obtainable for the wiper motor or the gearbox, but if the assembly only suffers from simple electrical faults such as worn brushes, broken wire and so on, repairs could be carried out by an auto-electrician.

2 Unless the cause of any defect can be positively identified by the home mechanic it will cost money merely to determine what's wrong and then it might not be possible to repair the fault. On balance, it would pay to renew the motor and gearbox when a defect arises after

a long period in service and only attempt repairing a relatively new assembly. In this case have the work done by a competent specialist.

22 Windscreen or rear window washer units – general

1 The windscreen washer unit is located in the top rear left-hand corner of the engine compartment and it is operated by an electric pump which draws cleaning fluid from the reservoir to which it is attached. The fluid is then conducted to the spray units by narrow bore pipes. The rear window washer unit (when fitted) is basically similar but is located in the left rear corner of the bodywork or, on estate cars, in the spare wheel well in the rear compartment (photos).

2 Malfunction is usually due to blocked jets on the screen delivery nozzles. These can be cleared with fine wire or a pin. Other causes of failure are blocked, kinked or disconnected pipes. The latter will be apparent when the pump is operated with fluid in the reservoir. In very cold weather, freezing of the washer fluid may cause failure (see below).

3 Should the pump fail to run when energised, check that current is available at the motor supply plug by using a 12 volt lamp and leads. Trace the cause of current failure. If the supply is satisfactory then the motor will have to be renewed as it is not repairable. Remove the

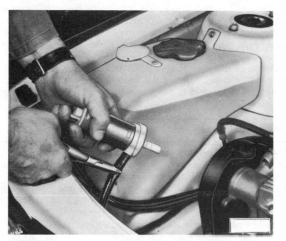

Fig. 10.24 Windscreen washer reservoir and pump (Sec 22)

motor by moving its top away from the reservoir and sliding it upwards. Cut the hose close to the pump. Immerse the end of the hose in hot water to make it more pliable before pushing it onto the new pump.

4   Do not use standard cooling system anti-freeze in the washer units as it will smear the glass and will attack the body paintwork. Special windscreen washer additives to aid windscreen cleaning and prevent freezing are available from most garages and accessory shops. Methylated spirit added to the water will also prevent freezing.

23 Horn – testing, removal and refitting

1   The horn is located on the engine left-hand mounting bracket.
2   Should the horn fail to work, check for a blown fuse by trying the windscreen wipers which are on the same fuse. If these work then the fault is in the horn circuit. Connect a test lamp across the two wires supplying the horn and get an assistant to operate the horn while you watch the light. If it works then the horn is defective and must be renewed as it is not repairable.
3   To remove the horn disconnect the battery earth lead, then disconnect the two electrical leads, undo the securing bolt and remove the horn from the car.
4   Refitting is a straightforward reversal of the removal procedure.

24 Horn button switch – removal and refitting

1   Disconnect the battery earth lead.
2   Carefully prise the centre fitting out of the steering wheel to reveal the electrical connections on the back of the horn button switch. Disconnect the two leads to remove the horn button switch (photo).
3   Refitting is the reverse of the removal procedure.

25 Instrument panel – removal and refitting

1   Disconnect the battery earth lead. It should not be necessary to remove the steering wheel, although this has been done for the sake of clarity in the photos which follow.
2   Reach behind the instrument panel and disconnect the speedometer drive cable by depressing the retaining spring and pulling the drive out of the instrument panel (photo).
3   On cars which have a facia panel fitted, remove the lighting switch located in the lower right corner of the panel by squeezing the switch retaining clips behind the panel, pulling the switch out of the panel and then disconnecting the electrical connector from the back of the switch. Remove the two retaining screws in the top of the panel and remove the panel (photos).
4   Undo the single retaining screw in the top of the instrument panel, ease the top of the panel out of the facia and carefully pull the panel towards you. Disconnect the multi-pin connector at the back of the instrument panel and remove the panel from the car (photos).

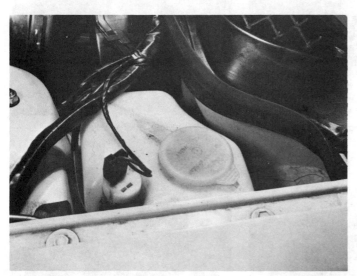

22.1A Windscreen washer reservoir

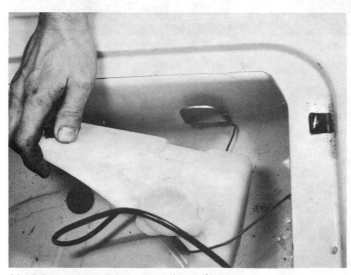

22.1B Rear washer fluid reservoir (Estate)

24.2 Steering wheel centre fitting

Fig. 10.25 Bimetallic instrument voltage stabiliser securing screw is arrowed (Sec 25)

The electronic voltage stabiliser is located at the other end of the panel

5   Instrument lamps and warning light bulbs can now be changed if required. Turn the lamps anti-clockwise to remove and vice versa to refit (photo). Other components in the instrument panel can also be changed such as the printed circuit, the voltage stabilizer and individual instruments.

6   Refitting is the reverse of the removal procedure.

7   Slight differences exist in the panels for different models in the range but the same principles of removal and refitting will apply.

26 Fuses – general

1   The fuses are mounted in a panel located at the lower right-hand corner of the facia under a removable cover (photo). The circuits protected are marked on the inside of the cover (photo).

2   To inspect or change a fuse simply remove the cover by lifting it at its bottom edge. These cars use a special type of fuse and spares will have to be obtained from your local dealer.

3   Before renewing a blown fuse, trace and rectify the cause and

25.2 Speedometer drive cable connector

25.3A Removing lighting switch

25.3B Extracting facia panel screws

25.3C Removing the facia panel

25.4A Extracting instrument panel screw

25.4B Withdrawing instrument panel

25.4C Instrument panel connector plug

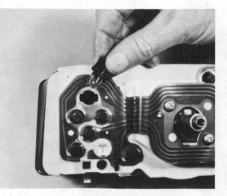
25.5 Instrument panel bulb and holder

26.1A Fuse block cover

26.1B Circuit identification on fuse block cover

27.3A Headlamp connector plug

27.3B Removing headlamp rubber cover

27.3C Headlamp bulb securing clip

27.3D Removing headlamp bulb

27.5 Front parking lamp bulb

always use a fuse of the correct value as listed in the Specifications. Never substitute a fuse of a higher rating or use such things as a piece of wire, metal foil or a pin to act as a makeshift, as more serious damage or even fire may result.

27 Headlights and parking lamps – bulb renewal

1   If a headlight bulb has to be removed and/or renewed, avoid touching the glass of the bulb with bare fingers but extract it using a piece of clean dry cloth or polythene. If a bulb is accidentally touched, clean it with methylated spirit.
2   Raise the bonnet and support it on its prop.
3   Disconnect the cable connector from the back of the headlight and then prise off the rubber cover to reveal the bulb securing clips. Lift the clips to release the bulb and remove it from the headlight assembly (photos).
4   Refitting is the reverse of removal, but note that the metal rim on the bulb has a projection which must align with the corresponding groove in the headlight assembly. After fitting a new bulb the headlight alignment must be checked and, if necessary, adjusted. See the next Section for details.
5   Renewal of the parking lamp bulb is simply a matter of pulling the bulb holder from the rear of the headlamp reflector (photo).

28 Headlights – alignment

1   The headlight beam adjustment is most important, not only for your own safety but for that of other road users as well. Accurate beam alignment can only be obtained using optical beam setting equipment and you should regard any adjustments made without such equipment as purely temporary.
2   To make a temporary adjustment, position the car on level ground about 10ft (3 metres) in front of a vertical wall or a piece of board secured vertically. The wall or board should be square to the centre-line of the car and the car should be normally laden. Check that the

tyre pressures are correct.
3   Draw a vertical line on the board or card in line with the centre-line of the car.
4   Bounce the car on its suspension several times to ensure correct levelling and then accurately measure the height between the ground and the centre of the headlights.
5   Draw a horizontal line across the wall or board at the same height as the headlight centres and on this line mark a cross on either side of the centre line at the same distance apart as the headlight centres.
6   Now locate the adjusters on each headlight. There are two diagonally opposite each other on each headlight (photo).
7   Switch the headlights on to full beam and, using the adjusters, adjust each headlamp to align the beam to shine just below the corresponding cross on the wall or board.
8   Bounce the car on its suspension again to check that the beams return to the correct position. At the same time check the operation of the dipswitch to confirm that the beams dip to the nearside. Switch off the headlights on completion.
9   Holts Amber Lamp is useful for temporarily changing the headlight colour to conform with the normal usage on Continental Europe.

29 Headlights – removal and refitting

1   Raise and support the bonnet, disconnect the electrical lead connectors from the back of the main and the parking light bulbs. Disconnect the earth connection from the headlight.
2   Remove the protective cover from the back of the headlight and remove the bulbs.

Rectangular headlamps

3   Remove the front direction indicator bulb after disconnecting its electrical supply and then remove the direction indicator lens by squeezing the retaining clips at the back and pushing the lens forward out of the bodywork.
4   Unscrew and remove the headlight retaining screws and lift the headlight forward out of the car (photos).

28.6 Headlamp beam adjuster screw

29.4A Removing headlamp securing screw

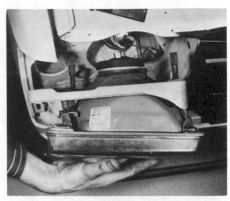

29.4B Removing headlamp unit

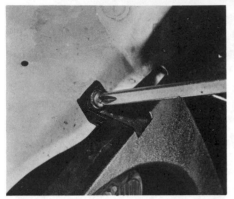

29.5A Removing trim plate screw (round headlamp)

29.5B Removing trim plate (round headlamp)

29.6 Removing round type headlamp from mounting stud

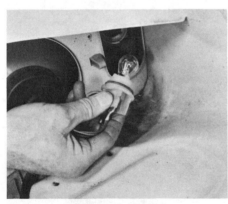

30.2 Front direction indicator bulb

30.4 Removing front direction indicator lamp unit

31.2 Removing rear lamp unit from Estate

31.4 Rear lamp bulb holder

31.5 Rear lamp bulbs and printed circuit

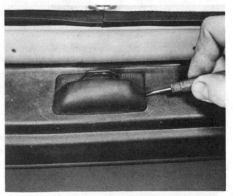

32.1 Prising out rear number plate lamp

Round headlamps

5   Remove the trim panel from around the headlamp (photos).
6   Pull the headlamp from its mounting studs by jerking it off the stud ball ends (photo).

All headlamps

7   Refititng is the reverse of the removal procedure. Check the operation of the lights on completion and refer to the previous Section for the procedure for alignment.

30 Front direction indicator bulb and light unit – removal and refitting

Bulb renewal

1   Raise and support the bonnet.
2   Remove the bulb holder by twisting and pulling it out of the lens unit (photo). Remove the bulb from the bulb holder by depressing and turning to disengage the bayonet fitting
3   Refitting is the reverse of the removal procedure.

Light unit

4   After removing the bulb holder as above, squeeze the four plastic clips on the lens unit to free them from the slots in the bodywork and remove the unit from the car (photo).
5   Refitting is the reverse of removal.

31 Rear light clusters – removal, refitting and bulb renewal

1   The rear direction indicator, stop and tail lights are mounted in a single unit each side of the car.

Light unit

2   To remove the light unit, undo and remove the retaining screws and then remove the unit from the vehicle (photo). Refitting is the reverse of removal.

Bulb renewal

3   Access to the bulbs is gained through the rear compartment. Where a cover is fitted, unclip it to get to the bulb holder in the rear quarter.
4   Remove the bulb holder by rolling it slightly from the outside towards the inside of the car to release the clip and then pull the holder free (photo).
5   The bulbs are, from top to bottom, direction indicator, stop and tail (this is a double filament bulb) and, where fitted, the reversing light. The wattage of each of the bulbs is marked on the bulb holder and the bulbs are removed by depressing and turning to free the bayonet fitting. The bulb holder can be removed after disconnecting the electrical connector at the back (photo).
6   Refitting is the reverse of removal.

32 Rear number plate light – removal and refitting

1   With a small screwdriver inserted under the right-hand edge of the light (photo) depress the retaining catch and lever the light out of the rear bumper.
2   The bulb can then be removed from its holder for renewal or the light assembly can be removed after disconnecting the electrical leads (photo).
3   Refitting is the reverse of removal.

33 Interior light/boot light/engine compartment light bulbs – removal and refitting

1   Carefully press and prise the light unit from its location.
2   The festoon bulb can be extracted from the holders for replacement (photo).
3   If the unit is to be removed, detach the earth cable from the battery, then disconnect the wires from the light unit.
4   Refitting is a direct reversal of the removal procedure, but check for correct operation on completion.

34 Windscreen wiper/washer switch and direction indicator switch – removal and refitting

1   The windscreen wiper/washer switch is mounted on the right-hand side of the steering column and the direction indicator switch on the left, but their removal and refitting are similar. First disconnect the battery earth lead.
2   Undo and remove the screws securing the two halves of the steering column shroud and ease the rubber ring from off the ignition/steering lock switch. Remove the two shroud halves (photo).
3   Depress the catches retaining the switch in its mounting and remove the switch from the mounting (photo).
4   Disconnect the multi-pin plug from the back of the switch to permit the switch to be removed (photo).
5   Refitting is the reverse of the removal procedure.

35 Switches and relays – general

Reversing light switch

1   The reversing light switch is screwed into the front of the gearbox case just above the engine left-hand front mounting bracket and it is operated internally by the reverse gear selector when reverse gear is engaged.
2   To remove the switch, first disconnect the electrical leads from the switch terminals and then unscrew the switch from the gearbox case.
3   Refitting is the reverse of removal, but note that the switch must be tightened to the specified torque.

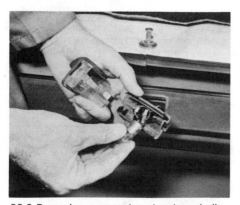

32.2 Removing rear number plate lamp bulb

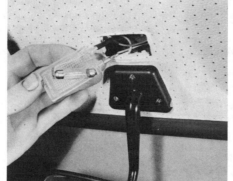

33.2 Interior lamp bulb (front)

34.2 Removing steering column lower shroud

34.3 Releasing wiper/washer switch

34.4 Disconnecting wiper switch plug

35.8 Courtesy lamp switch

35.10A Removing facia panel switch plate screw

35.10B Removing switch plate

Oil pressure switch

4   This switch is located on the front of the engine at the left-hand end of the block. On the 1196 cc engine it is screwed into the block but on the 1297 cc engine it is screwed into the oil pump case.

5   To remove the switch, first disconnect the electrical lead from the switch terminal and then unscrew the switch from its location.

6   Reverse the procedure to refit the switch, but note that on 1297 cc engines it must be tightened to the specified torque.

Interior light door switch

7   Plunger type switches are fitted to the front door pillars to operate the interior light when a door is opened.

8   To remove a switch, unscrew the retaining screw and pull the switch and the rubber shroud free of the door pillar. It will then be possible to disconnect the electrical leads from the back of the switch (photo).

Fig. 10.26 Ashtray surround securing screws (Sec 35)

Central panel switches

9   Depending on the standard of fit, the central panel may contain the following switches: foglight, rear foglight, hazard warning lights, rear wash/wipe, and driver's seat heating. Renewal of these switches is straightforward after the switch panel has been removed.

10   To remove the switch panel, first disconnect the battery earth lead, then extract two screws from the ashtray surround plate. Withdraw the switch plate by passing a screwdriver under the top of the foglamp switch cut-out and then the rear wash/wipe switch cut-out to extract the two screws. Pull the switch plate out from its bottom edge (photos).

11   Remove the switch concerned by releasing the retaining clip or clips, extracting the switch from the central panel and then disconnecting the electrical connector from the back of the switch.

12   Refitting is the reverse of the removal procedure.

Relays

13   Relays, depending on the equipment fitted, are located under the fuse box at the right-hand lower corner of the facia (photo).

14   Renewal of a relay simply consists of reaching behind the facia and pulling the appropriate relay out of its location, and refitting the new one in the reverse way.

36   Ignition switch/steering lock – renewal

1   To renew either the ignition switch or the steering lock cylinder, first remove the lower half of the steering column shroud by undoing and removing the securing screws.

Ignition switch

2   Undo and remove the two grub screws securing the switch assembly to the steering lock housing. Carefully remove the ignition switch, taking note of the position of the switch mating piece as it is

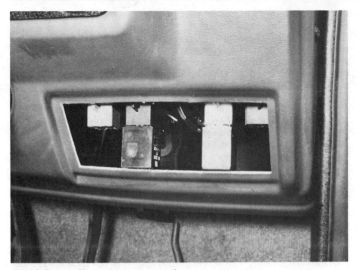

35.13 Relays (fuse block removed)

removed. It is important that the lock cylinder is not disturbed or removed while the ignition switch is removed as damage can result.

3   Disconnect the electrical plug from the ignition switch.

4   When refitting a new switch, position the mating piece in the same way as it was noted when being removed, fit the switch to the steering lock and secure it with the two grub screws. Refit the electrical plug to the switch.

Steering lock cylinder

5   Disconnect the battery earth lead and, after removing the lower half of the steering column shroud, insert the ignition key and turn it to the 'I' position.

6   Using a piece of wire or a drill shank (3 mm dia), depress the lock spring retaining the cylinder and carefully withdraw the cylinder from its housing. It is important that the ignition switch is not removed or disturbed while the lock cylinder is not fitted.

7   Before fitting a new lock cylinder insert the ignition key and turn it to the 'I' position. Insert the assembly into the steering lock housing and press it down until the retaining spring engages before removing the key.

8   Reconnect the battery earth lead and test the operation of the ignition switch before fitting the lower half shroud.

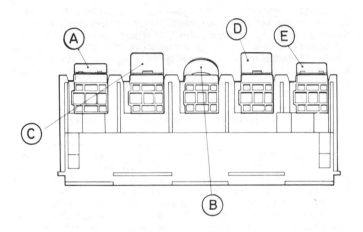

Fig. 10.27 Relay identification (Sec 35)

A   *Foglamp relay*
B   *Headlamps 'on' warning buzzer relay*
C   *Direction signal/hazard flasher relay*
D   *Washer/time delay relay*
E   *Spotlamp relay*

37 Radios and tape players – fitting (general)

A radio or tape player is an expensive item to buy, and will only give its best performance if fitted properly. It is useless to expect concert hall performance from a unit that is suspended from the dashpanel by string with its speaker resting on the back seat or parcel shelf! If you do not wish to do the fitting yourself, there are many in-car entertainment specialists who will do the fitting for you.

Make sure the unit purchased is of the same polarity as the vehicle. Ensure that units with adjustable polarity are correctly set before commencing the fitting operations.

It is difficult to give specific information with regard to fitting, as final positioning of the radio/tape player, speakers and aerial is entirely a matter of personal preference. However, the following paragraphs give guidelines to follow which are relevant to all fittings:

Radios

Most radios are a standardised size of 7 in wide by 2 in deep. This ensures that they will fit into the radio aperture provided in these cars (photo). Alternatively, a special console can be purchased which will fit between the dashpanel and the floor. These consoles can also be used for additional switches and instrumentation if required.

Some radios will have mounting brackets provided, together with instructions; others will need to be fitted using drilled and slotted metal strips, bent to form mounting brackets. These strips are available from most accessory shops. The unit must be properly earthed by fitting a separate earthing lead between the casing of the radio and the vehicle frame.

Use the radio manufacturer's instructions when wiring the radio into the vehicle's electrical system. A 1 or 2 amp in-line fuse must be fitted in the radio's feed wire; a choke may also be necessary (see next Section).

The type of aerial used and its fitted position, is a matter of personal preference. In general, the taller the aerial the better the reception. It is best to fit a fully retractable aerial; especially if a mechanical car-wash is used or if you live in an area where cars tend to be vandalised. In this respect, electric aerials which are raised and lowered automatically when switching the radio on or off are convenient, but are more likely to give trouble than the manual type.

When choosing a position for the aerial, the following points should be considered:

(a)   *The aerial lead should be as short as possible; this means that the aerial should be mounted at the front of the car*

(b)   *The aerial must be mounted as far away from the distributor and HT leads as possible*

(c)   *The part of the aerial which protrudes beneath the mounting point must not foul the roadwheels, or anything else*

(d)   *If possible, the aerial should be positioned so that the coaxial lead does not have to be routed through the engine compartment*

37.0 Radio being installed

Fig. 10.28 Front wing aerial locating diagram. Dimensions in mm (Sec 37)

(e) *The plane of the panel on which the aerial is mounted should not be so steeply angled that the aerial cannot be mounted vertically (in relation to the end-on aspect of the car). Most aerials have a small amount of adjustment available*

Having decided on a mounting position, a relatively large hole will have to be made in the panel. The exact size of the hole will depend upon the specific aerial being fitted, although generally, the hole required is of ¾ in (19 mm) diameter. A 'tank-cutter' of the relevant diameter is the best tool to use for making the hole. This tool needs a small diameter pilot hole drilled through the panel, through which the tool clamping bolt is inserted. When the hole has been made the raw edges should be de-burred with a file and then painted to prevent corrosion.

Fit the aerial according to the manufacturer's instructions. If the aerial is very tall, or if it protrudes beneath the mounting panel for a considerable distance, it is a good idea to fit a stay beneath the aerial and the vehicle frame. This stay can be manufactured from the slotted and drilled metal strips previously mentioned. The stay should be securely screwed or bolted in place. For best reception, it is advisable to fit an earth lead between the aerial and the vehicle frame.

It will probably be necessary to drill one or two holes through bodywork panels in order to feed the aerial lead into the interior of the car. Where this is the case, ensure that the holes are fitted with rubber grommets to protect the cable and to stop possible entry of water.

Positioning and fitting of the speaker depends mainly on its type. Generally, the speaker is designed to fit directly into the aperture already provided in the car. Where this is the case, fitting the speaker is just a matter of removing the protective grille from the aperture and screwing or bolting the speaker in place. Take great care not to damage the speaker diaphragm whilst doing this. It is a good idea to fit a gasket beneath the speaker frame and the mounting panel. In order to prevent vibration, some speakers will already have such a gasket fitted.

If a 'pod' type speaker was supplied with the radio, this can be secured to the mounting panel with self-tapping screws.

When connecting a rear mounted speaker to the radio, the wires should be routed through the vehicle beneath the carpets or floor mats, preferably along the side of the floorpan where they will not be trodden on by passengers. Make the relevant connections as directed by the radio manufacturer.

For the best results from speakers designed to be recessed into a panel, mount them so that the back of the speaker protrudes into an enclosed chamber within the car (eg door interiors or the boot cavity).

To fit recessed type speakers in the front doors, first check that there is sufficient room to mount the speakers in each door without it fouling the latch or window winding mechanism. Hold the speaker against the skin of the door, and draw a line around the periphery of the speaker. With the speaker removed draw a second cutting line, within the first, to allow enough room for the entry of the speaker back, but at the same time providing a broad seat for the speaker flange. When you are sure that the cutting line is correct, drill a series of holes around its periphery. Pass a hacksaw blade through one of the holes

and then cut through the metal between the holes until the centre section of the panel falls out.

De-burr the edges of the hole and then paint the raw metal to prevent corrosion. Cut a corresponding hole in the door trim panel - ensuring that it will be completely covered by the speaker grille. Now drill a hole in the door edge and a corresponding hole in the door surround. These holes are to feed the speaker leads through - so fit grommets. Pass the speaker leads through the door trim, door skin and out through the holes in the side of the door and door surround. Refit the door trim panel and then secure the speaker to the door using self-tapping screws. If the speaker is fitted with a shield to prevent water dripping on it, ensure that this shield is at the top.

By now you will have several yards of additional wiring in the car, use PVC tape to secure this wiring out of harm's way. Do not leave electrical leads dangling. Ensure that all new electrical connections are properly made (wires twisted together will not do) and completely secure.

The radio should now be working, but before you pack away your tools it will be necessary to trim the radio to the aerial. If specific instructions are not provided by the radio manufacturer, proceed as follows: Find a station with a low signal strength on the medium-wave band, slowly turn the trim screw of the radio in or out until the loudest reception of the selected station is obtained. The set is then trimmed to the aerial.

Tape players

Fitting instructions for both cartridge and cassette stereo tape players are the same, and in general the same rules apply as when fitting a radio. Tape players are not usually prone to electrical interference like radios, although it can occur, so positioning is not so critical. If possible, the player should be mounted on an even keel. Also it must be possible for a driver wearing a seat belt to reach the unit in order to change or turn over tapes.

38 Radios and tape players – suppression of interference (general)

To eliminate buzzes and other unwanted noises costs very little and is not as difficult as sometimes thought. With a modicum of common sense and patience, and following the instructions in the following paragraphs, interference can be virtually eliminated.

The first cause for concern is the generator. The noise this makes over the radio is like an electric mixer and the noise speeds up when you rev up (if you wish to prove the point, you can remove the drivebelt and try it). The remedy for this is simple; connect a 1.0 F - 3.0 μF capacitor between earth (probably the bolt that holds down the generator base) and the *large* (B+) terminal on the alternator. This is most important for if you connect it to the small terminal, you will probably damage the alternator permanently.

A second common cause of electrical interference is the ignition system. Here a 1.0 μF capacitor must be connected between earth and the 'SW' or '+' terminal on the coil. This may stop the tick-tick-tick sound that comes over the speaker. Next comes the spark itself. The ignition HT leads are of suppressed type and no further action is required. Do not fit plug suppressor caps or cut the leads to fit in-line suppressors.

At this stage it is advisable to check that the radio is well earthed, also the aerial and to see that the aerial plug is pushed well into the set and that the radio is properly trimmed (see preceding Section). In addition, check that the wire which supplies the power to the set is as short as possible and does not wander all over the car. It is a good idea to check that the fuse is of the correct rating. For most sets this will be about 1 to 2 amps.

At this point, the more usual causes of interference have been suppressed. If the problem still exists, a look at the cause of interference may help to pinpoint the component generating the stray electrical discharges.

The radio picks up electromagnetic waves in the air; now some are made by radio stations and other broadcasters and some, not wanted, are made by the car. The home-made signals are produced by stray electrical discharges floating around in the car. Common producers of these signals are electric motors, ie the windscreen wipers, electric screen washers, heater fan or an electric aerial if fitted. Other sources of interference are electric fuel pumps, flashing turn signals and instruments. Turn signals are not normally suppressed. In recent years,

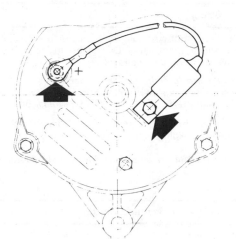

Fig. 10.29 Installation of radio interference suppressor to Delco alternator. Attachment points arrowed (Sec 38)

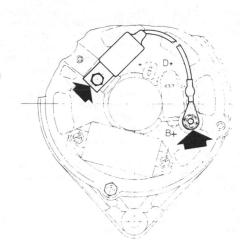

Fig. 10.30 Installation of radio interference suppressor to Bosch alternator. Attachment points arrowed (Sec 38)

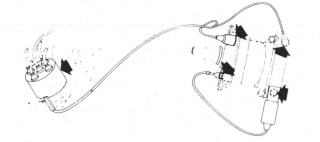

Fig. 10.31 Installation of radio interference suppressors to ignition coil and shield to distributor (Sec 38)

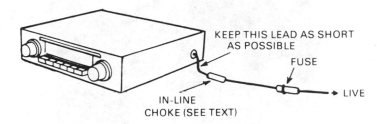

Fig. 10.32 Radio in-line choke (Sec 38)

radio manufacturers have included in the line (live) of the radio, in addition to the fuse, an 'in-line' choke. If your installation lacks one of these, put one in (Fig. 10.32).

All the foregoing components are available from radio shops or accessory shops. For a transistor radio, a 2A choke should be adequate. If you have an electric clock fitted, this should be suppressed by connecting a 0.5 μF capacitor directly across it as shown for a motor in Fig. 10.33.

If after all this you are still experiencing radio interference, first assess how bad it is, for the human ear can filter out unobtrusive unwanted noises quite easily. But if you are still adamant about eradicating the noise, then continue.

As a first step, a few 'experts' seem to favour a screen between the radio and the engine. This is OK as far as it goes, literally! The whole set is screened anyway and if interference can get past that then a small piece of aluminium is not going to stop it.

A more sensible way of screening is to discover if interference is coming down the wires. First, take the live lead; interference can get between the set and the choke (hence the reason for keeping the wires short). One remedy here is to screen the wire and this is done by buying screened wire and fitting that. The loudspeaker lead could be screened also to prevent pick-up getting back to the radio although this is unlikely.

Without doubt, the worst source of radio interference comes from the ignition HT leads, even if they have been suppressed. The ideal way of suppressing these is to slide screening tubes over the leads themselves. As this is impractical, we can place an aluminium shield over the majority of the lead areas.

Now for the really impossible cases, here are a few tips to try out. Where metal comes into contact with metal, an electrical disturbance is caused which is why good clean connections are essential. To remove interference due to overlapping or butting panels, you must

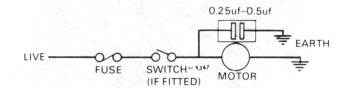

Fig. 10.33 Suppression of electric motors (Sec 38)

bridge the join with a wide braided earth strap (like that from the frame to the engine/transmission). The most common moving parts that could create noise and should be strapped are, in order of importance:

(a) *Silencer-to-frame*
(b) *Exhaust pipe-to-engine block and frame*
(c) *Air cleaner-to-frame*
(d) *Front and rear bumpers-to-frame*
(e) *Steering column-to-frame*
(f) *Bonnet and boot lids-to-frame*

These faults are most pronounced when the engine is idling or labouring under load. Although the moving parts are already connected with nuts, bolts, etc, these do tend to rust and corrode, this creating a high resistance interference source.

If you have a 'ragged' sounding pulse when mobile, this could be wheel or tyre static. This can be cured by buying some anti-static powder and sprinkling inside the tyres.

If the interference takes the shape of a high pitched screeching noise that changes its note when the car is in motion and only comes now and then, this could be related to the aerial, especially if it is of the telescopic or whip type. This source can be cured quite simply by pushing a small rubber ball on top of the aerial (yes, really!) as this breaks the electric field before it can form; but it would be much better to buy yourself a new aerial of a reputable brand. If, on the other hand, you are getting a loud rushing sound every time you brake, then this is brake static. This effect is most prominent on hot dry days and is cured only by fitting a special kit, which is quite expensive.

In conclusion, it is pointed out that it is relatively easy and therefore cheap, to eliminate 95 per cent of all noise, but to eliminate the final 5 per cent is time and money consuming. It is up to the individual to decide if it is worth it. Please remember also, that you cannot get a concert hall performance out of a cheap radio.

Finally, at the beginning of this Section are mentioned tape players; these are not usually affected by interference but in a very bad case, the best remedies are the first three suggestions plus using a 3 - 5 amp choke in the 'live' line and in incurable cases screen the live and speaker wires.

Note: *If your car is fitted with electronic ignition, then it is not recommended that either spark plug resistors or the ignition coil capacitor be fitted as these may damage the system. Most electronic ignition units have built in suppression and should, therefore, not cause interference.*

Fig. 10.34 Clock earthing point (arrowed) (Sec 39)

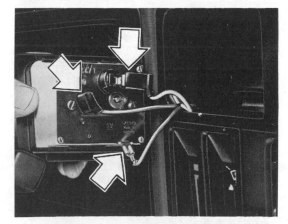

Fig. 10.35 Clock connections (arrowed) (Sec 39)

39 Clock – fitting

1   To fit a clock if not so originally equipped, prise out the blanking plate from the instrument panel. Disconnect the battery earth lead.
2   Make the following connections:

    (a) Clock earth to central earth connection
    (b) Positive terminal of clock to fuse block terminal 30
    (c) Clock light terminal to fuse block terminal 58

Terminals 30 and 58 are spare for connection of accessories and located at the lower right-hand side of the fuse box. Terminal 30 is not fused.
3   Reconnect the battery and check for correct operation.

40 Cigar lighter – removal and refitting

1   Extract the ashtray surround plate (two screws).
2   Disconnect the battery.
3   Disconnect the leads from the rear of the cigar lighter.
4   Insert a pair of round-nosed pliers into the lighter socket, expand the pliers and extract the socket.
5   Refit by reversing the removal operations.

41 Heated rear window – maintenance

1   Care should be taken to avoid damage to the element for the heated rear window or tailgate.
2   Avoid scratching with rings on the fingers when cleaning, and do not allow luggage to rub against the side of the glass.
3   Do not stick labels over the element on the inside of the glass.
4   If the element grids do become damaged, a special conductive paint is available from most motor factors to repair it.
5   Do not leave the heated rear window switched on unnecessarily, as it draws a high current from the electrical system.

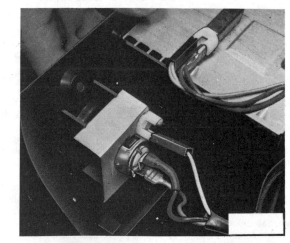

Fig. 10.36 Cigar lighter connections (Sec 40)

42 Fault diagnosis – electrical system

Symptom	Reason(s)
No voltage at starter motor	Battery discharged
	Battery defective internally
	Battery terminals loose or earth lead not securely attached to body
	Loose or broken connections in starter motor circuit
	Starter motor switch or solenoid faulty

Symptom	Reason(s)
Voltage at starter motor – faulty motor	Starter brushes badly worn, sticking, or brush wires loose Commutator dirty, worn or burnt Starter motor armature faulty Field coils earthed
Electrical defects	Battery in discharged condition Starter brushes badly worn, sticking, or brush wires loose Loose wires in starter motor circuit Starter motor pinion sticking on the screwed sleeve Dirt or oil on drive gear
Starter motor noisy or rough in engagement	Pinion or flywheel gear teeth broken or worn Starter drive main spring broken Starter motor retaining bolts loose
Alternator not charging*	Drivebelt loose and slipping, or broken Brushes worn, sticking, broken or dirty Brush springs weak or broken

* If all appears to be well but the alternator is still not charging, take the car to an automobile electrician for checking of the alternator and regulator

Symptom	Reason(s)
Battery will not hold charge for more than a few days	Battery defective internally Electrolyte level too low or electrolyte too weak due to leakage Plate separators no longer fully effective Battery plates severely sulphated Drivebelt slipping Battery terminal connections loose or corroded Alternator not charging properly Short in lighting circuit causing continual battery drain Regulator unit not working correctly
Ignition light fails to go out, battery runs flat in a few days	Drivebelt loose and slipping, or broken Alternator faulty

Failure of individual electrical equipment to function correctly is dealt with alphabetically below

Symptom	Reason(s)
Fuel gauge gives no reading (refer also to Chapter 3)	Fuel tank empty! Electric cable between tank sender unit and gauge earthed or loose Fuel gauge case not earthed Fuel gauge supply cable interrupted Fuel gauge unit broken
Fuel gauge registers full all the time	Electric cable between tank unit and gauge broken or disconnected
Horn operates all the time	Horn push either earthed or stuck down Horn cable to horn push earthed
Horn fails to operate	Blown fuse Cable or cable connection loose, broken or disconnected Horn has an internal fault
Horn emits intermittent or unsatisfactory noise	Cable connections loose Horn incorrectly adjusted
Lights do not come on	If engine not running, battery discharged Light bulb filament burnt out or bulbs broken Wire connections loose, disconnected or broken Light switch shorting or otherwise faulty
Lights come on but fade out	If engine not running, battery discharged
Lights give very poor illumination	Lamp glasses dirty Reflector tarnished or dirty Lamps badly out of adjustment Incorrect bulb with too low wattage fitted Existing bulbs old and badly discoloured Electrical wiring too thin not allowing full current to pass
Lights work erratically, flashing on and off, especially over bumps	Battery terminals or earth connections loose Lights not earthing properly Contacts in light switch faulty

Symptom	Reason(s)
Wiper motor fails to work	Blown fuse Wire connections loose, disconnected or broken Brushes badly worn Armature worn or faulty Field coils faulty
Wiper motor works very slowly and takes excessive current	Commutator dirty, greasy or burnt Drive to spindles too bent or unlubricated Drive spindle binding or damaged Armature bearings dry or unaligned Armature badly worn or faulty
Wiper motor works slowly and takes little current	Brushes badly worn Commutator dirty, greasy or burnt Armature badly worn or faulty
Wiper motor works but wiper blades remain static	Linkage disengaged or faulty Drive spindle damaged or worn Wiper motor gearbox parts badly worn

Wiring diagrams – explanatory notes

The following wiring diagrams are laid out using a grid reference system, with the bottom line being the earth track. Using grid reference 49 at the bottom of the diagram as an example, follow the line upwards past switch (S50) to lamp (H20), to a connector (X2) and finally to a number in a box (83). Referring back to grid reference 83 at the bottom of the diagram it will be seen that a number in a box (49) aligns with this reference. The line from this number is a continuation of grid reference 49 and shows the live feed to lamp (H20) through the 20 amp fuse F6.

Wiring diagrams for later models will be found in Chapter 13.

Key to Fig. 10.37 on pages 184 and 185

Number	Item	Current track	Number	Item	Current track
E1	RH sidelight	43	H12	RH rear direction indicator	66
E2	RH tail light	44	H13	LH front direction indicator	62
E3	Number plate light	45	H14	LH rear direction indicator	63
E4	LH sidelight	41	H20	Choke warning lamp	49
E5	LH tail light	42	K2	Flasher unit	60
E6	Engine compartment light	46, 48	L1	Ignition coil	9
E7	RH main beam	52	M1	Starter motor	5, 6, 7
E8	LH main beam	51	M2	Windscreen wiper motor	30, 31, 32, 33
E9	RH dipped beam	55	M3	Heater blower motor	38, 39
E10	LH dipped beam	54	M4	Radiator fan motor	17
E11	Instrument lights	46, 48	M5	Windscreen washer pump	29
E12	Selector lever light	75	P1	Fuel gauge	22
E13	Luggage compartment light	68	P2	Temperature gauge	20
E14	Passenger compartment light	70	P3	Clock	73
E15	Glovebox light	79	P4	Fuel gauge sender	21
E16	Cigar lighter light	77	P5	Temperature gauge sender	20
E17	RH reversing light	81	R1	Resistor cable	9
E18	LH reversing light	80	R2	Carburettor heater	82
E19	Heated rear window	36	R3	Cigarette lighter	76
E32	Clock light	74	S1	Starter switch	6, 7
E33	Ashtray light	78	S2	Light switch	46, 47
F1	Fuse (in fuse box)	42	S2.1	Passenger compartment light switch	69
F2	Fuse (in fuse box)	44	S3	Heater blower and heated rear window switch	36, 37, 38, 40
F4	Fuse (in fuse box)	68	S5.1	Windscreen wiper switch	30, 31, 32
F5	Fuse (in fuse box)	31	S5.2	Dipswitch	50, 51
F6	Fuse (in fuse box)	80	S5.3	Direction indicator switch	65
F7	Fuse (in fuse box)	57	S5.5	Horn switch	34
F8	Fuse (in fuse box)	37	S5.7	Windscreen washer switch	29
F9	Fuse (in fuse box)	38	S6	Distributor	9, 11
F10	Fuse (in fuse box)	17	S7	Reversing lamp switch	80
F14	Fuse (Italy only)	51	S8	Stop-light switch	57
F15	Fuse (Italy only)	52	S10	Starter inhibitor switch (automatic transmission)	7
F16	Fuse (Italy only)	54	S11	Brake fluid level switch	24
F17	Fuse (Italy only)	55	S13	Handbrake switch	26
F25	Voltage stabiliser	19	S14	Oil pressure switch	27
G1	Battery	1	S15	Luggage compartment light switch	68
G2	Alternator	13, 14, 15	S16	RH door switch	71
H1	Radio	72	S17	LH door switch	70
H2	Horn	34	S18	Glovebox light switch	79
H3	Direction indicator repeater	61	S29	Temperature switch (1.3 only)	17
H4	Oil pressure warning lamp	27	S50	Choke warning light switch (manual choke only)	49
H5	Brake warning lamp	25	S52	Hazard warning switch	59, 60, 61, 63, 64
H6	Hazard warning indicator lamp	61	X2	Auxiliary connector	49, 72, 73, 74
H7	No-charge warning lamp	15			
H8	High beam warning lamp	53			
H9	RH stop-light	58			
H10	LH stop-light	57			
H11	RH front direction indicator	65			

BL	Blue
BR	Brown
GE	Yellow
GN	Green
GR	Grey
HLB	Light blue
LI	Violet
RT	Red
SW	Black
WS	White

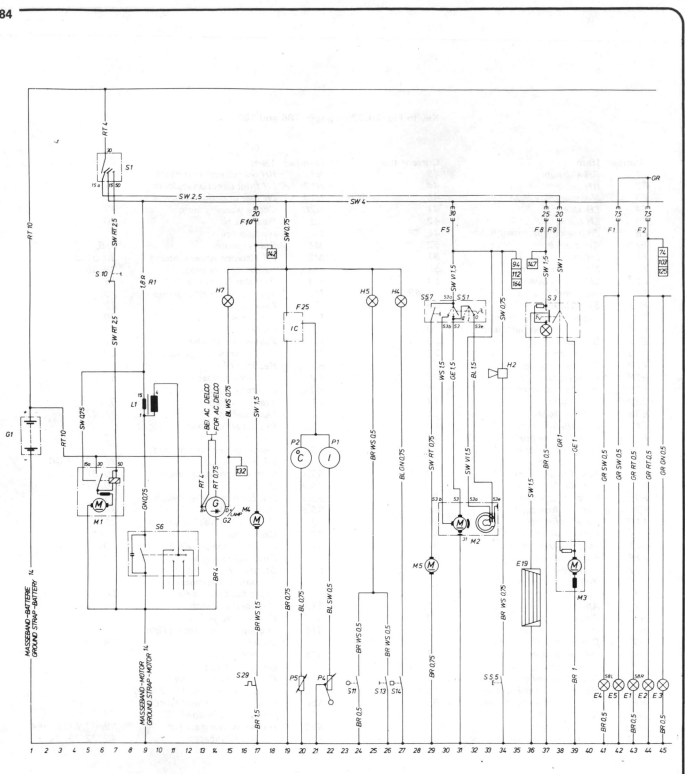

Fig. 10.37 Wiring diagram – basic equipment. (Not all items are fitted to all models). For key see page 183

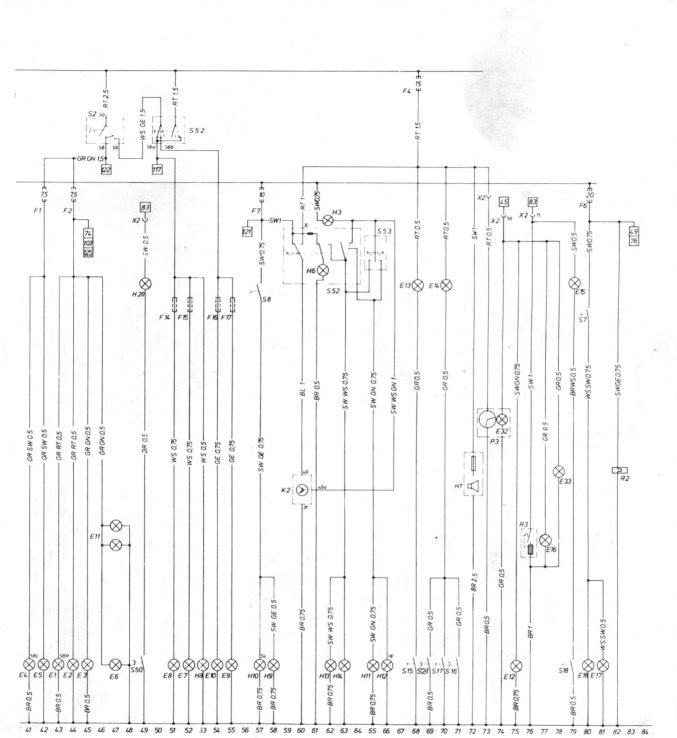

Fig. 10.37 (contd). Wiring diagram – basic equipment. (Not all items are fitted to all models). For key see page 183

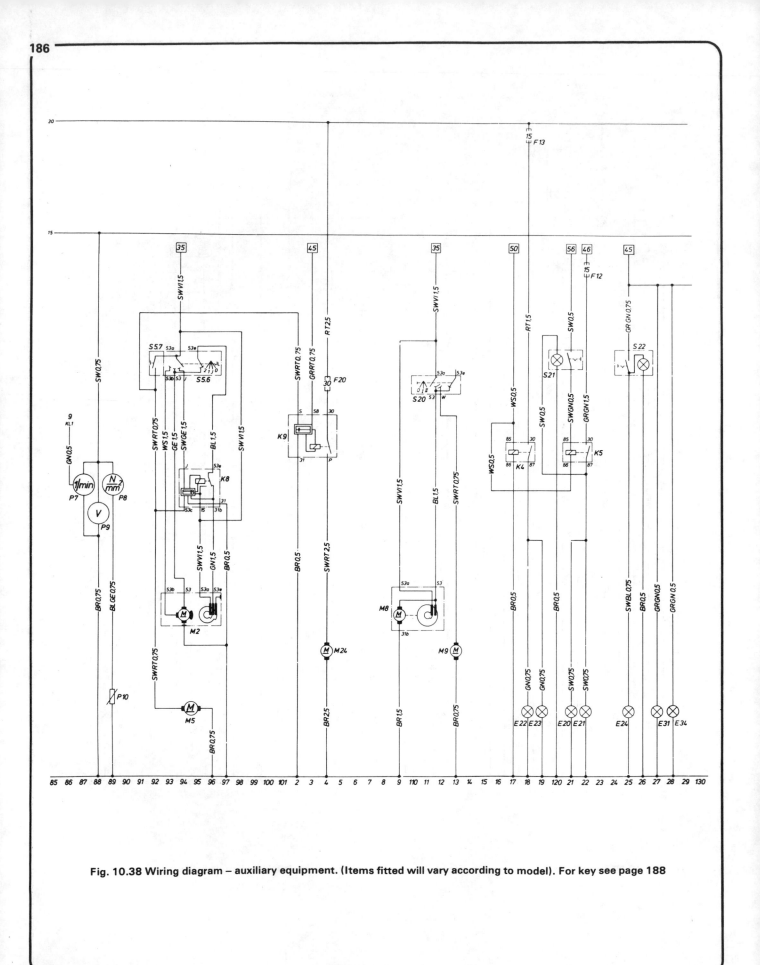

Fig. 10.38 Wiring diagram – auxiliary equipment. (Items fitted will vary according to model). For key see page 188

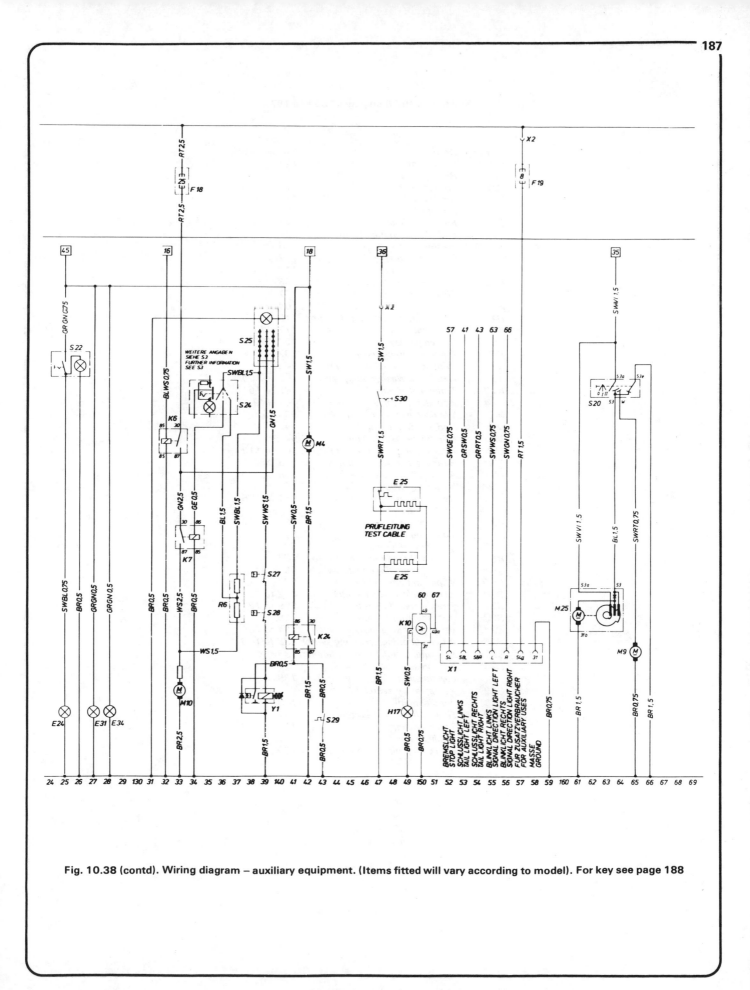

Fig. 10.38 (contd). Wiring diagram – auxiliary equipment. (Items fitted will vary according to model). For key see page 188

Key to Fig. 10.38 on pages 186 and 187

Number	Item	Current track
E20	LH foglamp	121
E21	RH foglamp	122
E22	LH spotlight	118
E23	RH spotlight	119
E24	Rear foglamp	125
E25	Front seat heating mat	147
E31	Switch illumination lamp	127
E34	Heater control lamp	128
F12	Fuse (in fuse box)	122
F13	Fuse (in fuse box)	118
F18	Fuse (air conditioning)	133
F19	Fuse (trailer socket)	157
F20	Fuse (time delay relay)	104
H17	Trailer turn signal indicator lamp	149
K4	Spotlight relay	117, 118
K5	Foglamp relay	121, 122
K6	Air conditioning relay	132, 133
K8	Windscreen washer delay relay	94 to 97
K9	Headlamp washer delay relay	102 to 104
K10	Trailer flasher unit	149 to 151
K24	Radiator fan relay	141, 142
M2	Windscreen wiper motor	93 to 97
M4	Radiator fan motor	142
M5	Windscreen washer pump	94, 95
M8	Rear wiper motor (except Estate)	109 to 112
M9	Rear window washer pump	113, 165
M10	Air conditioning blower motor	133
M24	Headlamp washer pump	104
M25	Rear wiper motor (Estate)	161 to 166
P7	Tachometer	86, 87
P8	Oil pressure gauge	89
P9	Voltmeter	88
P10	Oil pressure sender	89
R6	Air conditioning blower resistor	137
S5.6	Windscreen wiper delay switch	93 to 97
S5.7	Wiper unit contact switch	92
S20	Rear window wiper switch	112 to 114
S21	Front foglamp switch	119 to 121
S22	Rear foglamp switch	125, 126
S24	Air conditioning blower switch	134 to 136
S25	Air conditioning operating switch	138 to 140
S27	Pressure switch (air conditioning)	139
S28	Compressor cut-off (air conditioning)	139
S29	Temperature switch (air conditioning)	143
S30	Heated front seat switch	147
X1	Trailer socket	152 to 159
X2	Auxiliary connector	147, 157
Y1	Air conditioning compressor	139

BL	Blue
BR	Brown
GE	Yellow
GN	Green
GR	Grey
HLB	Light blue
LI	Violet
RT	Red
SW	Black
WS	White

Chapter 11 Suspension

For modifications, and information applicable to later models, see Supplement at end of manual

Contents

Specifications

Front suspension

Type	Independent, MacPherson strut with coil springs, and anti-roll bar on certain models
Steering angles and toe setting	Refer to Chapter 8

Rear suspension

Type	Independent with trailing link, coil spring and telescopic shock absorbers. Automatic level control system option. Anti-roll bar on certain models

Suspension angles and toe setting:
Camber*	0° to – 1°
Toe-in*	0 to 4.0 mm (0 to 0.157 in)

Set in production – non-adjustable

Roadwheels

Type	Pressed steel or cast alloy

Size:
Saloon/Hatchback (1.2 l)	$4\frac{1}{2}$J x 13
Saloon/Hatchback GL (1.2 l)	5J x 13
Saloon/Hatchback (1.3 l)	$5\frac{1}{2}$J x 13
Estate	$5\frac{1}{2}$J x 13

Tyres

Type	Steel belt radial

Size:
Saloon/Hatchback (1.2 l, 1.3 l)	155 SR 13
Saloon/Hatchback (1.3 l S)	155 SR 13
Saloon/Hatchback (1.3 l S/GL)	175/70 SR 13
Saloon/Hatchback (1.3 l S – Special Equipment)	185/60 HR 14
Estate (1.2 l)	155 SR 13
Estate (1.3 l)	175/70 SR 13

Tyre pressures (cold) in lbf/in² (kPa):

	Up to 3 occupants		Fully laden	
	Front	Rear	Front	Rear
Saloon/Hatchback:				
155 SR 13	24 (170)	24 (170)	27 (190)	32 (220)
175/70 SR 13	23 (160)	23 (160)	26 (180)	30 (210)
185/60 HR 14	24 (170)	24 (170)	27 (190)	30 (210)
Estate:				
155 SR 13	24 (170)	29 (200)	29 (200)	43 (300)
175/70 SR 13	23 (160)	26 (180)	26 (180)	37 (260)

Torque wrench settings

Front suspension

	Nm	lbf ft
Driveshaft/hub nut	100	74
Caliper mounting bolts	95	70
Disc shield bolts	4	3
Control arm balljoint nut	50	37
Tie-rod end balljoint nut	50	37
Control arm balljoint (replacement) fixing nuts	65	48
Anti-roll bar clamp bolts	40	29
Suspension arm front bolt	140	103
Suspension arm rear bolts	70	51
Suspension strut top mounting nuts	30	22
Strut piston rod nut	55	40
Strut tube ring nut	200	148

Rear suspension

	Nm	lbf ft
Suspension-to-body bolts	100	69
Anti-roll bar end bolts	80	59

Roadwheels

	Nm	lbf ft
Fixing bolts	90	66

1   Description

The front suspension is of MacPherson strut type with an anti-roll bar fitted to certain models.

The rear suspension incorporates an axle tube, single trailing links, progressive rate coil springs and hydraulic shock absorbers. An anti-roll bar is fitted to certain models.

A self-levelling system for the rear suspension is available as an optional extra, or as standard on certain versions destined for specified territories.

Roadwheels on standard models are of pressed steel, but light alloy wheels are available as special equipment. The wheels have safety bead rims and are bolted into position.

All models are equipped with steel-belted radial tyres.

2   Maintenance

1   Regularly inspect the front suspension struts and rear shock absorbers for sign of fluid leakage. If apparent, renew the assembly.
2   Inspect the suspension arm balljoint gaiter. If it is split, renew it immediately.
3   With the help of an assistant, periodically push and pull the suspension components to check for wear in the flexible bushes. If evident, renew the bushes immediately.
4   At the specified intervals, check the rear hub bearing adjustment (Section 8).

3   Front anti-roll bar – removal and refitting

1   Raise the front of the vehicle.
2   Unscrew and disconnect the anti-roll bar from the suspension arm links (photo).
3   Unbolt the anti-roll bar clamps from the body and withdraw the bar. If the steering is turned to full lock, the anti-roll bar can be withdrawn from under the wheel arch.
4   Refitting is a reversal of removal. Use new rubber cushions where necessary and tighten the securing nuts and bolts to the specified torque, making sure that the cushions at the top of the link conform to the dimension in the diagram (Fig. 11.2).
5   Fitting an anti-roll bar to a vehicle not originally equipped with one will require the fitting of a new suspension arm at the same time.

4   Front suspension control arm – removal and refitting

1   Raise the front of the vehicle and support it securely with axle stands.
2   Remove the roadwheel from the side being worked upon.
3   If an anti-roll bar is fitted, disconnect it from the suspension arm.

4   Using a balljoint separator, disconnect the suspension arm balljoint from the hub carrier (photos).
5   Unscrew the pivot bolt and the clamp bolts from the inboard end of the suspension arm. Remove the arm (photo).

3.2 Front anti-roll bar end links

Fig. 11.1 Front anti-roll bar clamp (Sec 3)

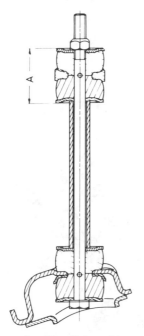

Fig. 11.2 Front anti-roll bar link cushion setting (Sec 3)

A – 38.0 mm (1.5 in)

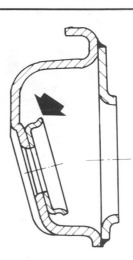

Fig. 11.3 Seat for rubber cushion on control arm (vehicles with anti-roll bar) (Sec 3)

4.4A Suspension control arm balljoint

4.4B Suspension control arm balljoint released

4.5 Front suspension arm pivots

6   The flexible bushes of the suspension arm may be renewed by pressing them out or by using a bolt, nut and distance pieces to draw them out. Use soapy water or brake fluid when installing the new ones, and make sure that the flat on the rear bush is aligned with the balljoint on the arm before pressing it into its bore.

7   If the suspension arm balljoint is worn, it can be renewed if the original rivets are drilled out (12.0 mm - 0.5 in dia. drill). The new balljoint is bolted on. Bolts are supplied with the new balljoint; make sure that the nuts are located on the underside of the control arm.

8   Commence reassembly by locating the arm loosely with the bolts finger tight. Make sure that the head of the pivot bolt is towards the front of the vehicle and always use a new self-locking nut. The longer arm of the bush clamp must point towards the centre of the vehicle.

9   The rubber pivot bush must have its flattened side against the body.

10 Connect the suspension arm swivel, tighten to the specified torque and insert the retaining clip.

11 Reconnect the anti-roll bar (if fitted) as described in Section 3.

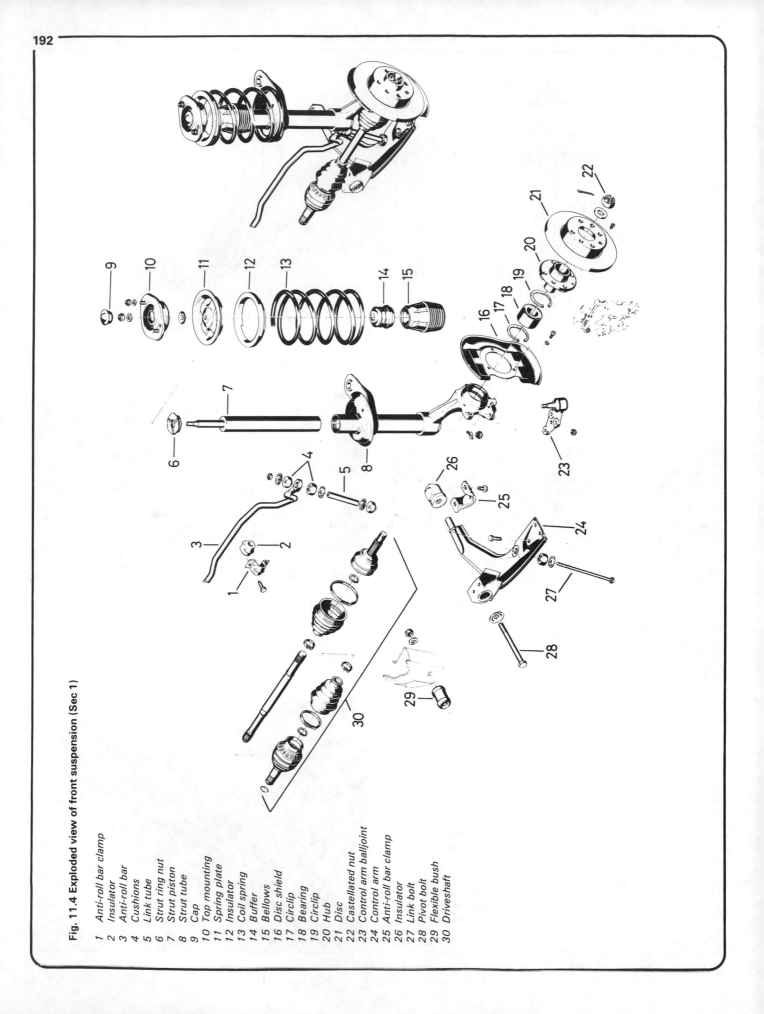

Fig. 11.4 Exploded view of front suspension (Sec 1)

1 Anti-roll bar clamp
2 Insulator
3 Anti-roll bar
4 Cushions
5 Link tube
6 Strut ring nut
7 Strut piston
8 Strut tube
9 Cap
10 Top mounting
11 Spring plate
12 Insulator
13 Coil spring
14 Buffer
15 Bellows
16 Disc shield
17 Circlip
18 Bearing
19 Circlip
20 Hub
21 Disc
22 Castellated nut
23 Control arm balljoint
24 Control arm
25 Anti-roll bar clamp
26 Insulator
27 Link bolt
28 Pivot bolt
29 Flexible bush
30 Driveshaft

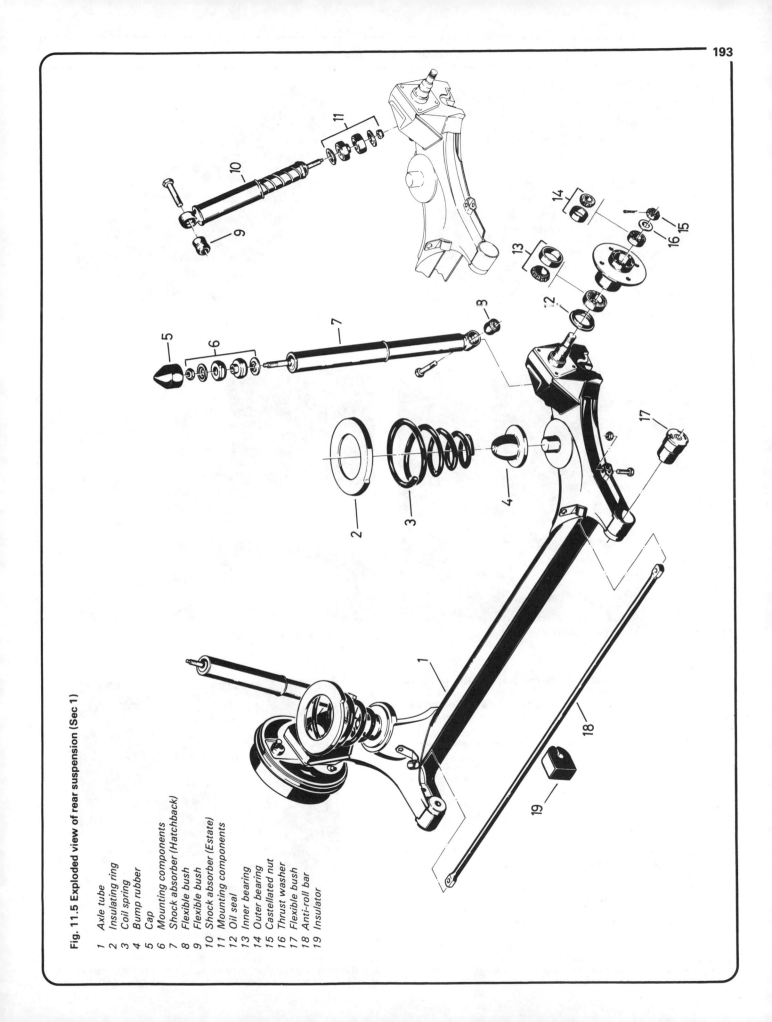

Fig. 11.5 Exploded view of rear suspension (Sec 1)

1 Axle tube
2 Insulating ring
3 Coil spring
4 Bump rubber
5 Cap
6 Mounting components
7 Shock absorber (Hatchback)
8 Flexible bush
9 Flexible bush
10 Shock absorber (Estate)
11 Mounting components
12 Oil seal
13 Inner bearing
14 Outer bearing
15 Castellated nut
16 Thrust washer
17 Flexible bush
18 Anti-roll bar
19 Insulator

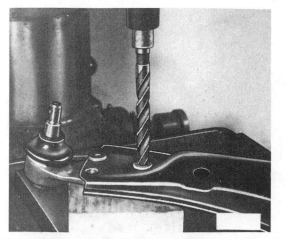

Fig. 11.6 Drilling out a control arm balljoint rivet (Sec 4)

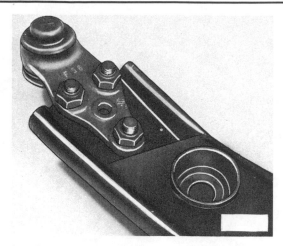

Fig. 11.7 New control arm balljoint fitted with bolts and nuts
(Sec 4)

5.3A Front strut showing tie-rod balljoint connection

5.3B Tie-rod end balljoint. Note nut securing clip

12 Jack up the outboard end of the control arm until it is horizontal
and tighten the pivot bolt to the specified torque.
13 Now tighten the pivot bush clamp bolts to the specified torque.
14 Refit the roadwheel and lower the vehicle to the ground.

5 Front suspension strut – removal and refitting

1 Raise the front of the vehicle and remove the roadwheel. Make
sure the vehicle is securely supported.
2 Extract the split pin from the castellated hub nut and unscrew the
nut. To prevent the hub from turning, either have an assistant apply the
footbrake or use a length of steel bolted to the hub as a lever in contact
with the floor.
3 Using a suitable balljoint separator, disconnect the tie-rod end
from the steering arm of the suspension strut (photos).
4 Unbolt the brake caliper, pull out the hose fixing clip and
disconnect the hose from its bracket. Tie the brake caliper up out of the
way to avoid strain on the flexible hose. Do not disconnect the
hydraulic hose.
5 Again using the balljoint separator, disconnect the suspension arm
balljoint from the hub carrier.
6 Separate the driveshaft from the hub carrier. This should simply
push out by hand, if not, use a two-legged extractor.
7 Unscrew and remove the mounting nuts at the top of the strut
inside the engine compartment.

Fig. 11.8 Strut top mounting nuts (Sec 5)

8 Withdraw the strut from under the wheel arch.
9 Refitting is a reversal of removal, but observe the connection of
the driveshaft to the hub carrier as described in Chapter 7, Section 2.

Fig. 11.9 Unscrewing strut piston nut (Sec 6)

Fig. 11.10 Removing strut top mounting (Sec 6)

Fig. 11.11 Top spring plate alignment mark (arrowed) (Sec 6)

Fig. 11.12 Abutment of strut spring bottom coil (Sec 6)

6   Front suspension strut – dismantling and reassembly

1   The coil spring from the original strut will be required for fitting to a new strut as struts are supplied new without the spring.

2   A new damper cartridge can be fitted to the original strut by carrying out the following procedure.

3   Grip the hub carrier in a vice so that the strut lies horizontally. Fit spring compressors. These are available from most motor accessory stores.

4   Compress the spring until tension is relieved from the top mounting. Prise out the sealing cap.

5   Hold the flats on the piston rod to prevent it rotating and then unscrew the strut top nut.

6   Take off the top mounting components with ball-bearing.

7   Remove the spring plate, buffer and bellows and spring.

8   Unscrew the ring nut from the top of the strut tube, this is very tight.

9   Withdraw the original cartridge and insert the new one.

10 Screw in the new threaded ring which is supplied with the cartridge. The threads are wax coated, do not clean this wax off. Tighten the nut to the specified torque.

11 Fit the spring, still compressed, the bellows, buffer and plate. The plate must be positioned so that the small hole aligns with the inboard hole for the driveshaft in the hub carrier. Check that the bottom coil of the spring abuts the stop on the seat.

12 Removal of the hub and disc is described in the next Section.

7   Front hub bearings – renewal

1   Raise the front of the vehicle and remove the roadwheel.

2   Remove the suspension strut as described in Section 5.

Fig. 11.13 Disc shield securing screws (Sec 7)

3   Extract the small retaining screw and remove the brake disc.

4   The hub must now be pressed out of the hub carrier. The hub bearings will be destroyed during this operation and half of the bearing inner assembly will remain on the hub.

5   Unscrew and remove the disc shield from the hub carrier.

6   Extract the two bearing retaining circlips from the hub carrier.

7   Now press the bearing out of the hub carrier.

8   Remove the bearing component from the hub.

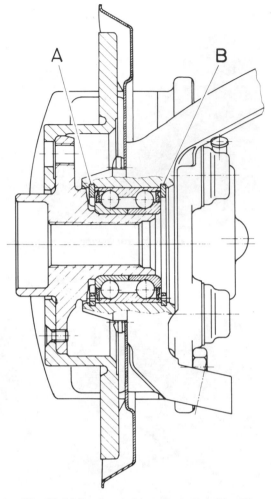

Fig. 11.14 Sectional view of front hub (Sec 7)

A Outboard circlip   B Inboard circlip

9   Commence reassembly by inserting the outboard circlip into the hub carrier, making sure that it seats correctly.
10 Press the bearing into the hub carrier, applying pressure to the bearing outer track. Fit the inboard circlip.
11 Refit the disc shield.
12 The hub must now be pressed into the hub carrier, but support the bearing centre track during the operations.
13 Fit the brake disc and screw.
14 The suspension strut can now be refitted to the vehicle.

8   Rear hub bearings – adjustment

1   Raise the rear of the vehicle and remove the wheel cover plate.
2   Prise off the centre dust cap.
3   Extract the split pin from the castellated nut.
4   Tighten the castellated nut to a torque of 25 Nm (18 lbf ft) while turning the roadwheel.
5   Unscrew the nut and retighten it finger tight.
6   Grip the top and bottom of the roadwheel and check for bearing 'rock' or endfloat. If evident, give a little more finger pressure to the nut and if this does not eliminate the play, suspect worn bearings.
7   Refit the split pin, the dust cap and the cover plate, and lower the car to the ground.

9   Rear hub bearings – renewal

1   Raise the rear of the vehicle and remove the roadwheel.
2   Extract the small securing screw and withdraw the brake drum. Back off the brake adjustment if necessary – see Chapter 9.
3   Tap off the dust cap from the end of the hub (photo).
4   Extract the split pin and unscrew the castellated nut (photo).
5   Withdraw the thrust washer.
6   Pull the hub towards you and then push it back. This will leave the outer bearing ready to be taken off the stub axle (photo).
7   Withdraw the hub (photo).
8   Prise out the oil seal from the inner end of the hub.
9   Extract the inner bearing race.
10 Press or drive out the bearing outer tracks from the inside of the hub. Wipe out all the old grease and install the new tracks squarely.
11 Press grease into the inner bearing race and locate it in position. Tap a new oil seal squarely into place and grease its lips.
12 Half fill the space between the two bearings with grease and then slide the hub onto the stub axle. Take care not to damage the oil seal lips.
13 Hold the hub horizontally and fit the outer bearing, which should have been liberally greased.
14 Fit the thrust washer and screw on the nut.
15 Adjust the bearings as described in the preceding Section.
16 Insert a new split pin and bend the ends around the nut so that the pin will not rub against the dust cap (photo).
17 Tap the dust cap into position.
18 Fit the brake drum and roadwheel. Adjust the brakes if necessary (Chapter 9) and lower the vehicle to the ground.

10 Rear anti-roll bar – removal and refitting

1   Raise the rear of the vehicle and remove one of the roadwheels.
2   Disconnect the ends of the anti-roll bar from both sides of the vehicle.
3   Withdraw the bar from under the wheel arch on the side from which the roadwheel was removed.
4   Refitting is a reversal of removal. Tighten the bolts to the specified torque.

9.3 Removing rear hub dust cap

9.4 Removing rear hub castellated nut

9.6 Removing rear hub outer bearing

9.7 Rear hub removed

9.16 Fitting new rear hub split pin

Fig. 11.15 Removing rear anti-roll bar (Sec 10)

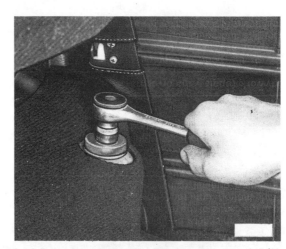

Fig. 11.16 Releasing rear shock absorber top mounting (Hatchback) (Sec 11)

11 Rear shock absorber (Saloon/Hatchback) – removal, testing and refitting

1 Working inside the vehicle, remove the cover from the shock absorber mounting.
2 Unscrew the mounting nut and remove the retainer and the nut.
3 Raise the rear of the vehicle.
4 If automatic level control is installed (see Section 16), discharge the air pressure from the system and then disconnect the pressure line from the shock absorber.
5 Unscrew the shock absorber lower mounting from the axle.
6 Prise the shock absorber up and out of the bracket.
7 To test a standard type shock absorber, grip it vertically by its bottom mounting in the jaws of a vice.
8 Fully extend and contract the unit at least six times. If there is any sign of lack of resistance, jerky movement or seizure, renew the shock absorber.
9 On vehicles equipped with automatic level control, testing of the units is best left to your dealer.
10 Refitting is a reversal of removal, but observe the setting of the top mounting nut (Fig. 11.19).
11 On vehicles with automatic level control, pump up the system as described in Section 16.

Fig. 11.17 Disconnecting rear shock absorber lower mounting (Hatchback) (Sec 11)

Fig. 11.18 Prising shock absorber out of rear axle bracket
(Hatchback) (Sec 11)

12 Rear shock absorber (Estate) – removal, testing and refitting

1   Raise the rear suspension arm slightly on a jack and disconnect
the shock absorber lower mounting (photo).
2   Unscrew the upper mounting bolt, which is accessible through a
hole in the body side member (photo).
3   If the vehicle is equipped with automatic level control, discharge
the air pressure from the system and then disconnect the pressure line
from the shock absorber. Refer to Section 16 if necessary.
4   Remove the shock absorber and test as described in the preceding
Section, paragraph 8 or 9.
5   Refitting is a reversal of removal, but observe the setting of the
lower mounting nut (Fig. 11.20).
6   On vehicles with automatic level control, pump up the system as
described in Section 16.

13 Rear roadspring (Saloon/Hatchback) – removal and refitting

1   If the vehicle is equipped with automatic level control, discharge
the air from the system (Section 16).

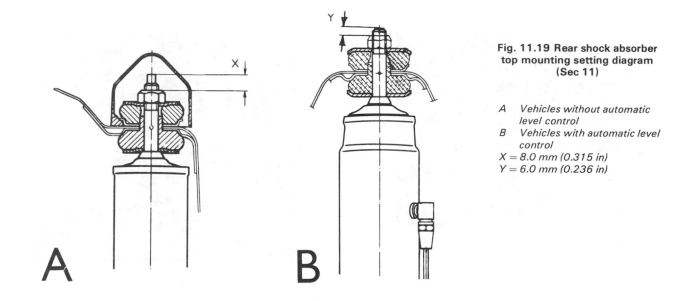

Fig. 11.19 Rear shock absorber
top mounting setting diagram
(Sec 11)

A   *Vehicles without automatic
level control*
B   *Vehicles with automatic level
control*
$X = 8.0$ mm (0.315 in)
$Y = 6.0$ mm (0.236 in)

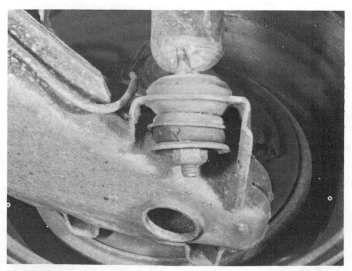

12.1 Rear shock absorber lower mounting (Estate)

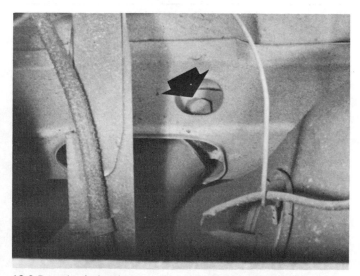

12.2 Rear shock absorber upper mounting (arrowed) on Estate

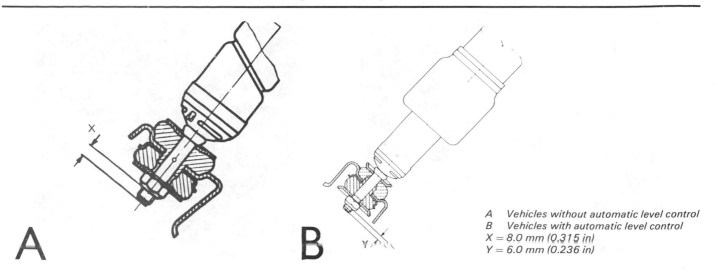

A   Vehicles without automatic level control
B   Vehicles with automatic level control
X = 8.0 mm (0.315 in)
Y = 6.0 mm (0.236 in)

Fig. 11.20 Rear shock absorber lower mounting setting diagram (Sec 12)

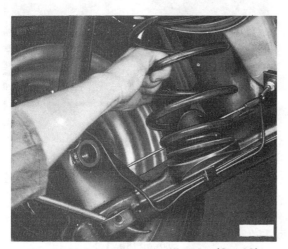

Fig. 11.21 Removing rear coil spring (Sec 13)

Fig. 11.22 Rear coil spring with bump rubber (Sec 13)

2   Disconnect the lower end of the shock absorber as described previously. Raise the rear of the vehicle.
3   Pass a lever through the shock absorber bracket on the axle and prise the axle down so that the spring and rubber insulating rings can be withdrawn from the vehicle.
4   To refit, engage the rubber insulator on the lower smaller coil of the spring and reverse the removal operations. Refer to Section 11 when reconnecting the shock absorber. On vehicles with automatic level control, pump up the system.

14 Rear roadspring (Estate) – removal and refitting

1   If the vehicle is equipped with automatic level control, discharge the system air pressure (Section 16).
2   Raise the rear of the vehicle and disconnect the shock absorber lower mounting on the side from which the spring is to be removed.
3   Completely remove the shock absorber from the opposite side of the vehicle.
4   Returning to the other side of the vehicle, withdraw the spring and rubber insulator.
5   The second roadspring may now be removed if required.
6   Refitting is a reversal of removal, but refer to Section 12 for the shock absorber lower mounting settings.
7   On vehicles with automatic level control, pump up the system as described in Section 16.

15 Rear suspension assembly – removal and refitting

1   Raise the rear of the vehicle. If it is equipped with automatic level control, discharge the system (see Section 16).
2   Remove the rear roadwheels.
3   Slacken the handbrake equaliser nut until the cable can be slipped out of the groove in the equaliser.
4   Detach the handbrake cable from the guides on the floor panel and the hooks on the fuel tank.
5   Release the exhaust system from its hangers.
6   Disconnect the brake hydraulic line from the flexible hose at the axle bracket. Cap the open end of the line to prevent loss of fluid.
7   Raise the suspension arm, remove the shock absorbers at the roadsprings as described in earlier Sections.
8   Support the weight of the rear axle and unbolt it from its anchor brackets on the underside of the vehicle (photo).
9   Lower the assembly and remove it from under the vehicle. The looped part of the handbrake cable should be slid over the exhaust silencer and off the tailpipe as the exhaust hanger was previously disconnected.
10   The suspension assembly may now be dismantled as necessary and as described in earlier Sections of this Chapter and in Chapter 9.
11   Reassembly and refitting are reversals of removal and dismantling. Adjust the handbrake cable and the pressure proportioning valve and bleed the brakes, all as described in Chapter 9.

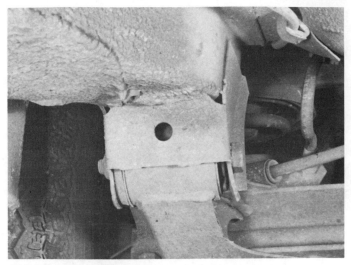

15.8 Rear suspension attachment to anchor brackets

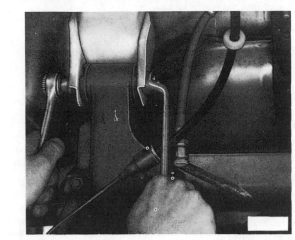

Fig. 11.23 Unscrewing rear suspension from body anchor bracket (Sec 15)

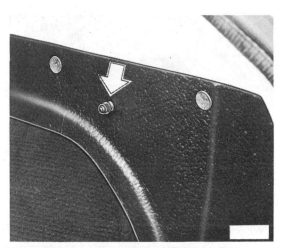

Fig. 11.24 Typical discharge and pressurising valve for automatic level control system (Sec 16)

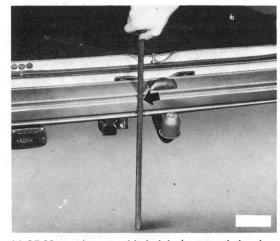

Fig. 11.25 Measuring rear ride height (automatic level control system) (Sec 16)

Fig. 11.26 Pressurising automatic level control system (Sec 16)

12 Adjust the shock absorber mounting settings as described in Sections 11 or 12 of this Chapter. Pressurise the automatic level control system if so equipped (Section 16).

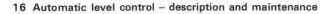

16 Automatic level control – description and maintenance

1   On vehicles equipped with this system, the vehicle riding level is controlled at the rear by an interconnecting pipeline between the two shock absorbers. The system is pressurised with air.
2   The system pressurising valve is similar to a tyre valve and is located on the trim panel within the luggage area.
3   Always discharge the system air pressure at the valve before disconnecting the pipeline and on completion, pump up the pressure to 11.4 lbf/in² (80 kPa) with the vehicle unloaded and standing on level ground.
4   Measure the distance between the centre of the rear bumper bar and the ground and record the measurement. If the vehicle is now loaded, the pressure in the automatic level control system must be increased until the ride height matches the original dimension taken when the vehicle was unladen.
5   On no account should the pressure be increased above 71 lbf/in² (500 kPa) however.
6   After the load has been removed, the system pressure should once again be lowered by depressing the centre pin in the valve until a reading of 11.4 lbf/in² (80 kPa) is recorded.

17 Wheels and tyres – maintenance

1   Whenever the roadwheels are removed, it is a good idea to clean the insides of the wheels to remove accumulations of mud and in the case of the front ones, disc pad dust.

2   Check the condition of the wheel for rust and repaint if necessary.

3   Examine the wheel bolt holes. If these are tending to become elongated, or the dished recesses in which the nuts seat have worn or become overcompressed, then the wheel will have to be renewed.

4   With a roadwheel removed, pick out any embedded flints from the tread and check for splits in the sidewalls or damage to the tyre carcass generally.

5   Where the depth of tread pattern is 1 mm or less, the tyre must be renewed.

6   In production, the wheels are balanced on the vehicle and in order to maintain this balance it is essential to mark the relationship of each roadwheel to its hub before removing it for the first time. Do this with a spot of quick-drying paint on the wheel and hub at adjacent points.

7   Rotating of the roadwheels to even out wear may be a worthwhile idea if the wheels have been balanced off the car. Include the spare wheel in the rotational pattern. Move the wheels front-to-rear, not side-to-side of the car.

8   It is recommended that wheels are rebalanced halfway through the life of the tyres to compensate for the loss of tread rubber, due to wear.

9   Finally, always keep the tyres (including the spare) inflated to the recommended pressures and always refit the dust caps on the tyre valves. Tyre pressures are best checked first thing in the morning when the tyres are cold.

18 Suspension angles and wheel alignment – general

1   Due to the need for special gauges, rear suspension camber and toe is best checked by your dealer.

2   Before checking the angles, the front seats of the vehicle must be loaded with 70 kg (154 lb) each and the fuel tank filled, also the car depressed several times on its suspension.

3   Any variation from the specified tolerances (see Specifications) can only be due to damage or gross wear in the suspension components as the camber angle and rear toe setting are not adjustable.

4   For front suspension and steering angles, refer to Chapter 8, Section 10.

19 Fault diagnosis – suspension

Symptom	Reason(s)
Vehicle wanders	Incorrect wheel alignment Worn front control arm balljoints
Heavy or stiff steering	Incorrect front wheel alignment Incorrect tyre pressures
Wheel wobble or vibration	Roadwheels out of balance Roadwheel buckled Incorrect front wheel alignment Faulty strut or shock absorber Weak coil spring
Excessive pitching or rolling on corners or during braking	Faulty strut or shock absorber Weak or broken coil spring Discharged automatic level control system (where fitted)

Chapter 12 Bodywork

Contents

1 Description

The body is of all-steel welded construction without a separate chassis frame.

Vehicles are available in 2 or 4-door Saloon, 3 or 5-door Hatchback and 3 and 5-door Estate version.

The front wings are detachable for renewal after damage or due to corrosion by extracting the securing bolts.

2 Bodywork – maintenance

1 The general condition of a vehicle's bodywork is the one thing that significantly affects its value. Maintenance is easy but needs to be regular. Neglect, particularly after minor damage, can lead quickly to further deterioration and costly repair bills. It is important also to keep watch on those parts of the vehicle not immediately visible, for instance the underside, inside all the wheel arches and the lower part of the engine compartment.

2 The basic maintenance routine for the bodywork is washing – preferably with a lot of water, from a hose. This will remove all the loose solids which may have stuck to the vehicle. It is important to flush these off in such a way as to prevent grit from scratching the finish. The wheel arches and underframe need washing in the same way to remove any accumulated mud which will retain moisture and tend to encourage rust. Paradoxically enough, the best time to clean the underframe and wheel arches is in wet weather when the mud is thoroughly wet and soft. In very wet weather the underframe is usually cleaned of large accumulations automatically and this is a good time for inspection.

3 Periodically, except on vehicles with a wax-based underbody protective coating, it is a good idea to have the whole of the underframe of the vehicle steam cleaned, engine compartment included, so that a thorough inspection can be carried out to see what minor repairs and renovations are necessary. Steam cleaning is available at many garages and is necessary for removal of the accumulation of oily grime which sometimes is allowed to become thick in certain areas. If steam cleaning facilities are not available, there are one or two excellent grease solvents available such as Holts Engine Cleaner or Holts Foambrite which can be brush applied. The dirt can then be simply hosed off. Note that these methods should not be used on vehicles with wax-based underbody protective coating or the coating will be removed. Such vehicles should be inspected annually, preferably just prior to winter, when the underbody should be washed down and any damage to the wax coating repaired using Holts

Undershield. Ideally, a completely fresh coat should be applied. It would also be worth considering the use of such wax-based protection for injection into door panels, sills, box sections, etc, as an additional safeguard against rust damage where such protection is not provided by the vehicle manufacturer.

4 After washing paintwork, wipe off with a chamois leather to give an unspotted clear finish. A coat of clear protective wax polish, like the many excellent Turtle Wax polishes, will give added protection against chemical pollutants in the air. If the paintwork sheen has dulled or oxidised, use a cleaner/polisher combination such as Turtle Extra to restore the brilliance of the shine. This requires a little effort, but such dulling is usually caused because regular washing has been neglected. Care needs to be taken with metallic paintwork, as special non-abrasive cleaner/polisher is required to avoid damage to the finish. Always check that the door and ventilator opening drain holes and pipes are completely clear so that water can be drained out. Bright work should be treated in the same way as paint work. Windscreens and windows can be kept clear of the smeary film which often appears, by the use of a proprietary glass cleaner like Holts Mixra. Never use any form of wax or other body or chromium polish on glass.

3 Bodywork repair – minor damage

The photographic sequences on pages 206 and 207 illustrate the operations detailed in the following sub-sections.
Note: *For more detailed information about bodywork repair, the Haynes Publishing Group publish a book by Lindsay Porter called The Car Bodywork Repair Manual. This incorporates information on such aspects as rust treatment, painting and glass fibre repairs, as well as details on more ambitious repairs involving welding and panel beating.*

Repair of minor scratches in bodywork

If the scratch is very superficial, and does not penetrate to the metal of the bodywork, repair is very simple. Lightly rub the area of the scratch with a paintwork renovator like Turtle Wax New Color Back, or a very fine cutting paste like Holts Body + Plus Rubbing Compound, to remove loose paint from the scratch and to clear the surrounding bodywork of wax polish. Rinse the area with clean water.

Apply touch-up paint, such as Holts Dupli-Color Color Touch or a paint film like Holts Autofilm, to the scratch using a fine paint brush; continue to apply fine layers of paint until the surface of the paint in the scratch is level with the surrounding paintwork. Allow the new paint at least two weeks to harden: then blend it into the surrounding paintwork by rubbing the scratch area with a paintwork renovator or a very fine cutting paste, such as Holts Body + Plus Rubbing Compound

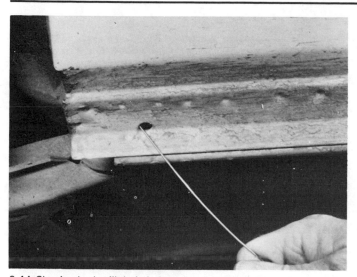

2.4A Clearing body sill drain hole

2.4B Clearing door drain hole

or Turtle Wax New Color Back. Finally, apply wax polish from one of the Turtle Wax range of wax polishes.

Where the scratch has penetrated right through to the metal of the bodywork, causing the metal to rust, a different repair technique is required. Remove any loose rust from the bottom of the scratch with a penknife, then apply rust inhibiting paint, such as Turtle Wax Rust Master, to prevent the formation of rust in the future. Using a rubber or nylon applicator fill the scratch with bodystopper paste like Holts Body + Plus Knifing Putty. If required, this paste can be mixed with cellulose thinners, such as Holts Body + Plus Cellulose Thinners, to provide a very thin paste which is ideal for filling narrow scratches. Before the stopper-paste in the scratch hardens, wrap a piece of smooth cotton rag around the top of a finger. Dip the finger in cellulose thinners, such as Holts Body + Plus Cellulose Thinners, and then quickly sweep it across the surface of the stopper-paste in the scratch; this will ensure that the surface of the stopper-paste is slightly hollowed. The scratch can now be painted over as described earlier in this Section.

Repair of dents in bodywork

When deep denting of the vehicle's bodywork has taken place, the first task is to pull the dent out, until the affected bodywork almost attains its original shape. There is little point in trying to restore the original shape completely, as the metal in the damaged area will have stretched on impact and cannot be reshaped fully to its original contour. It is better to bring the level of the dent up to a point which is about ⅛ in (3 mm) below the level of the surrounding bodywork. In cases where the dent is very shallow anyway, it is not worth trying to pull it out at all. If the underside of the dent is accessible, it can be hammered out gently from behind, using a mallet with a wooden or plastic head. Whilst doing this, hold a suitable block of wood firmly against the outside of the panel to absorb the impact from the hammer blows and thus prevent a large area of the bodywork from being 'belled-out'.

Should the dent be in a section of the bodywork which has a double skin or some other factor making it inaccessible from behind, a different technique is called for. Drill several small holes through the metal inside the area – particularly in the deeper section. Then screw long self-tapping screws into the holes just sufficiently for them to gain a good purchase in the metal. Now the dent can be pulled out by pulling on the protruding heads of the screws with a pair of pliers.

The next stage of the repair is the removal of the paint from the damaged area, and from an inch or so of the surrounding 'sound' bodywork. This is accomplished most easily by using a wire brush or abrasive pad on a power drill, although it can be done just as effectively by hand using sheets of abrasive paper. To complete the preparation for filling, score the surface of the bare metal with a screwdriver or the tang of a file, or alternatively, drill small holes in the affected area. This will provide a really good 'key' for the filler paste.

To complete the repair see the Section on filling and re-spraying.

Repair of rust holes or gashes in bodywork

Remove all paint from the affected area and from an inch or so of the surrounding 'sound' bodywork, using an abrasive pad or a wire brush on a power drill. If these are not available a few sheets of abrasive paper will do the job just as effectively. With the paint removed you will be able to gauge the severity of the corrosion and therefore decide whether to renew the whole panel (if this is possible) or to repair the affected area. New body panels are not as expensive as most people think and it is often quicker and more satisfactory to fit a new panel than to attempt to repair large areas of corrosion.

Remove all fittings from the affected area except those which will act as a guide to the original shape of the damaged bodywork (eg headlamp shells etc). Then, using tin snips or a hacksaw blade, remove all loose metal and any other metal badly affected by corrosion. Hammer the edges of the hole inwards in order to create a slight depression for the filler paste.

Wire brush the affected area to remove the powdery rust from the surface of the remaining metal. Paint the affected area with rust inhibiting paint like Turtle Wax Rust Master; if the back of the rusted area is accessible treat this also.

Before filling can take place it will be necessary to block the hole in some way. This can be achieved by the use of aluminium or plastic mesh, or aluminium tape.

Aluminium or plastic mesh or glass fibre matting, such as the Holts Body + Plus Glass Fibre Matting, is probably the best material to use for a large hole. Cut a piece to the approximate size and shape of the hole to be filled, then position it in the hole so that its edges are below the level of the surrounding bodywork. It can be retained in position by several blobs of filler paste around its periphery.

Aluminium tape should be used for small or very narrow holes. Pull a piece off the roll and trim it to the approximate size and shape required, then pull off the backing paper (if used) and stick the tape over the hole; it can be overlapped if the thickness of one piece is insufficient. Burnish down the edges of the tape with the handle of a screwdriver or similar, to ensure that the tape is securely attached to the metal underneath.

Bodywork repairs – filling and re-spraying

Before using this Section, see the Sections on dent, deep scratch, rust holes and gash repairs.

Many types of bodyfiller are available, but generally speaking those proprietary kits which contain a tin of filler paste and a tube of resin hardener are best for this type of repair, like Holts Body + Plus or Holts No Mix which can be used directly from the tube. A wide, flexible plastic or nylon applicator will be found invaluable for imparting a smooth and well contoured finish to the surface of the filler.

Mix up a little filler on a clean piece of card or board – measure the hardener carefully (follow the maker's instructions on the pack) otherwise the filler will set too rapidly or too slowly. Alternatively, Holts No Mix can be used straight from the tube without mixing, but daylight is required to cure it. Using the applicator apply the filler paste to the prepared area; draw the applicator across the surface of the filler to achieve the correct contour and to level the filler surface. As soon as a contour that approximates to the correct one is achieved, stop working the paste – if you carry on too long the paste will become sticky and begin to 'pick up' on the applicator. Continue to add thin layers of filler paste at twenty-minute intervals until the level of the filler is just proud of the surrounding bodywork.

Once the filler has hardened, excess can be removed using a metal plane or file. From then on, progressively finer grades of abrasive paper should be used, starting with a 40 grade production paper and finishing with 400 grade wet-and-dry paper. Always wrap the abrasive paper around a flat rubber, cork, or wooden block – otherwise the surface of the filler will not be completely flat. During the smoothing of the filler surface the wet-and-dry paper should be periodically rinsed in water. This will ensure that a very smooth finish is imparted to the filler at the final stage.

At this stage the 'dent' should be surrounded by a ring of bare metal, which in turn should be encircled by the finely 'feathered' edge of the good paintwork. Rinse the repair area with clean water, until all of the dust produced by the rubbing-down operation has gone.

Spray the whole repair area with a light coat of primer, either Holts Body+Plus Grey or Red Oxide Primer – this will show up any imperfections in the surface of the filler. Repair these imperfections with fresh filler paste or bodystopper, and once more smooth the surface with abrasive paper. If bodystopper is used, it can be mixed with cellulose thinners to form a really thin paste which is ideal for filling small holes. Repeat this spray and repair procedure until you are satisfied that the surface of the filler, and the feathered edge of the paintwork are perfect. Clean the repair area with clean water and allow to dry fully.

The repair area is now ready for final spraying. Paint spraying must be carried out in a warm, dry, windless and dust free atmosphere. This condition can be created artificially if you have access to a large indoor working area, but if you are forced to work in the open, you will have to pick your day very carefully. If you are working indoors, dousing the floor in the work area with water will help to settle the dust which would otherwise be in the atmosphere. If the repair area is confined to one body panel, mask off the surrounding panels; this will help to minimise the effects of a slight mis-match in paint colours. Bodywork fittings (eg chrome strips, door handles etc) will also need to be masked off. Use genuine masking tape and several thicknesses of newspaper for the masking operations.

Before commencing to spray, agitate the aerosol can thoroughly, then spray a test area (an old tin, or similar) until the technique is mastered. Cover the repair area with a thick coat of primer; the thickness should be built up using several thin layers of primer rather than one thick one. Using 400 grade wet-and-dry paper, rub down the surface of the primer until it is really smooth. While doing this, the work area should be thoroughly doused with water, and the wet-and-dry paper periodically rinsed in water. Allow to dry before spraying on more paint.

Spray on the top coat using Holts Dupli-Color Autospray, again building up the thickness by using several thin layers of paint. Start spraying in the centre of the repair area and then work outwards, with a side-to-side motion, until the whole repair area and about 2 inches of the surrounding original paintwork is covered. Remove all masking material 10 to 15 minutes after spraying on the final coat of paint.

Allow the new paint at least two weeks to harden, then, using a paintwork renovator or a very fine cutting paste such as Turtle Wax New Color Back or Holts Body+Plus Rubbing Compound, blend the edges of the paint into the existing paintwork. Finally, apply wax polish.

4 Bodywork repair – major damage

1   Because the body is built on the monocoque principle, major damage must be repaired by a competent body repairer with the necessary jigs and equipment.
2   In the event of a crash that resulted in buckling of body panels, or damage to the roadwheels, the car must be taken to your dealer or body repairer where the bodyshell and suspension alignment may be checked.
3   Bodyshell and/or suspension misalignment will cause excessive wear of the tyres, steering system and possibly transmission. The handling of the car will also be affected adversely.

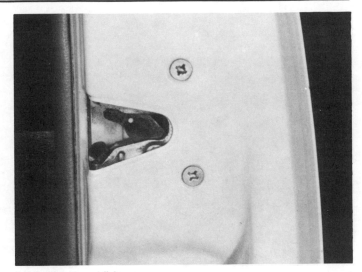

5.3 Door lock and fixing screws

5 Door and lid hinges, locks and controls – lubrication

1   Oil the hinges of the bonnet, boot and doors with a drop, or two, of light oil, periodically. A good time is after the car has been washed.
2   Oil the bonnet release catch pivot pin and safety catch pivot pin, periodically.
3   Do not over-lubricate door latches and strikers. Normally a little oil on the latch dovetail and a thin smear of high melting point grease on the striker is adequate (photo). Make sure that before lubrication they are wiped thoroughly clean and corrected adjusted.

6 Bonnet – removal and refitting

1   Open the bonnet and support it in the fully open position.
2   Mark the position of the hinges on the underside of the bonnet.
3   With the help of an assistant, support the weight of the bonnet and unbolt and remove it from the vehicle.
4   It is unlikely that the bonnet hinges will ever have to be removed but if they are, the wiper arm and linkage will first have to be withdrawn (Chapter 10) and the rivets drilled out of the hinged holder brackets.
5   Refitting is a reversal of removal, but check the bonnet alignment (even gap between edge of bonnet and wing) before finally tightening the hinge bolts.
6   When closing the bonnet, it should close smoothly and positively with moderate hand pressure. If it does not, align the dovetail and plate and adjust the projection of the dovetail by releasing its locknut and turning it by using a screwdriver in its end slot. The standard setting is as shown in Fig. 12.2. The bump rubbers may need some adjustment for height after the preceding operation.

7 Bonnet release cable – renewal

1   Remove the cable clip from the top of the front cross rail (photo).
2   Using a screwdriver, prise the cable end fitting out of the release slide.
3   Working inside the vehicle, pull the bonnet release handle out of its retainer.
4   Release the cable end fitting from the handle.
5   Pull the cable assembly through its grommet in the engine compartment rear bulkhead into the engine compartment.
6   Fit the new cable by reversing the removal operations, then adjust the cable at its rail securing clip to conform with the dimension given in Fig. 12.6.
7   The cable should release the bonnet with a gentle pull on the control handle. If it is stiff, check the setting of the catch dovetail as described in the preceding Section.

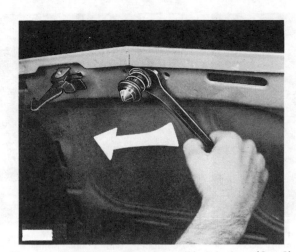

Fig. 12.1 Releasing bonnet dovetail bolt locknut (Sec 6)

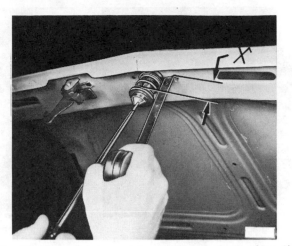

Fig 12.2 Adjusting bonnet dovetail bolt projection (Sec 6)

$X = 39.0$ mm (1.5 in)

7.1 Bonnet release cable clip (arrowed)

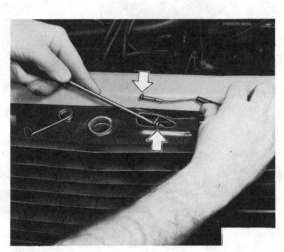

Fig. 12.3 Prising out bonnet release cable end fitting (Sec 7)

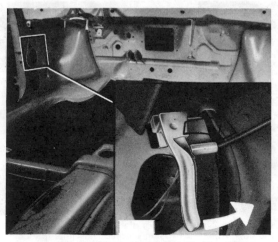

Fig. 12.4 Bonnet release handle (Sec 7)

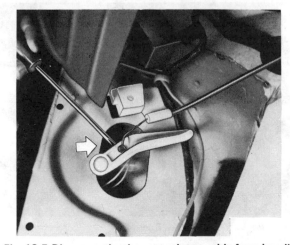

Fig. 12.5 Disconnecting bonnet release cable from handle (Sec 7)

1

This photographic sequence shows the steps taken to repair the dent and paintwork damage shown above. In general, the procedure for repairing a hole will be similar; where there are substantial differences, the procedure is clearly described and shown in a separate photograph.

2

First remove any trim around the dent, then hammer out the dent where access is possible. This will minimise filling. Here, after the large dent has been hammered out, the damaged area is being made slightly concave.

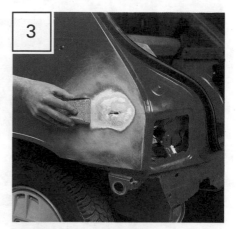

3

Next, remove all paint from the damaged area by rubbing with coarse abrasive paper or using a power drill fitted with a wire brush or abrasive pad. 'Feather' the edge of the boundary with good paintwork using a finer grade of abrasive paper.

4

Where there are holes or other damage, the sheet metal should be cut away before proceeding further. The damaged area and any signs of rust should be treated with Turtle Wax Hi-Tech Rust Eater, which will also inhibit further rust formation.

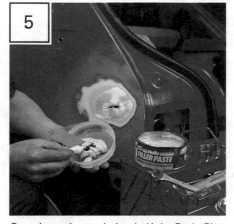

5

For a large dent or hole mix Holts Body Plus Resin and Hardener according to the manufacturer's instructions and apply around the edge of the repair. Press Glass Fibre Matting over the repair area and leave for 20-30 minutes to harden. Then ...

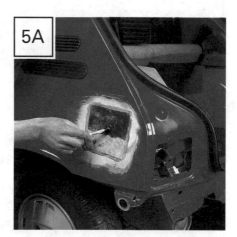

5A

... brush more Holts Body Plus Resin and Hardener onto the matting and leave to harden. Repeat the sequence with two or three layers of matting, checking that the final layer is lower than the surrounding area. Apply Holts Body Plus Filler Paste as shown in Step 5B.

5B

For a medium dent, mix Holts Body Plus Filler Paste and Hardener according to the manufacturer's instructions and apply it with a flexible applicator. Apply thin layers of filler at 20-minute intervals, until the filler surface is slightly proud of the surrounding bodywork.

5C

For small dents and scratches use Holts No Mix Filler Paste straight from the tube. Apply it according to the instructions in thin layers, using the spatula provided. It will harden in minutes if applied outdoors and may then be used as its own knifing putty.

6

Use a plane or file for initial shaping. Then, using progressively finer grades of wet-and-dry paper, wrapped round a sanding block, and copious amounts of clean water, rub down the filler until glass smooth. 'Feather' the edges of adjoining paintwork.

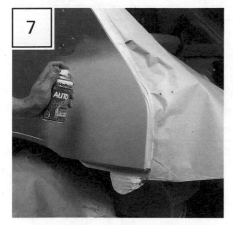

7 Protect adjoining areas before spraying the whole repair area and at least one inch of the surrounding sound paintwork with Holts Dupli-Color primer.

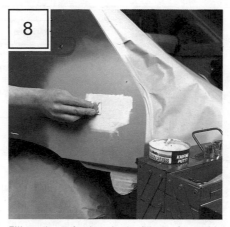

8 Fill any imperfections in the filler surface with a small amount of Holts Body Plus Knifing Putty. Using plenty of clean water, rub down the surface with a fine grade wet-and-dry paper – 400 grade is recommended – until it is really smooth.

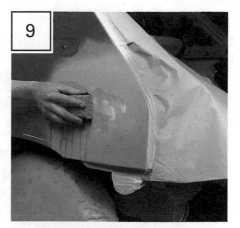

9 Carefully fill any remaining imperfections with knifing putty before applying the last coat of primer. Then rub down the surface with Holts Body Plus Rubbing Compound to ensure a really smooth surface.

10 Protect surrounding areas from overspray before applying the topcoat in several thin layers. Agitate Holts Dupli-Color aerosol thoroughly. Start at the repair centre, spraying outwards with a side-to-side motion.

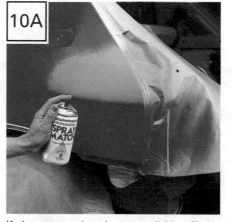

10A If the exact colour is not available off the shelf, local Holts Professional Spraymatch Centres will custom fill an aerosol to match perfectly.

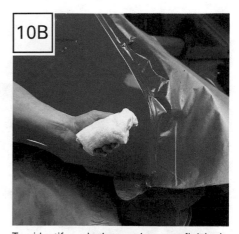

10B To identify whether a lacquer finish is required, rub a painted unrepaired part of the body with wax and a clean cloth.

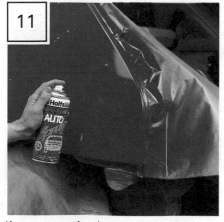

11 If *no* traces of paint appear on the cloth, spray Holts Dupli-Color clear lacquer over the repaired area to achieve the correct gloss level.

12 The paint will take about two weeks to harden fully. After this time it can be 'cut' with a mild cutting compound such as Turtle Wax Minute Cut prior to polishing with a final coating of Turtle Wax Extra.

14 When carrying out bodywork repairs, remember that the quality of the finished job is proportional to the time and effort expended.

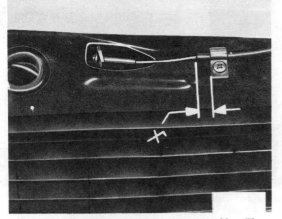

Fig. 12.6 Cable/clip setting on top rail (Sec 7)

X = 10.0 mm (0.394 in)

8 Radiator grille – removal and refitting

1   The grille is held in place at its upper edge by clips and the bottom is secured by pegs engaging in sockets.
2   Disconnect the grille clips and lift the grille up and away from the front of the vehicle (photo).

9 Front bumper – removal and refitting

1   The bumpers are constructed of impact-resistant plastic and are mounted on brackets which are bolted to the side members of the body.
2   Removal is simply a matter of unbolting the brackets from both sides.
3   When refitting, check that the bumper is perfectly level before finally tightening the bolts.

10 Rear bumper – removal and refitting

1   The rear bumper is bolted directly to the rear body panel by means of brackets (photos).
2   Access to the mounting nuts is obtained from within the luggage area spare wheel compartment (photos).
3   Note the bumper end retaining clip (photo).

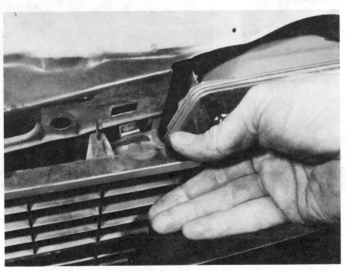

8.2 Unclipping radiator grille

Fig. 12.7 Radiator grille securing points in body (arrowed) (Sec 8)

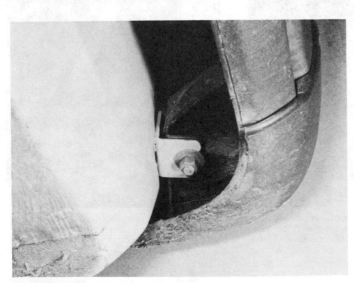

10.1A Rear bumper outboard mounting bracket

10.1B Rear bumper inboard mounting bracket

10.2A Releasing rear bumper bracket bolt

10.2B Withdrawing the rear bumper

10.3 Rear bumper end fixing clip

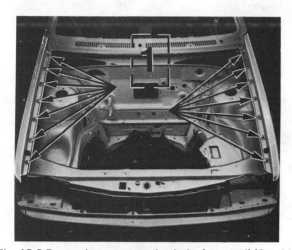

Fig. 12.8 Front wing top mounting bolts (arrowed) (Sec 11)

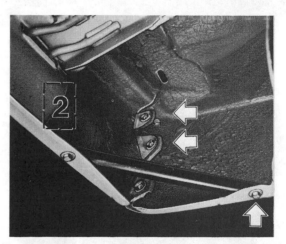

Fig. 12.9 Front wing-to-spoiler bolts (arrowed) (Sec 11)

11 Front wing – removal and refitting

1   Remove the front bumper as described in Section 9.
2   Open the bonnet and unscrew the seven bolts from the top edge of the wing.
3   Remove the four bolts which hold the front of the wing to the spoiler.
4   Remove the four bolts which hold the wing to the base of the windscreen pillar. Two of these bolts are located on the outside of the pillar and two on the inside.
5   Remove the wing and pull off the old flange sealing tape.
6   Refit by reversing the removal operations, and use a new piece of flange sealing tape.
7   The wing (supplied in primer) should now be sprayed to match the colour of the rest of the bodywork and the underside of the wing protected by the application of sealing compound.

12 Door trim panel – removal and refitting

1   Using a length of wire with a hook at its end, insert it behind the winder handle bezel and extract the retaining clip, then remove the handle (photo).
2   Extract the screws and remove the armrest (photo).
3   Gently prise off the trim plate from around the remote control handle (photo).
4   Unscrew and remove the lock plunger from the top edge of the trim panel.
5   Insert a wide flat blade between the trim panel and the door at its bottom edge and release the panel retaining clips. Work your way around the panel, releasing all the clips using either the blade or the fingers. If the blade is used, slide it up against each clip in turn as in this position the clip is less likely to tear out of the trim panel.

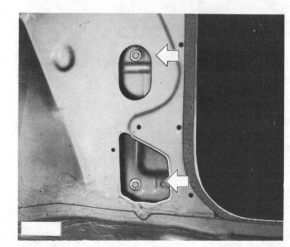

Fig. 12.10 Front wing rear mounting bolts (arrowed) (Sec 11)

6   Remove the panel and then carefully peel away the waterproof sheet (photo). Remove the regulator coil spring (photo).
7   Refitting is a reversal of removal but to install the window winder handle, push the clip fully home in its groove in the handle boss, locate the handle on its spindle and then strike it into position on the splines with the hand (photo).

13 Front door glass – removal and refitting

1   Remove the trim panel as described in the preceding Section. Peel off the waterproof sheet.

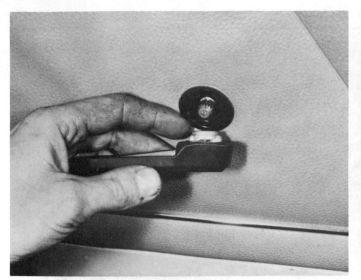

12.1 Removing window regulator handle

12.2 Extracting armrest screw

12.3 Lock remote control handle escutcheon plate

12.6A Removing door trim panel

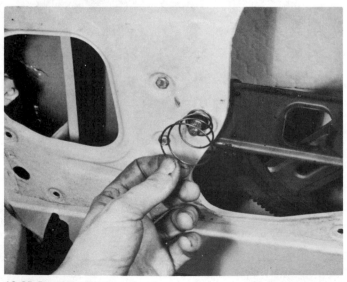

12.6B Regulator handle coil spring

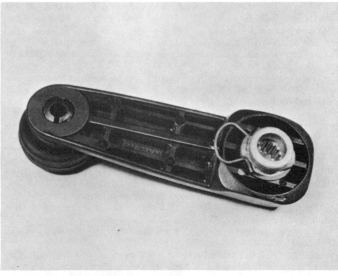

12.7 Clip for window regulator handle.

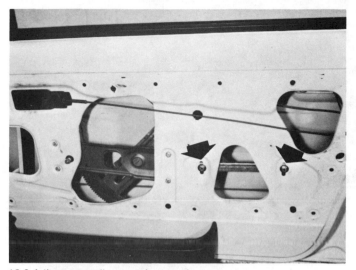

13.2 Adjustment rail screws (arrowed)

Fig. 12.11 Removing door weatherstrip (Sec 13)

2   Extract the screws and remove the adjustment rail from the regulator scissors (photo).
3   Using a wooden or plastic lever, prise off the outer weatherstrip.
4   Withdraw the glass from the door towards the outside of the vehicle, swivelling the glass as shown in Fig. 12.12, which will cause the scissors rollers to slip out of the glass bottom channel.
5   Refit by reversing the removal operations. Adjust the closure by moving the adjustment rail within the limits of its mounting screw slots.

14   Front door window regulator – removal and refitting

1   Remove the door trim panel as previously described and peel off the waterproof sheet.
2   Temporarily fit the regulator handle and wind the glass up about halfway. Wedge the glass to prevent it dropping once the regulator mechanism is removed.
3   Extract the regulator screws and bolts, slide the scissors rollers out of the glass channel and then withdraw the regulator mechanism through the aperture in the door (photos).
4   Refit by reversing the removal operations, and apply grease to the sliding surfaces.
5   The glass can be adjusted for correct closure by moving the position of the adjustment rail within the limits of its mounting screw slots.

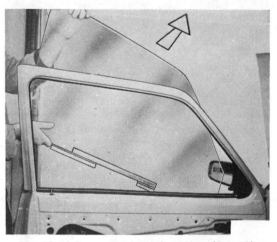

Fig. 12.12 Removing front door glass (Sec 13)

Fig. 12.13 Front door glass wedged (Sec 14)

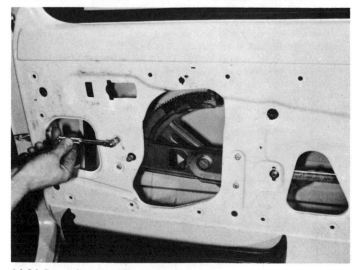

14.3A Removing a regulator screw

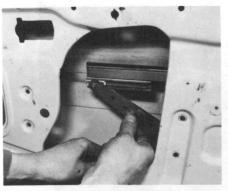

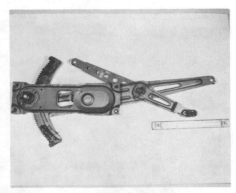

14.3B Removing scissors roller from glass channel

14.3C Withdrawing the regulator mechanism

14.3D Window regulator mechanism withdrawn

Fig. 12.14 Window guide rail fixing screws (1, 2 and 3) (Sec 15)

A   Guide rail

Fig. 12.15 Removing window guide rail (Sec 15)

15 Rear door glass and regulator – removal and refitting

1   Remove the door trim panel as previously described. Peel away the waterproof sheet.
2   Extract the screws and remove the adjustment rail from the regulator scissors.
3   Using a wooden or plastic lever, prise off the outer weatherstrip.
4   Withdraw the glass from the door towards the outside of the vehicle, swivelling the glass to release the scissors rollers from the glass channel.
5   Remove all the bolts and screws and withdraw the window regulator mechanism through the aperture in the door.
6   Remove the window guide rail. To do this extract the fixing screws from the points indicated (Fig. 12.14).
7   Remove the fixed glass from the window frame, also the weatherseals.
8   Refitting is a reversal of removal, but after screwing in the adjustment screw for the window rear guide rail, set the inclination of the window glass by turning the screw and locknut.

Fig. 12.16 Removing rear door glass (Sec 15)

16 Front door lock and exterior handle – removal and refitting

1   Remove the door interior trim panel as described in Section 12 and peel away the waterproof sheet.
2   Temporarily refit the regulator handle and wind the window fully up.
3   Remove the lower section of the glass guide rail at the rear end of the door. To do this, extract the fixing screw and pull the seal out of the rail. According to model the rail fixing screw may be located on the door panel or on the door edge.

4   Disconnect the remote control linkage by sliding the lever assembly towards the front of the vehicle and pulling it out of its hole in the panel (photo).
5   Disconnect the link rods from the lock.
6   Extract the lock securing screws and withdraw the lock from the door aperture.
7   The exterior handle is held by two nuts and can be removed after they are unscrewed.
8   Refitting is a reversal of removal.

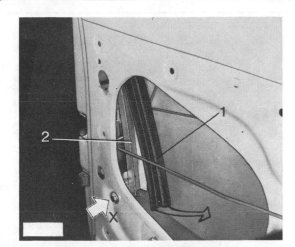

Fig. 12.17 Pulling seal out of glass guide rail (Sec 16)

1   Seal
2   Rail
X   Rail fixing screw

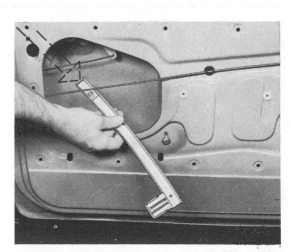

Fig. 12.18 Removing lower section of glass guide rail (Sec 16)

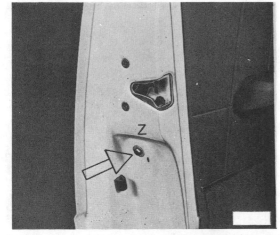

Fig. 12.19 Guide rail fixing screw Z (alternative) (Sec 16)

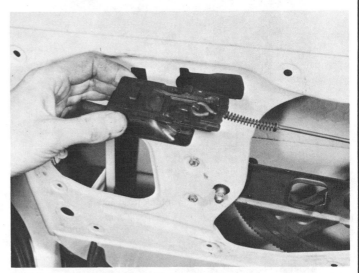

16.4 Removing remote control lever assembly

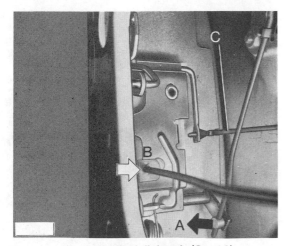

Fig. 12.20 Lock link rods (Sec 16)

A   Outside door handle rod
B   Inside remote control rod
C   Lock cylinder rod

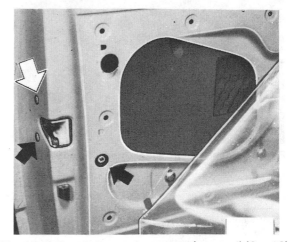

Fig. 12.21 Door lock securing screws (arrowed) (Sec 16)

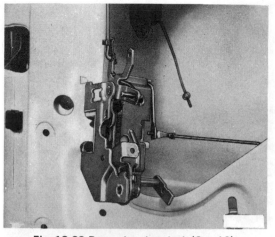

Fig. 12.22 Removing door lock (Sec 16)

Fig. 12.23 Exterior handle mounting nuts (2) (Sec 16)

1　Link rod

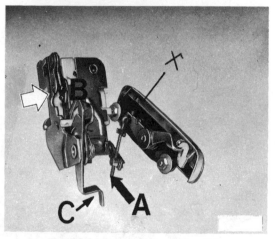

Fig. 12.24 Rear door lock (Sec 17)

A　Exterior handle rod　　*C　Child safety lock*
B　Plunger link　　*X　Exterior handle*

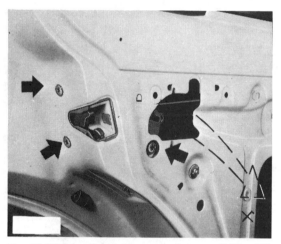

Fig. 12.25 Rear door lock screws (arrowed) (Sec 17)

X　Direction of removal

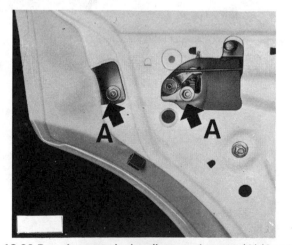

Fig. 12.26 Rear door exterior handle mounting nuts (A) (Sec 17)

17　Rear door lock and exterior handle – removal and refitting

1　The operations are similar to those described for the front door in the preceding Section except that once released, the lock must be swivelled around the rear guide rail of the window before it can be removed.

2　Once the lock is removed, the exterior handle can be withdrawn after having unscrewed the mounting stud nuts.

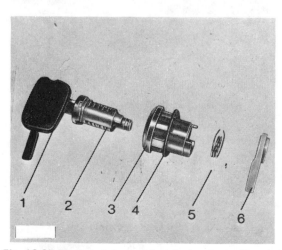

Fig. 12.27 Exploded view of door lock cylinder (Sec 18)

1　Key　　　　　*4　Seal*
2　Cylinder　　*5　Spring*
3　Housing　　*6　Arm*

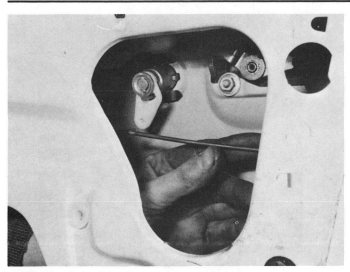

18.2 Lock cylinder link rod

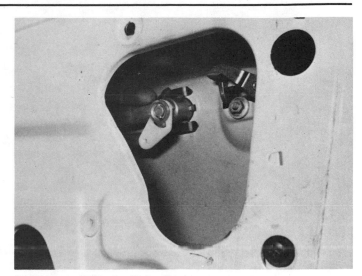

18.3A Removing lock cylinder clip

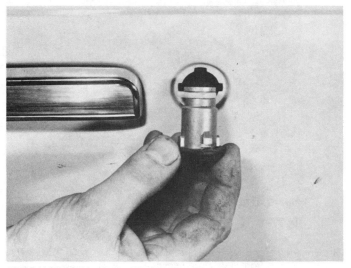

18.3B Withdrawing lock cylinder

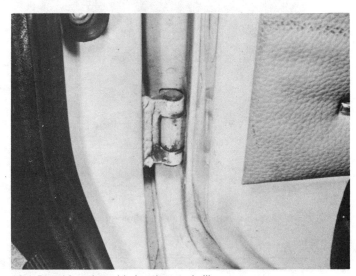

19.1 Door hinge is welded to door and pillar

18 Front door lock cylinder – removal and refitting

1   Remove the door interior trim panel and waterproof sheet.
2   Disconnect the link rod from the arm of the lock cylinder (photo).
3   Pull out the lock securing clip and withdraw the cylinder from the door (photos).
4   If the arm is removed from the lock and the ignition key inserted, the cylinder can be withdrawn from the housing.
5   Refitting is a reversal of removal.

19 Doors – removal and refitting

1   The door hinges are welded onto the door frame and the body pillar so that there is no provision for adjustment or alignment, although closure can be adjusted by moving the position of the striker (photo).
2   To remove a door, open it fully and support it under its lower edge on blocks covered with pads of rag.
3   Disconnect the door check and drive out the hinge pins. Remove the door.
4   If the door can be moved up and down on its hinge due to wear in the pivot pins or holes, it may be possible to drill out the holes and fit slightly oversize pins.

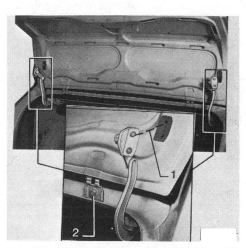

Fig. 12.28 Boot lid hinges (1 and 2) (Sec 20)

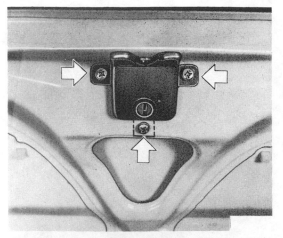

Fig. 12.29 Boot lid lock screws (arrowed) (Sec 21)

Fig. 12.30 Removing boot lock (Sec 21)

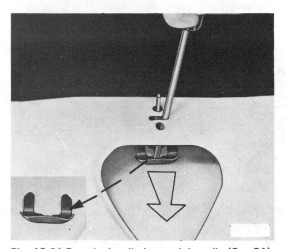

Fig. 12.31 Boot lock cylinder retaining clip (Sec 21)

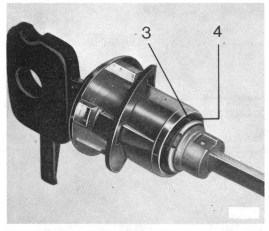

Fig. 12.32 Boot lock cylinder components (Sec 21)

3   Wave washer   4   Circlip

20 Boot lid – removal and refitting

1   Open the lid and mark the position of the hinges on the underside of the boot lid, also the position of the smaller hinges on the body top panel.
2   With the help of an assistant, support the lid and unbolt and remove it.
3   Refit by reversing the removal operations, but use new sealing washers under the smaller hinge bolts to prevent the entry of water from the drain channel.

21 Boot lid lock – removal and refitting

1   Open the lid and extract the three screws which hold the lock to the underside of the boot lid.
2   Withdraw the lock from the lid aperture.
3   The lock cylinder can be withdrawn once the spring retaining clip is extracted.
4   The cylinder can be removed from the housing if the circlip is first extracted and the key fully inserted.
5   Refitting is a reversal of removal.

22 Boot lid torsion rods – removal and refitting

1   These counterbalance spring rods are under considerable tension and should be removed with care.
2   Make up a tool which will engage with the long hooked ends of the rod.

3   Engage the tool with the first hooked end and twist it to release the torsion rod from the two notches in the anchor bracket.
4   Slowly release the rod and tool until there is no longer any tension and then remove the tool.
5   Release the opposite torsion rod in a similar way. Support the boot lid to prevent it from dropping.
6   Refitting is the reversal of removal.

23 Tailgate – removal and refitting

1   Open the tailgate fully and support it on a length of wood. Disconnect the heated rear window leads and washer/wiper leads and tubes (as applicable).
2   Disconnect the gas-filled struts at the tailgate. Do this by extracting the circlip and pulling the socket off the ball-stud (Estate) or prising out the plastic wedge (Hatchback) (photos).
3   With the help of an assistant, support the tailgate and extract the small circlips from the hinge pins (photo).
4   Tap the hinge pins out and lift the tailgate away.
5   Refit by reversing the removal operations. Check that an even gap exists all round, otherwise adjust the tailgate by moving it within the limits of its elongated bolt holes.
6   Reconnect the disconnected leads and washer tubes.

24 Tailgate lock (Hatchback) – removal and refitting

This is removed and refitted in a very similar way to that described for the boot lid in Section 21.

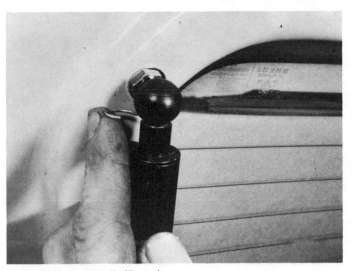

23.2A Tailgate strut clip (Estate)

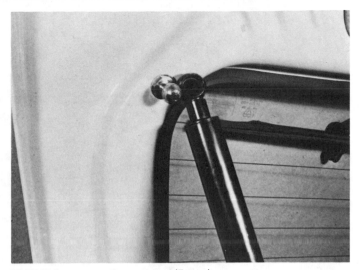

23.2B Tailgate strut disconnected (Estate)

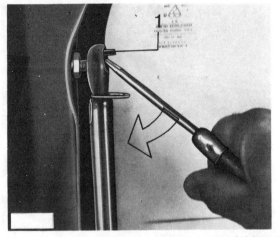

Fig. 12.33 Removing tailgate strut plastic wedge (1) (Sec 23)

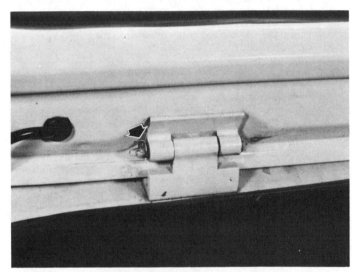

23.3 Tailgate hinge, circlip arrowed

25 Tailgate lock cylinder (Hatchback) removal and refitting

1   Remove the lock as described in Section 21.
2   If a trim panel is fitted to the inside of the tailgate, remove it as described for the door trim panel in Section 12.
3   Prise out the cylinder retaining clip and withdraw it.
4   The cylinder can be withdrawn from the housing if the circlip is first extracted and the ignition key inserted.
5   Refitting is a reversal of removal.

26 Tailgate lock (Estate) – removal and refitting

1   Open the tailgate and remove the trim panel.
2   Extract the lock fixing screws, disconnect the link rod and remove the lock (photo).
3   Refitting is a reversal of removal.

27 Tailgate handle and lock cylinder (Estate) – removal and refitting

1   Open the tailgate fully and remove the interior trim panel.
2   Disconnect the link rod and unscrew the handle mounting nuts (photo).

26.2 Tailgate lock fixing screws

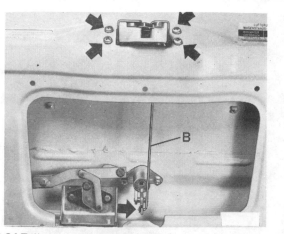

Fig. 12.34 Tailgate handle fixing screws (arrowed) and link rod (B)
(Sec 27)

27.2 Tailgate handle link rod and lock cylinder (Estate)

3   The lock cylinder can be withdrawn from the handle assembly if
the circlip is first extracted.
4   Refitting is a reversal of removal and dismantling. Make sure that
the sealing gasket is in good order, otherwise renew it.

28 Windscreen glass – removal and refitting

1   If the windscreen is to be removed and/or replaced for any reason,
it is a job which is better left to an auto glass replacement specialist.
They will do the job in half the time and most important, ensure that
it is correctly fitted with no leakages around the surround rubber every
time it rains! However if you wish to do it yourself proceed as follows.
2   Where a windscreen is to be replaced due to shattering, the facia
air vents should be covered before attempting removal. Adhesive
sheeting is useful to stick to the outside of the glass to enable large
areas of crystalised glass to be removed.
3   Where the screen is to be removed intact or is of laminated type,
then an assistant will be required. First release the rubber surround
from the bodywork by running a blunt, small screwdriver around and
under the rubber weatherstrip both inside and outside the car. This
operation will break the adhesive of the sealer originally used. Take
care not to damage the paintwork or catch the rubber surround with
the screwdriver. Remove the windscreen wiper arms and interior
mirror and place a protective cover on the bonnet. Salvage your tax
disc.
4   Have your assistant push the inner lip of the rubber surround off
the flange of the windscreen body aperture. Once the rubber surround
starts to peel off the flange, the screen may be forced gently outwards
by careful hand pressure. The second person should support and
remove the screen complete with rubber surround and metal beading
as it comes out.
5   Remove the bright moulding from the rubber surround.
6   Fit a new rubber weatherseal to the glass and ensure that all old
sealant is removed from the body flange. Scrape it away and then
clean it off with a fuel-soaked cloth.
7   Apply a bead of sealant to the body flange all round the
windscreen aperture.
8   Cut a piece of strong cord greater in length than the periphery of
the glass and insert it into the body flange locating the channel of the
rubber surround.
9   Offer the windscreen to the body aperture and pass the ends of
the cord, previously fitted and located at bottom centre, into the
vehicle interior.
10 Press the windscreen into place, at the same time have an
assistant pull the cords to engage the lip of the rubber channel over the
body flange.
11 Remove any excess sealant with a paraffin-soaked rag.
12 Refit the bright moulding to the rubber surround. A special tool
will facilitate this operation but take care not to tear the lips of the
rubber.
13 Refit the windscreen wipers, the interior mirror and the tax disc.

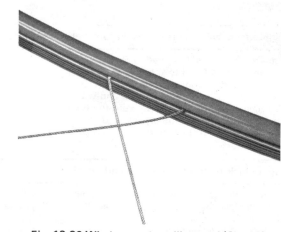

Fig. 12.35 Applying sealant to windscreen body flange (Sec 28)

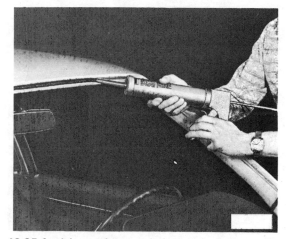

Fig. 12.36 Windscreen installing cord (Sec 28)

29 Rear window glass – removal and refitting

The operations are very similar to those described in the preceding
Section, but remove the wiper arm (if applicable) and disconnect the
heated element electrical leads before commencing work.

30 Centre console – removal and refitting

1   Remove the plastic plugs from the bottom of the tidy tray (photo).
2   Unscrew and remove the fixing screws (photo).
3   The console can now be lifted by sliding the bellows up the gearchange lever.
4   If the centre console must be removed completely, then the gear lever knob will first have to be unscrewed.
5   Refitting is a reversal of removal.

31 Body side protective trim – removal and refitting

1   The side trim is held in place by spring clips which are riveted to the body panel.
2   The trim strip can be removed by prising outwards and downwards, but take care not to damage the paintwork.
3   New clips can be fitted using pop rivets. Push the clips forward in their slots until they contact the stop. Seal the rivet head with suitable compound.

32 Sliding roof panel – removal and refitting

1   Move the control handle to position A (Fig. 12.39). Slide back the roof.

30.1 Removing centre console screw cap

30.2 Removing centre console screw

Fig. 12.37 Body side trim clips (Sec 31)

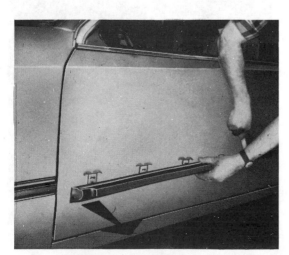

Fig. 12.38 Removing body side trim (Sec 31)

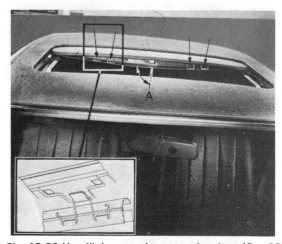

Fig. 12.39 Headlining attachment and springs (Sec 32)
A   Control handle position

2   Remove the recessed handle escutcheon plate.
3   Release the headlining at the retaining springs and fold down the edge.
4   Unscrew the front and rear guide plates from the sliding panel.
5   Pull the headlining aside and fold it upwards at the front edge.
6   Pull the sliding panel forward until the front edges of the slides B are at the same height as the rounded edge of the projection C (Fig. 12.41).
7   Swivel the panel and remove it from the vehicle.
8   To refit, first grease the slide rails.
9   Offer the panel to the roof aperture, making sure that the support levers D point outwards (Fig. 12.43).
10   Attach the front and rear retaining plates, making sure that the carrier arms for the lateral control shafts are towards each other.
11   The remainder of refitting is the reverse of the removal procedure.

33 Sliding roof panel lining – removal and refitting

1   Remove the panel from the vehicle as described in the preceding Section.
2   Detach the retaining springs at the front edge, prising them out with a screwdriver.
3   Using a screwdriver, bend open the retaining tabs on the rear slide rail.
4   Extract the wire staples from the lining and pull out the front slide rail and the wire suport.
5   Refitting the rear lining is a reversal of removal, but make sure that the cut-outs point towards the front as shown (Fig. 12.48) when installing the front slide rail.

34 Sliding roof control gear – removal and refitting

1   Remove the sliding panel and the lining as previously described.
2   Extract the springs and the shaft support levers.
3   Bend open the hinge pin retaining tabs and tap the pins out of the hinge bearings.

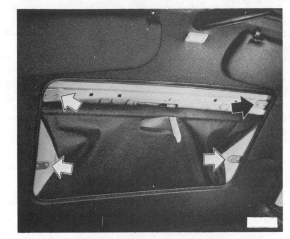

Fig. 12.40 Sliding roof guide plates (Sec 32)

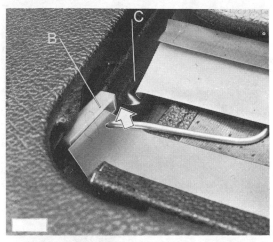

Fig. 12.41 Sunroof slide (B) and projection (C) (Sec 32)

Fig. 12.42 Removing the sliding roof panel (Sec 32)

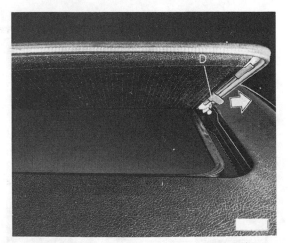

Fig. 12.43 Refitting the roof panel (Sec 32)

D   Support levers

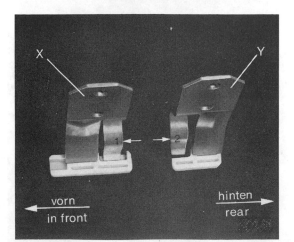

Fig. 12.44 Sliding roof retaining plates (X and Y) (Sec 32)

1   Carrier arm   2   Carrier arm

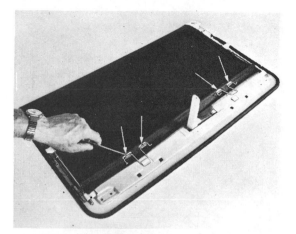

Fig. 12.45 Detaching sliding panel front retaining springs (Sec 33)

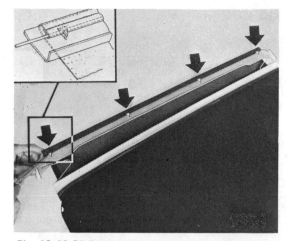

Fig. 12.46 Sliding panel rear slide tail tabs (Sec 33)

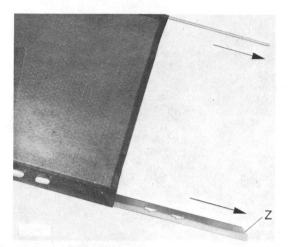

Fig. 12.47 Withdrawing front slide rail (Z) and support wire (Sec 33)

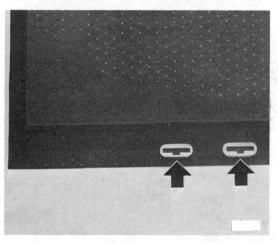

Fig. 12.48 Front slide rail cut-outs (Sec 33)

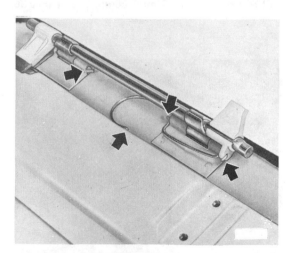

Fig. 12.49 Sliding roof springs and shaft support levers (Sec 34)

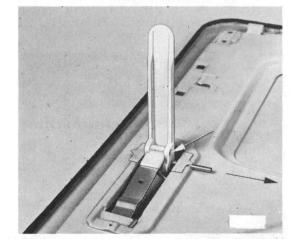

Fig. 12.50 Removing sliding roof control handle pivot pin (Sec 34)

4   Drive out the control handle pivot pins.
5   Remove both the push bar control shafts.
6   Extract the control handle equaliser spring.
7   Pull out the left-hand and right-hand push bars from the panel shaft. As they are pulled out, the push bar and control handle can be withdrawn.
8   Refitting is a reversal of removal.

35 Safety belts – general

1   Periodically inspect the safety belts for fraying or other damage. If evident, renew the belt.
2   Cleaning of the belt fabric should be done with a damp cloth and a little detergent, nothing else.
3   Never alter the original belt anchorage and if the belts are ever removed, always take careful note of the sequence of mounting components. If the washers or collars are incorrectly positioned, the belt will not swivel as it has been designed to do.

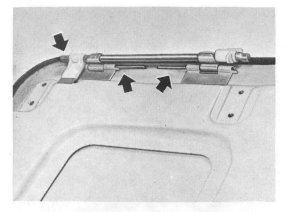

Fig. 12.51 Sliding roof push bar control shaft (Sec 34)

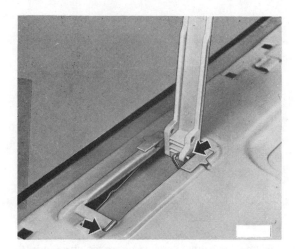

Fig. 12.52 Sliding roof control handle equaliser spring (Sec 34)

Fig. 12.53 Removing sliding roof control handle (Sec 34)

Fig. 12.54 Exterior mirror remote control handle (Sec 36)

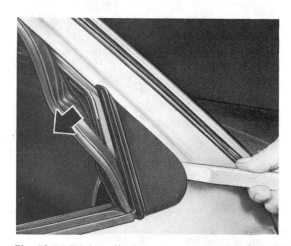

Fig. 12.55 Prising off mirror screw cover plate (Sec 36)

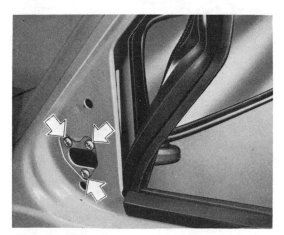

Fig. 12.56 Exterior mirror screws (Sec 36)

36 Exterior mirror – removal and refitting

1   The mirror is mounted at the lower front corner of the front door window aperture.

2   The mirror may be remotely controlled from the interior by a knob pushed onto a control spindle.

3   The mirror mounting screws are covered by a plastic plate which can be removed by levering it off.

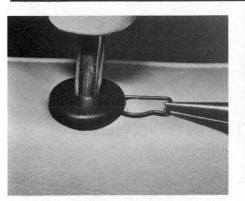

37.1 Extracting headrest spring clip

38.1 Front seat frame clamp

38.2 Front seat plastic sliding blocks

39.1 Rear seat cushion fixings

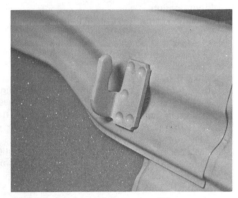

39.3 Rear seat back lower fixings

39.4 Rear seat back upper hooks

37 Headrests — adjustment

The headrests on the front seats are adjustable for height by extracting the spring clips from both headrest pillars, which are grooved to receive them (photo).

38 Front seats — removal and refitting

1   Unbolt the two front clamps (photo).
2   Slide the seat to the rear until the plastic blocks disengage from the floor rails (photo).

3   Refitting is a reversal of removal.

39 Rear seat — removal and refitting

1   Extract the screws from the lower edge at each side of the seat cushion. Remove the plastic retainer pieces (photo).
2   Remove the seat cushion.
3   Bend the two tongues straight at the lower outer ends of the seat back (photo).
4   Pull the bottom edge of the seatback forward and then lift it off the upper retaining hooks (photo).
5   Refitting is a reversal of removal.

Chapter 13 Supplement:
Revisions and information on later models

Contents

1 Introduction

This supplement contains information which is additional to, or a revision of, material in the first twelve Chapters. Although most of the material relates to additions to the range of engines and transmissions available, some items (eg the camshaft lubrication modification) apply retrospectively to the appropriate models from the start of production.
The Sections in the Supplement follow the same order as the Chapters to which they relate. The Specifications are all grouped together for convenience, but they follow Chapter order.
It is recommended that before any particular operation is undertaken, reference be made to the appropriate Section(s) of the Supplement. In this way any changes to procedure or components can be noted before referring to the main Chapters.
Not all engines and transmissions described here are necessarily available in the UK.

2 Specifications

The specifications below are supplementary to, or revisions of, those at the beginning of the preceding Chapters

OHC engine (1.6 and 1.8)

General

	16S	18E
Bore (nominal size)	80.0 mm (3.15 in)	84.8 mm (3.34 in)
Stroke	79.5 mm (3.13 in)	79.5 mm (3.13 in)
Displacement	1598 cc (97.5 cu in)	1796 cc (109.6 cu in)
Maximum power (DIN)	66 kW @ 5800 rpm	85 kW @ 5800 rpm
Maximum torque (DIN)	126 Nm @ 3800 to 4200 rpm	151 Nm @ 4800 rpm
Compression ratio	9.2 : 1	9.5 : 1

Crankshaft

Endfloat	0.07 to 0.30 mm (0.0028 to 0.0118 in)
Main bearing running clearance	0.015 to 0.040 mm (0.0006 to 0.0016 in)

Camshaft

Endfloat	0.04 to 0.14 mm (0.0016 to 0.0055 in)
Cam lift:	
16S	6.12 mm (0.2409 in)
18E	6.95 mm (0.2736 in)

Pistons

Clearance in bore	0.02 to 0.04 mm (0.0008 to 0.0016 in)

Valves and guides

Valve head diameter:	
Exhaust (16S)	32 mm (1.26 in)
Exhaust (18E) and inlet (16S)	35 mm (1.38 in)
Inlet (18E)	41 mm (1.61 in)
Valve stem diameter (nominal)	8 mm (0.315 in)
Valve clearance in guide:	
Inlet	0.015 to 0.042 mm (0.0006 to 0.0017 in)
Exhaust	0.03 to 0.06 mm (0.0012 to 0.0024 in)
Valve guide installed height	80.95 to 81.85 mm (3.187 to 3.222 in)

Lubrication system

Oil pump clearance (outer gear to housing)	0.03 to 0.10 mm (0.0012 to 0.0039 in)
Oil filter	Champion G102

Torque wrench settings

As for the 1.3 engine except for the following:

	Nm	lbf ft
Cylinder head bolts:		
Stage 1 (cold)	25	18
Stage 2 (cold)	Through 60°	Through 60°
Stage 3 (cold)	Through 60°	Through 60°
Stage 4 (cold)	Through 60°	Through 60°
Stage 5 (hot)	Through 30° to 50°	Through 30° to 50°
Big-end cap bolts	50	36
Crankshaft pulley/damper bolt	60	44
Coolant pump bolts	25	18
Intake manifold nuts	22	16
Thermostat housing bolts	15	11

Cooling system (1.6 and 1.8)

Coolant capacity

16S (manual transmission)	7.8 litres (13.7 pints)
16S (automatic transmission)	7.6 litres (13.4 pints)
18E	7.6 litres (13.4 pints)

Torque wrench settings

	Nm	lbf ft
Coolant pump bolts	25	18
Thermostat housing bolts	15	11
Temperature sender	8	6

Fuel and exhaust systems

General

Fuel octane requirement (1.6, 1.8)	98 RON (UK 4-star)
Idle speed (later models):	
1.3, automatic choke, automatic transmission	900 to 950 rpm
1.3, manual choke, manual transmission	850 to 900 rpm
1.3, manual choke, automatic transmission	800 to 850 rpm
1.6, manual transmission	900 to 900 rpm
1.6, automatic transmission	800 to 850 rpm
1.8 (fuel injection)	900 to 950 rpm

Fast idle speed (later models):
    1.3, automatic transmission .... 2600 ± 50 rpm
    1.3, manual choke, manual transmission .... 2500 ± 50 rpm
    1.6, automatic transmission .... 2300 ± 50 rpm
    1.6, manual transmission .... 2100 ± 50 rpm
Exhaust gas, CO level at idle:
    1.3 and 1.6 .... 1.0 to 1.5%
    1.8 (fuel injection) .... Not exceeding 0.5%

Air cleaner element
1598 cc OHC engines .... Champion W103
1796 cc injection (1983-on) .... Champion U511

Varajet II carburettor – 1.3 engine

Carburettor code number:	Manual transmission	Automatic transmission
Up to August 1981	96 010 017	–
August 1981 to August 1982	96 002 017	96 002 018
August 1982 on	96 002 117	96 002 118

Choke operation (August 1982 on) .... Manual
Automatic choke setting (earlier models) .... See text
Float level (August 1981 on) .... 4.5 to 6.5 mm (0.177 to 0.256 in)
Main jet (Stage I, August 1981 on) .... 2.01 mm (marked 201)
Jet needle (Stage I, August 1981 on) .... 1.51 mm (marked 151)
Jet needle (Stage II, August 1981 on) .... 2.20 mm (marked G)
Idle jet (August 1981 on) .... 0.575 mm

Varajet II carburettor – 1.6 engine
Code number:
    Manual transmission 96 002 101
    Automatic transmission 96 002 102
Idle jet .... 0.65 mm
Main jet (Stage I) .... 2.04 mm (marked 204)
Jet needle (Stage I) .... 1.51 mm (marked 151)
Main jet (Stage II) .... 3.20 mm
Jet needle (Stage II) .... 2.20 mm (marked G)
Choke valve gap .... 2.8 to 3.4 mm (0.110 to 0.134 in)
Float level .... 4.5 to 6.5 mm (0.177 to 0.256 in)
Automatic choke setting .... See text

Fuel injection system – 1.8 engine
System type .... Bosch LE Jetronic
Fuel pressure .... 2.5 bar (36 lbf/in²)
Fuel filter .... Champion L201

Torque wrench settings

	Nm	lbf ft
Fuel pump bolts (1.6 engine)	15	11
Carburettor securing nuts (1.6 engine)	15	11
Intake manifold nuts (1.6 and 1.8 engines)	22	16
Fuel injectors	32	24
Airflow meter bolts	10	7

Ignition system
System type
1.3 from mid-1982, all 1.6 and 1.8 .... Electronic (breakerless). Bosch JHFU 4 or equivalent

HT leads
1196 cc and 1297 cc male distributor cap (1982-on) .... Champion CLS 11, boxed set
1598 cc .... Champion CLS 8, boxed set
1796 cc injection .... Champion CLS 4, boxed set

Spark plugs
Type (1.6 and 1.8) .... Champion RN7YCC or RN7YC
Electrode gap:
    RN7YCC .... 0.8 mm (0.032 in)
    RN7YC .... 0.7 mm (0.030 in)

Ignition timing*
12S (ohv) engine from September 1982 .... 10° BTDC
1.6 and 1.8 .... 10° BTDC
* Static or at idle speed, vacuum pipe disconnected

Ignition coil (breakerless system)
Primary (LT) resistance .... 0.4 ohms approx
Secondary (HT) resistance .... 7000 ohms approx

Clutch (1.6 and 1.8)
Friction disc (driven plate)
Diameter:
    1.6 .... 203 mm (8 in)

1.8 .... 216 mm (8.5 in)
Allowable lateral run-out .... 0.15 mm (0.006 in)

Torque wrench setting	Nm	lbf ft
Transmission cover sealing plug (5-speed)	30	22

Manual transmission

Transmission type
12S and 13S engines .... F10/4 (4-speed) or F10/5 (5-speed)
16S engine .... F16/4 (4-speed) or F16/5 (5-speed)
18E engine F16/5 (5-speed)

Gear ratios (:1)

	F10/4 & 10/5	F16/4	F16/5	F16/5 (sport)
1st	3.55	3.55	3.42	3.42
2nd	1.96	2.16	1.95	2.16
3rd	1.30	1.37	1.28	1.48
4th	0.89	0.97	0.89	1.12
5th (when applicable)	0.71	–	0.71	0.89
Reverse	3.18	3.33	3.33	3.33

Final drive ratio
F10/4 .... 3.94 or 4.18 : 1
F10/5 .... 4.18 : 1
F16/4 .... 3.74 or 3.94 : 1
F16/5 .... 3.74 or 3.94 : 1

Oil capacity
F10/5 .... 1.7 litres (3 pints) approx
F16/4 .... 2.0 litres (3.5 pints) approx
F16/5 .... 2.1 litres (3.7 pints) approx

Oil type/specification
4-speed .... Gear oil, viscosity SAE 80, to API GL3 or GL4 (Duckhams Hypoid 80)
5-speed (not GTE) .... Gear oil, viscosity SAE 80 to API GL3 or GL4 (Duckhams Hypoid 75W/90S)
5-speed (GTE) .... Special transmission oil, GM part No 90 188 629 (Duckhams Hypoid 75W/90S)

Torque wrench settings
As given in Chapter 6, except for the following:

	Nm	lbf ft
Vibration damper on selector housing cover (1.8 only)	20	15
End cover sealing plug (5-speed)	30	22
5th gear selector fork pivot socket screws	22	16
5th gear pawl socket screws	9	7
Differential bearing flange to transmission casing (F16)	25	18

Automatic transmission

General
Maker's designation .... 125 THM
Transmission type .... Torque converter with chain drive to geartrains. Three forward gears and one reverse

Gear ratios
1st .... 2.84 : 1
2nd .... 1.60 : 1
3rd .... 1.00 : 1
Reverse .... 2.07 : 1
Final drive .... 3.33 or 3.74 : 1

Shift speeds (mph)*

	Light throttle	Kickdown
1st to 2nd	10 to 13	33 to 40
2nd to 3rd	18 to 21	63 to 70
3rd to 2nd	15 to 18	54 to 62
2nd to 1st	8 to 12	25 to 33

* Speeds quoted are for 16S engine; 13S engine speeds are slightly lower

Transmission fluid
Type .... Dexron II type ATF (Duckhams D-Matic)
Quantity:
    Filling from dry .... 9.0 litres (15.9 pints) approx
    Drain and refill .... 6.3 litres (11.1 pints) approx

Torque wrench settings

	Nm	lbf ft
Fluid pan bolts	16	12
Fluid cooling hose connections to transmission	38	28
Torque converter housing-to-engine bolts	75	55
Torque converter-to-driveplate bolts	60	44
Fluid cooling hose to cooler	22	16
Mounting bracket bolts to transmission	22	16
Mounting bolts to bodyframe	40	29

Steering
Torque wrench settings

	Nm	lbf ft
Balljoint (tie-rod) nut:		
Steel steering knuckle	50	37
Cast iron steering knuckle	60	44

Braking system (1.6 and 1.8)
Disc brakes (front)

Disc thickness (new):	
16S	12.7 mm (0.50 in)
18E	20.0 mm (0.79 in) ventilated
Disc thickness after refinishing:	
16S	11.7 mm (0.46 in)
18E	19.0 mm (0.75 in)
Minimum safe working thickness:	
16S	10.7 mm (0.42 in)
18E	18.0 mm (0.71 in)

Drum brakes (rear)

Drum internal diameter (13S Estate with automatic transmission, 16S EState and certain 18E models):	
New	230 mm (9.06 in)
After refinishing	231 mm (9.10 in) maximum
Drum effective width (as above)	50 mm (1.97 in)

Hydraulic system

Caliper piston diameter (18E)	52 mm (2.05 in)

Torque wrench settings

	Nm	lbf ft
Brake pressure proportioning valves (screwed into master cylinder):		
GMF type	40	30
ATE type	12	9

Suspension, wheels and tyres
Tyre pressures – 1.6 and 1.8

Cold pressures in lbf/in² (bar)	Up to 3 occupants		Fully laden	
	Front	Rear	Front	Rear
1.6 Hatchback:				
155 SR 13	27 (1.9)	27 (1.9)	30 (2.1)	34 (2.4)
175/70 SR 13	26 (1.8)	26 (1.8)	29 (2.0)	33 (2.3)
185/60 HR 14	27 (1.9)	27 (1.9)	30 (2.1)	33 (2.3)
175/65 SR 14	27 (1.9)	30 (2.1)	30 (2.1)	34 (2.4)
1.6 Estate:				
155 SR 13	27 (1.9)	32 (2.2)	32 (2.2)	46 (3.2)
175/70 SR 13	26 (1.8)	29 (2.0)	29 (2.0)	40 (2.8)
1.8 (185/60 HR 14)	29 (2.0)	29 (2.0)	32 (2.2)	34 (2.4)

Torque wrench settings
Refer to Chapter 11 for values not given below

	Nm	lbf ft
Control arm balljoint nut:		
With steel steering knuckle	50	37
With cast iron steering knuckle	75	55
Tie-rod end balljoint nut:		
With steel steering knuckle	50	37
With cast iron steering knuckle	60	44
Rear shock absorber fixed mounting:		
Lower mounting bolt:		
Saloon to June 83	60	44
Saloon from June 83	70	52
Upper mounting bolt:		
Estate to June 83	60	44
Estate from June 83	70	52

Bodywork
Torque wrench settings

	Nm	lbf ft
Bonnet hinge strap	20	15
Tailgate hinge strap	20	15
Tailgate lock striker	20	15
Bumper brackets	12	9
Seat belt mountings	35	26
Tailgate strut ball-studs	20	15
Front seat mountings	20	15

3 Routine maintenance

1 The maintenance schedule at the beginning of the book is still relevant, with the reservations below where applicable. Owners of models fitted with electronic ignition can ignore references to the contact breaker points.

2 The service interval recommended by the manufacturer has been increased to 9000 miles or 6 months, whichever comes first. It is the author's opinion that the DIY owner would be well advised to continue to observe intervals of no more than 6000 miles.

3 Antifreeze with an ethylene glycol base can usually be left in the cooling system for up to 2 years, provided that its concentration is checked (and made good if necessary) at the end of the first year. Refer to the antifreeze maker's instructions.

4 When automatic transmission is fitted, the fluid level should be checked every 6000 miles. Renew the fluid at intervals of 54 000 miles or every 3 years, or more frequently if operating under severe conditions.

5 The fuel filter on fuel injection models should be changed every 24 000 miles or two years, whichever comes first.

4 Engine – general

Identification

1 The engine number may be interpreted by reference to Fig. 13.1.

Unleaded high octane petrol

2 All engines can be successfully run on unleaded high octane petrol, but the following points should be noted.

OHV engines

3 After 5 tankfuls of unleaded petrol, a tankful of full leaded high octane fuel must be used.

OHC engines

4 These engines can be run exclusively on unleaded petrol.

Carburettor engines

5 If detonation (pinking or knock) occurs, the ignition timing should be retarded by up to 5° (see later in this Chapter).

Under-bonnet view of 1.6 engine with air cleaner removed

1 Wiper motor	6 Coolant expansion tank	11 Battery
2 Suspension strut	7 Washer fluid reservoir	12 Alternator
3 Carburettor	8 Fuel pump	13 Dipstick
4 Brake vacuum servo	9 Timing belt cover	14 Oil filler cap
5 Brake master cylinder	10 Distributor	15 Ignition coil

Fuel injection engines
6   Using unleaded petrol can cause high speed knock which cannot be heard, but can lead to engine damage; the ignition **must be** retarded by 5° (see later in this Chapter).

Cylinder block core plugs – renewal
Front core plugs
7   Remove the radiator and fan assembly (Chapter 2, Section 5).
8   Remove the exhaust manifold (Chapter 3, Section 17).
9   Remove the right-hand engine mounting.
10 Remove the core plugs by hammering a screwdriver through and prising them free.
11 Fit the new core plugs by simply hammering them into position. The use of a sealant is not usually necessary.
12 Refit the disconnected ancillaries by reference to the appropriate Chapters.
Rear core plugs
13 Drain the coolant (Chapter 2, Section 2).
14 Remove the inlet manifold (Chapter 3, Section 17).
15 Remove the coolant distribution hose which runs across the rear of the engine.
16 Remove the core plugs by hammering a screwdriver through and prising them free. Note that it may be possible to gain better access by removing the starter and alternator (Chapter 10).
17 Fit the new core plugs by simply hammering them into position. The use of a sealant is not usually necessary.
18 Refit the disconnected ancillaries by reference to the appropriate Chapters. Refill the cooling system (Chapter 2, Section 4).

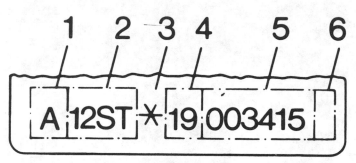

Fig. 13.1 Key to engine identification number (Sec 4)

1   *Engine code for special territories*
2   *Engine displacement code:*
    N = low compression
    S = high compression
    T = modified power output
3   *Low lead operation*
4   *Manufacturing plant code*
5   *Engine serial number*
6   *Blank*

---

5   OHV engine

Engine mounting tightening sequence
1   When refitting the engine and transmission to the car, the engine mountings should be tightened in the following sequence:

   (a)   Right-hand side
   (b)   Rear
   (c)   Left-hand side
   (d)   Front strut (when fitted)

2   Failure to follow the above sequence may lead to excessive noise and vibration.

Timing chain tensioner
3   A different type of timing chain tensioner may be found fitted to later engines. Unlike the tensioner shown in Chapter 1, which is operated both by a spring and by oil pressure, the later type operates only by spring pressure.

4   When fitting this type of tensioner, ensure that the oil splash hole is not blocked (Fig. 13.2). Tension the device as follows.
5   Fit the bottom bolt only, leaving it finger tight. Insert a feeler gauge between the free end of the spring and the grooved section of the tensioner (Fig. 13.3).

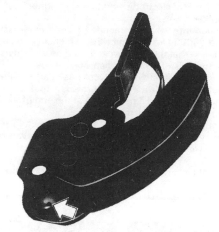

Fig. 13.2 Alternative type of timing chain tensioner. Oil hole (arrowed) must not be blocked (Sec 5)

Fig. 13.3 Feeler blade (arrowed) inserted between free end of timing chain tensioner spring and grooved section of tensioner (Sec 5)

6   Press the tensioner towards the chain until the top bolt can be inserted. Tighten both bolts and remove the feeler gauge. The spring will now take up its correct position.

---

6   OHC engine

Introduction of 1598 cc and 1796 cc engines
1   The 1598 cc engine (also known as '1600' or '1.6') became available in the UK at the beginning of 1982. The 1796 cc engine was not introduced until early 1983. Both engines are very similar to the 1297 cc ohc engine described in Chapter 1.
2   The procedures given in Chapter 1 can be followed for the larger engines, making due allowance for differences in peripheral components (especially the fuel injection system on the 1.8) and with regard to the following specific differences:

(a) The oil filter on the 1.3 has an Imperial thread, but on the larger engines it has a metric thread. The two types are not interchangeable

(b) There is a torsional damper on the larger engines instead of a single crankshaft pulley. When removing the engine it may be advantageous to remove the damper first

(c) Certain fasteners are tightened to a higher torque on the larger engines. Refer to the Specifications at the beginning of this Chapter for details

(d) The washer under the plug of the oil pressure relief valve is only found on the 1.3 engine

(e) The thermostat housing differs – see Section 7 of this Chapter

3 Reference should also be made to the rest of this Chapter in order to note modifications which may apply regardless of engine size.

Engine removal leaving automatic transmission in the vehicle

4 Proceed as described in Chapter 1, Section 43, paragraphs 1 to 12.

5 Disconnect the kickdown cable from the carburettor.

6 Unscrew and remove the torque converter cover plate. On 1.6 engines only, unbolt and remove the torsional damper from the crankshaft.

7 Unbolt the engine driveplate from the torque converter. Hold the driveplate from rotating by jamming the starter ring gear with a heavy screwdriver blade. New connecting bolts must be used at reconnection.

8 Support the transmission on a jack.

9 Attach a suitable hoist to the engine and just take its weight.

10 Unbolt the engine from the transmission.

11 Disconnect the engine mountings.

12 Separate the engine and transmission just enough to clear the positioning dowels and then turn the engine slightly until it can be lifted from the engine compartment.

Engine removal complete with automatic transmission

13 This procedure is not recommended, due to the weight and unwieldiness of the combined units.

Camshaft journal modification

14 If the camshaft has to be renewed on early 1.3 or 1.6 engines, the rear journal must be modified as follows. (Engines produced from mid-1982 are already modified.)

15 Remove the camshaft lockplate and position the old camshaft so that its end face is flush with the inner face of the rear journal. Clamp the camshaft in this position with self-locking pliers.

16 Make a centre punch mark in the position shown in Fig. 13.4 (1.3 engines) or Fig. 13.5 (1.6 engines).

17 Using a drill 3 mm (0.118 in) in diameter, drill into the camshaft and housing (at the point where the punch mark was made) to a depth of 16 mm (0.63 in). **Do not** drill beyond this depth, nor through the whole journal width.

18 Clean away any swarf and withdraw the old camshaft. Clean up the journal surface with emery cloth to remove any burrs, and clean the camshaft housing thoroughly.

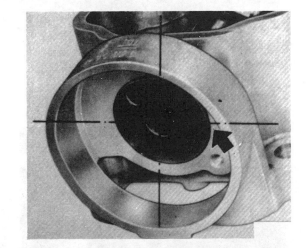

Fig. 13.4 Camshaft housing drilling point (1.3 engine) (Sec 6)

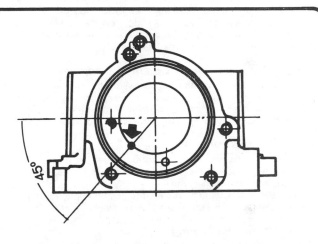

Fig. 13.5 Camshaft housing drilling point (1.6 engine) (Sec 6)

Fig. 13.6 Drilling the camshaft housing (Sec 6)

Fig. 13.7 The modified camshaft housing (Sec 6)

Camshaft housing cover filter

19 A filter is incorporated in the camshaft housing cover on 1.6 and 1.8 models. It is part of the positive crankcase ventilation system.

20 Whenever the cover is removed, wash the filter in petrol and allow it to dry. Renew the filter if it is clogged so badly that washing will not clear it.

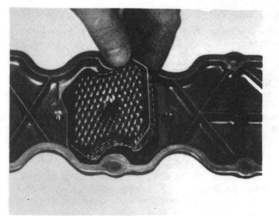

Fig. 13.8 Camshaft housing filter (Sec 6)

Cylinder head gasket modification – 1.3 engine

21 On 1.3 engines produced after May 1982, the kidney-shaped hole in the head gasket near No 4 cylinder (on the spark plug side) is replaced by two round holes. Do not worry, therefore, if you encounter this difference when renewing a head gasket.

Cylinder head overhaul – 1.6 and 1.8 engines

22 Always renew the sealing ring between the cylinder head and the thermostat housing when the head is removed for overhaul. Reference to Section 7 will show that a considerable amount of work is involved if it is wished to renew the sealing ring with the cylinder head installed.

Oil filter bypass valve renewal

23 The oil filter bypass valve is located under the oil filter, in the oil filter mounting block. If it is wished to remove the valve, screw an M10 tap into it and extract the valve.

24 The new valve should be driven into position up to its stop, using a drift approximately 15 mm (0.6 in) in diameter.

Crankshaft needle bearing

25 From engine No 14 089 444, 1.6 engines are no longer fitted with a needle bearing (pilot bearing) in the centre of the crankshaft rear flange.

26 From engine number 13S1212647, January 1984, some 1.3 engines are no longer fitted with a needle roller bearing in the crankshaft rear flange. The engines affected are identified by a blue dot on the camshaft cover and a P stamped under the transmission number.

7 Cooling system

1 The main difference between the cooling system components on the 1.3 engine and those on the 1.6 and 1.8 is the thermostat housing. The housing on the larger engine contains the thermostat in a recess at the end furthest from the engine, the hose union forming the cover to the recess.

2 The thermostat housing also carries the coolant temperature sender unit and a bleed screw. The latter should be slackened when filling the cooling system until coolant free of air bubbles emerges; it should then be tightened. A hose connects the bleed screw to the expansion tank.

Thermostat removal and refitting – 1.6 and 1.8 engines

3 Partially drain the cooling system, as described in Chapter 2.

4 Disconnect the radiator top hose from the thermostat housing.

5 Remove the 3 bolts which secure the thermostat cover to the housing. Lift off the cover.

6 The thermostat may now be removed and tested if wished, as described in Chapter 2.

7 Refitting is a reversal of the removal procedure. Use a new thermostat sealing ring, and remember to slacken the bleed screw on the thermostat housing when refilling the cooling system.

Thermostat housing removal and refitting – 1.6 and 1.8 engines

8 Remove the camshaft toothed belt, as described in Chapter 1.

9 Disconnect all hoses from the thermostat housing, noting their positions for subsequent reconnection.

10 Remove the two screws securing the thermostat housing and lift off the housing. Extract the sealing ring.

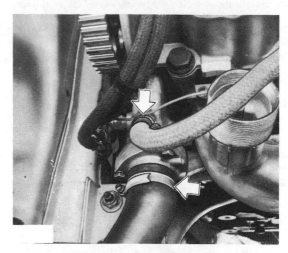

Fig. 13.9 Thermostat housing on 1.6/1.8 engines. Radiator top hose and bleed hose arrowed (Sec 7)

Fig. 13.10 Thermostat housing screws (arrowed) (Sec 7)

11 Refitting is a reversal of the removal procedure. Use a new sealing ring and tighten the thermostat housing screws to the specified torque.

Temperature gauge gives false high reading

12 If it is found that the temperature gauge shows a dangerously high temperature when no overheating is in fact taking place, this may be due to a fault in the instrument voltage stabiliser. The condition may be diagnosed as follows.

13 Disconnect the lead from the coolant temperature sender. (This is located behind the coolant pump on ohv engines, on the intake manifold on 1.3 engines and on the thermostat housing on 1.6 and 1.8 engines.)

14 A voltmeter, range 0 to 15 volts approx, is now required. Connect the positive (+) lead of the voltmeter to the lead disconnected from

Fig. 13.11 Sealing ring at thermostat housing flange on cylinder head (arrowed) (Sec 7)

the temperature gauge sender, and the negative (-) lead to bare metal in the engine bay. Do not allow the positive connection to touch any metal.

15 Switch on the ignition. The voltmeter should read 10 volts. If the reading is 12 or 13 volts, the instrument voltage stabiliser is at fault.

16 Before renewing the instrument voltage stabiliser, check that the centre terminal of the stabiliser is earthed. Remove the instrument panel (Chapter 10) and inspect the stabiliser. Solder a piece of copper wire between the centre terminal of the stabiliser and the resistor (Fig. 13.12) if such a wire is not already in place. If you are not skilled in soldering electronic components, leave the job to someone who is. Recheck the voltage as described above.

17 Early vehicles are fitted with a larger voltage stabiliser without exposed terminals. The above procedure does not apply to these units.

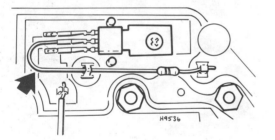

Fig. 13.12 Instrument voltage stabiliser earth lead (arrowed) (Sec 7)

Radiator removal and refitting – automatic transmission models

18 Removal is as described in Chapter 2, but additionally disconnect the transmission oil cooler lines and plug them. Take care to avoid the entry of dirt.

19 Reconnect the lines on refitting. Check and if necessary top up the transmission fluid level.

8 Fuel and exhaust systems – carburettor models

Automatic choke setting

1 The setting of the automatic choke cover recommended in Chapter 3 (one gradation towards R) has been changed several times. In addition, a modified choke cover with greater heat storage capacity (and therefore a slower cooling rate) was introduced in January 1981.

2 Vehicles now leave the factory with the choke cover set to the centre mark, midway between L and R. If problems are encountered with poor driveability when cold, the setting may be changed to a maximum of two gradations towards R.

3 Over-choking of a warm engine may be improved by fitting the modified choke cover mentioned above, if not already done.

4 Proprietary kits are available to convert the automatic choke to manual operation. In the long run this may prove the best course of action.

Varajet II carburettor with manual choke

5 From mid-1982, all 1.3 models are fitted with manual choke Varajet carburettors. Except as detailed below, adjustment and overhaul procedures are unchanged.

Fig. 13.13 Varajet carburettor with manual choke (Sec 8)

Fast idle speed adjustment

6 The engine must be at normal operating temperature, and the normal idle speed and mixture adjustments must be correct.

7 Remove the air cleaner and plug its vacuum line at the carburettor. Connect a tachometer to the engine.

8 Pull out the choke control until the mark on the fast idle cam is in line with the fast idle adjustment screw (Fig. 13.14).

9 Hold the choke valve plate in the open position with a rubber band, then start the engine. The engine speed should be as given in the Specifications for the fast idle condition.

10 If adjustment is necessary, remove the tamperproof cap from the head of the fast idle adjusting screw, then turn the screw until the desired engine speed is obtained. Fit a new tamperproof cap on completion where this is required by law.

11 Stop the engine, remove the rubber band and refit the air cleaner.

Choke pull-down adjustment

12 Remove the air cleaner and connect a vacuum pump (a modified bicycle pump or similar) to the choke vacuum unit.

13 Pull the choke control knob right out.

14 Apply vacuum to the vacuum unit. The choke valve plate should be seen to open slightly. When the maximum opening is achieved, measure the gap between the choke valve plate and the carburettor wall, as described in Chapter 3, Section 11, paragraph 8. The same dimensions and adjustment procedures apply.

15 Remake the original vacuum connection and refit the air cleaner.

Throttle linkage damper (automatic transmission models)

16 Automatic transmission models are equipped with a throttle linkage damper, the purpose of which is to stop the throttle snapping

Fig. 13.14 Varajet fast idle cam mark aligned with screw (arrow) (Sec 8)

shut suddenly when the pedal is released.

17 Correct adjustment of the damper is carried out as follows. Release the damper locknut and unscrew the damper until the damper pin is only just touching the throttle lever. From this position, screw the damper back in between 3 and 4 complete turns, then secure with the locknut.

Vacuum unit damping valve

18 On later versions of the automatic choke carburettor, a damping valve was introduced in order to overcome a tendency to misfire during hard acceleration between 2700 and 3500 rpm. This valve (Part No. 96 009 298) may be fitted to earlier model carburettors.

Part load regulator screw adjustment

19 Problems such as jerking or hesitation at light throttle openings, or excessive fuel consumption despite moderate driving habits, may be due to incorrect adjustment of the part load regulator screw.

20 It is emphasised that this adjustment should not be attempted until all other possible causes of the problems mentioned have been investigated.

21 Remove the carburettor from the vehicle.

22 Prise out the metal plug covering the part load regulator screw (adjacent to the fuel inlet union).

23 If stalling or hesitation is the reason for adjustment – ie the mixture is too weak – turn the screw one-quarter turn anti-clockwise.

24 If excessive fuel consumption is the problem – ie the mixture is too rich – turn the screw one-quarter turn clockwise.

25 Refit the carburettor and test drive the vehicle to see if any improvement has occurred. If necessary a further adjustment can be made, but **do not** deviate from the original setting by more than half a turn of the screw.

Air cleaner (dual barrel carburettor type)

26 Individual components are now available to renew faulty parts in an automatically temperature-controlled air cleaner (photos).

27 To renew the vacuum unit, depress the retaining tabs and take off the cap.

28 Bend back the tabs to release the vacuum unit and remove it (photos).

29 The thermostat (sensor) can be withdrawn after extracting its retaining spring ring (photo).

Basic idle setting – GM Varajet II

30 If the specified idle speed and mixture cannot be achieved (as described in Chapter 3, Section 10) the basic idle setting should be checked. This is not a routine operation and should only be necessary when setting up a carburettor from scratch.

31 Connect a vacuum gauge to the distributor vacuum take-off point on the carburettor.

32 Allow the engine to idle and reduce the idle speed by screwing the bypass screw (Fig. 3.2) fully home. Do not force the screw onto its seat or it may be damaged. Adjust the idle mixture screw to give a CO level of 1 to 2%.

33 At this point the engine speed should be 550 to 650 rpm, and the vacuum gauge should indicate between 1 and 20 mbar (0.03 to 0.59 in Hg). If not, break the tamperproof cap from the throttle valve stop screw (Fig. 3.16) and adjust the screw, aiming for 600 rpm and 10 mbar (0.3 in Hg).

34 Disconnect the vacuum gauge and reconnect the distributor pipe.

35 Repeat the normal idle adjustments described in Chapter 3, Section 9 to bring the speed and mixture back within specified limits.

36 Disconnect the test gear and fit new tamperproof caps, where required.

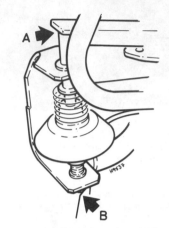

A   Damper pin
B   Locknut

Fig. 13.15 Throttle linkage damper fitted to automatic transmission models (Sec 8)

Fig. 13.16 Vacuum unit damping valve (arrowed) (Sec 8)

Fig. 13.17 Part load regulator screw (arrowed) (Sec 8)

8.26A Vacuum hose connection to underside of air cleaner

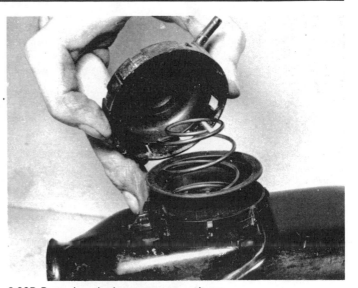

8.26B Removing air cleaner vacuum unit cap

8.28A Vacuum unit anchor tab

8.28B Removing vacuum unit

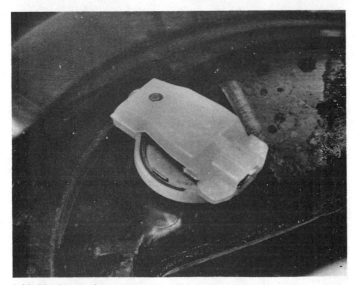

8.29 Air cleaner thermostat

9 Fuel injection system

General description

1   A Bosch LE Jetronic fuel injection system is fitted to 1.8 models.
2   This system is designed to ensure minimum exhaust emission levels throughout the engine speed range, as the fuel is metered precisely according to engine speed and load.
3   The main components of the system are:

  (a) A **control unit** which incorporates an electronic thrust cut-off, triggered by the throttle valve switch. This device further reduces fuel consumption. A cold start boost eliminates the need for a separate cold start valve and a thermotime switch

  (b) **Injection valves,** one to each cylinder, ensure precise metering of the fuel

  (c) **Airflow meter.** This incorporates the air temperature sensor

  (d) **Control relay.** This comprises an electronic timing element and a switch relay which cuts off the fuel supply immediately after the engine stops

  (e) An electrically-operated **fuel pump**

4   In addition and essential to the system are a fuel filter, a throttle valve switch, an auxiliary air valve, a pressure regulator, and temperature sensors to monitor both intake air and coolant.

Precautions

5 Although the fuel injection system is virtually trouble-free, observing the following essential requirements will keep it operating efficiently:

(a) *Never attempt to start the engine unless the battery terminals are securely connected*
(b) *Never disconnect the battery as a means of stopping the engine*
(c) *Never pull out the wiring harness plug from the control unit if the ignition is switched on*
(d) *If you are testing cylinder compression, first pull the plug from the control relay to interrupt the power supply*

Idle speed and mixture adjustment

6 With the engine at normal operating temperature, connect a tachometer to it if one is not already fitted as standard equipment.

7 Check the idle speed against that given in the Specifications. If necessary, correct it by turning the regulating screw on the throttle connecting piece (Fig. 13.18).

8 To check the mixture (CO level), connect an exhaust gas analyser in accordance with its maker's instructions. Again the engine must be at normal operating temperature, and the ignition system must be correctly adjusted.

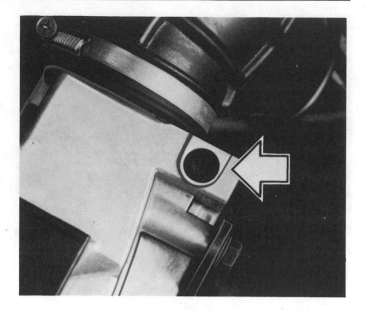

Fig. 13.19 Mixture adjusting screw (Sec 9)

Fig. 13.18 Fuel injection system idle speed adjusting screw (Sec 9)

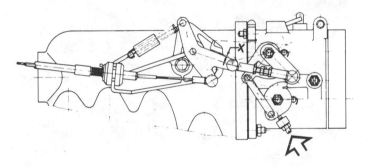

Fig. 13.20 Throttle valve linkage – stop screw arrowed (Sec 9)

X = 0.5 mm (0.02 in)

9 If the CO content deviates from that specified, remove the cap from the mixture adjusting screw on the airflow sensor (Fig. 13.19). Turn the screw in a clockwise direction to enrich the mixture or anti-clockwise to weaken it.

10 On completion of the adjustment, fit a new cap to the bypass screw.

11 Failure to bring the CO content within the specified tolerances will indicate a fault in the system, or a well worn engine.

Throttle valve adjustment

12 Make sure that the throttle valve plate is closed. Refer to Fig. 13.20.

13 Unscrew the throttle valve stop screw and locknut until the screw is clear of the cap, then screw it back in again until it just contacts the cam. Screw it in a further quarter of a turn, then tighten the locknut without altering the position of the screw.

14 Release the locknuts on the connecting rod and adjust its length by rotating it until dimension X is as shown in Fig. 13.20. Tighten the locknuts on completion.

Throttle valve switch adjustment

15 Release the switch mounting screws and rotate the switch in an anti-clockwise direction until resistance is felt. Tighten the screws.

16 Have an assistant open the throttle valve slightly by depressing the accelerator pedal. A click should be heard from the switch. A click should also be heard when the pedal is released.

Component removal and refitting

17 It is not possible to repair the main components of the fuel injection system. In the event of a fault occurring, it is best to have the fault isolated by your GM dealer or a fuel system specialist as special equipment will be necessary. However, once the problem has been diagnosed, there is no reason why the defective components cannot be renewed by carrying out the following instructions.

Throttle valve housing

18 Release the securing clips and disconnect the flexible ducting which connects the throttle valve housing with the airflow sensor (photo).

19 Disconnect the coolant hose from the throttle control housing. If the ends of the hoses are retained in their highest position there will be no loss of coolant. If the engine is still warm when this work is being carried out then the system pressure must be released before disconnecting the hoses. Do this by gently unscrewing the expansion bottle cap.

20 Pull the distributor vacuum hose from the throttle valve housing (photo).

21 Disconnect the brake servo vacuum hose, the crankcase ventilation system hose and the auxiliary air valve hose (photos).

22 Disconnect and plug the fuel hoses from the distribution tube pipe stubs. Note that the hose with the white band is located nearer the alternator. Do not connect these hoses incorrectly (photo).

9.18 Disconnecting the throttle valve housing duct

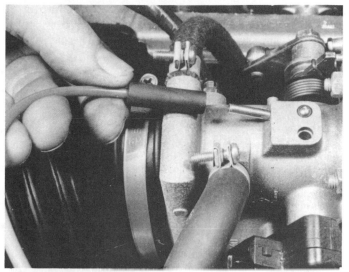

9.20 Disconnecting the distributor vacuum advance hose from the throttle valve housing

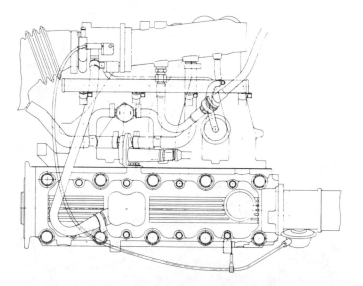

Fig. 13.21 1.8 fuel injection engine showing hose connections (Sec 9)

9.21A Disconnecting the crankcase ventilation hose

A   Coolant hose

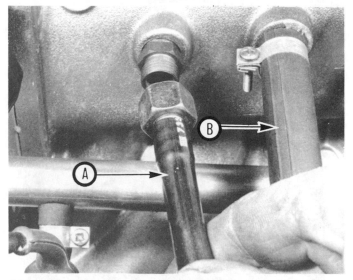

9.21B Brake servo vacuum hose (A) and auxiliary air valve hose (B)

9.22 Engine compartment fuel hoses

23 Release the wiring harness by disconnecting all the plugs and the earth connections (photos). These include:

    (a) Airflow sensor plug
    (b) Coolant temperature sensor
    (c) Fuel injectors
    (d) Throttle valve switch
    (e) Auxiliary air valve
    (f) Cam cover earth screw

24 Disconnect the throttle cable from the throttle valve housing. The ball coupling on the end of the cable is retained by a wire clip. The outer cable end fitting is retained in its bracket by an E-clip locating in a groove in the end fitting. This arrangement provides the adjustment for tensioning the cable (photos).

25 Unscrew the throttle valve housing fixing nuts. The lower ones are difficult to reach, but present no problem to remove if a small socket or ring spanner is used.

26 Lift the throttle housing away (photos).

27 Peel off the flange gasket; renew it on reassembly.

28 Refitting is a reversal of removal, but note the wiring harness connections. Number 4 fuel injector is nearest the flywheel housing (photo).

Throttle valve switch

29 Disconnect the three-pin wiring plug.

30 Unscrew the two mounting screws and pull the switch from the throttle valve spindle.

31 Refitting is a reversal of removal, but adjust the switch as described in paragraph 15.

Fuel pump

32 The fuel pump is located just forward of the fuel tank.

33 Clamp the fuel hoses on either side of the pump to prevent loss of fuel when they are disconnected. Self-locking grips are useful for this. Disconnect the hoses.

34 Unscrew the pump mounting clamp bolts and withdraw the pump from its flexible insulator. Disconnect the electrical plug as the pump is withdrawn.

35 Alternatively, the pump can be removed complete with filter and damper diaphragm unit if the mounting strap nuts are unscrewed and the assembly removed from its flexible mountings.

Fuel filter

36 The fuel filter is adjacent to the fuel pump.

37 Clamp the fuel hoses to prevent loss of fuel when they are disconnected. Self-locking grips are useful for this. Disconnect the hoses and remove the filter.

38 Refitting is a reversal of removal. Observe the AUS (out) marking on the filter showing the direction of fuel flow (photo).

Fuel injectors

39 Make sure that the engine is cool to eliminate the danger of fuel igniting. Do not smoke, and guard against external sources of ignition (eg pilot lights).

40 Release the hose clamps and pull the fuel distribution pipe from the hoses of the injectors. Catch as much fuel as possible.

41 Disconnect the wiring plug.

42 Unscrew the retaining bolts and withdraw the injector from its holder, taking care not to damage the needle valve.

43 Refitting is a reversal of removal, but renew the sealing rings if there is any doubt about their condition.

Airflow sensor

44 The airflow sensor is located between the air cleaner and the throttle valve housing.

45 Pull the wiring harness plug from the airflow sensor. Release the securing band and remove the rubber trunking.

46 Release the toggle locks and remove the airflow sensor with the upper part of the air cleaner housing.

47 Unbolt the airflow sensor from the air cleaner housing.

48 Check the airflow sensor flap valve for free movement, without any jerkiness.

Control unit

49 The control unit is located at the side of the front footwell.

50 Remove the trim panel from the side of the front footwell on the passenger side.

51 Pull the wiring plug from the control unit by pressing aside the retaining spring. Extract the three screws and remove the control unit.

Control temperature sensor

52 This sensor, located next to the alternator, is an additional sensor fitted to vehicles equipped with a fuel injection system.

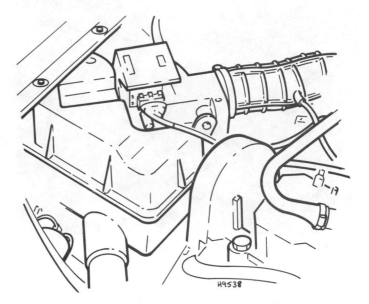

Fig. 13.22 Airflow temperature sensor (Sec 9)

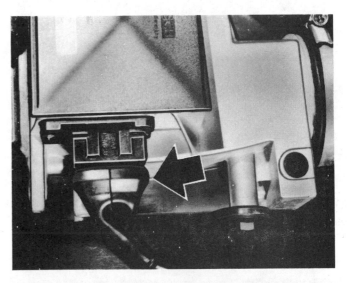

Fig. 13.23 Control relay wiring plug (arrowed) (Sec 9)

Fig. 13.24 Fuel pressure regulator (Sec 9)

9.23A Airflow sensor plug

9.23B Coolant temperature sensor plug

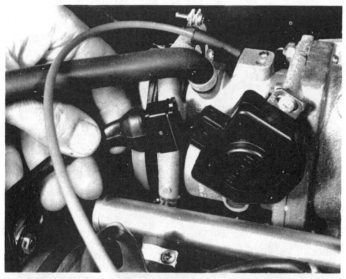

9.23C Throttle valve switch and plug

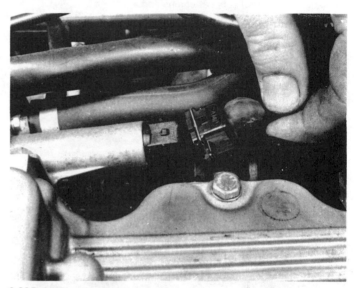

9.23D Auxiliary air valve

9.23E Cam cover earthing point

9.24A Control linkage on throttle valve housing

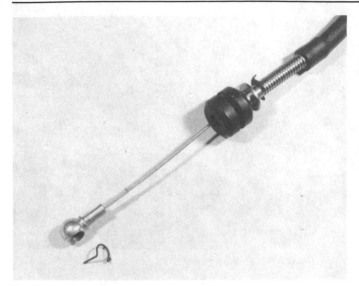

9.24B Throttle control cable at engine end

9.26A Removing the throttle valve housing

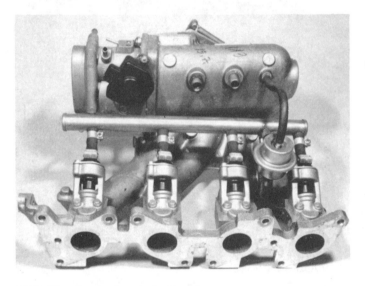

9.26B Throttle valve housing removed

9.26C View of throttle valve plate

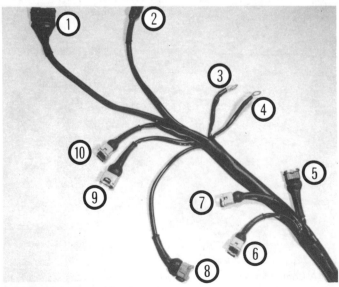

9.28 Fuel injection wiring harness

1 Airflow sensor	6 No 4 injector
2 Throttle valve switch	7 No 3 injector
3 Earth to cam cover	8 Coolant sensor
4 Earth to cam cover	9 No 2 injector
5 Auxiliary air valve	10 No 1 injector

53 Partially drain the cooling system, about 3 litres (5 pints) should be sufficient.
54 Disconnect the electrical lead and unscrew the sensor.
55 Refitting is a reversal of removal.
56 Top up and bleed the cooling system.

Auxiliary air valve
57 This valve is located on the side of the camshaft housing.
58 Pull the connecting plug from the valve.
59 Disconnect the hoses. Unscrew the two mounting bolts and remove the valve.
60 A check can be made on the serviceability of the valve by observing the regulator disc. With the valve cold, the disc should be open; with the valve hot (by connection to a 12V battery) the disc should be closed.
61 Refitting is a reversal of removal.

Control relay
62 The relay is located on the front suspension strut turret (photo).

9.38 Fuel filter (1) pressure regulator (2) and fuel pump (3)

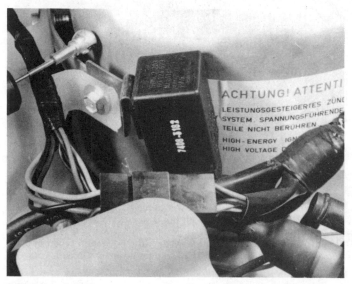

9.62 Control relay

63 Pull the wiring plug from the relay, unscrew the mounting bolt and remove the relay.
64 Refitting is a reversal of removal.

Fuel pressure regulator
65 The fuel pressure regulator is located between injectors 3 and 4.
66 Clamp the fuel hose to prevent loss of fuel. Self-locking grips are useful for this.
67 Disconnect the fuel hoses and the vacuum hose from the pressure regulator.
68 Refitting is a reversal of removal.

10 Ignition system

Breakerless ignition system – description

1 All 1.6 and 1.8 engines, and later 1.3 engines, are equipped with electronic (breakerless) ignition. Either an AC Delco or a Bosch system may be fitted. Both systems are similar in that they require virtually no maintenance or adjustment.
2 The main components are a control unit, an ignition coil and a camshaft-driven distributor.
3 Instead of the reluctor and pick-up on the AC Delco induction

system, the Bosch system incorporates a permanent magnet, a detector/amplifier, and four vanes. When a vane is masking the detector/amplifier no voltage is induced in the detector, and under these conditions the control unit passes current through the low tension windings of the coil.
4 Rotation of the distributor will uncover the detector and cause it to be influenced by the magnetic field of the permanent magnet. The Hall effect induces a small voltage in the detector plate which is then amplified and triggers the control unit to interrupt the low tension current in the coil.
5 The control unit in the Bosch system incorporates a circuit which switches off the low tension circuit if the time between consecutive signals, exceeds 1.5 seconds. The coil and internal circuits are therefore protected if the ignition is left switched on inadvertently.
6 It is not recommended that this type of distributor is dismantled beyond the limits of the operations described in the following paragraphs.

Breakerless ignition system – precautions

7 In view of the high voltage used in this system, care must be used when handling wiring or components with the ignition switched on. This is particularly important to anyone equipped with a cardiac pacemaker.
8 When cranking the engine with the HT leads disconnected – for example, when making a compression test – either disconnect the plug from the ignition control unit, or securely earth the coil HT terminal. If the coil is energised with the HT leads 'floating' there is a risk of insulation damage.
9 If it is wished to connect an independent tachometer to the breakerless ignition system, an adaptor cable may be needed in order to make contact with the ignition coil negative terminal (terminal 1, green lead). This is necessary if a completely insulated multiple plug is used to connect the coil into the ignition system.
10 When using such an adaptor cable, remember that dangerous voltages may be present at terminal 1. Always switch the ignition off before connecting or disconnecting equipment.

Ignition timing – breakerless system

11 Stroboscopic timing is carried out as described in Chapter 4, Section 8, paragraph 10 onwards. The distributor is retained by a clamp plate on 1.3 models, and by mounting flange nuts on 1.6 and 1.8 models.
12 Static timing as described in Chapter 4 is not possible with breakerless ignition. The position of the rotor arm stud when No 1 piston is firing is denoted by a mark on the rim of the distributor body.
13 Checking and adjusting the dwell angle is not required with breakerless distributors. The ignition timing itself should rarely need adjusting, except overhaul or renewal of the distributor or related engine components.

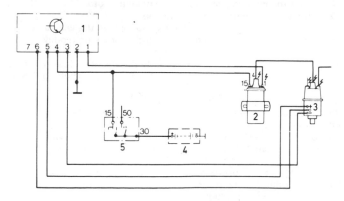

Fig. 13.25 Electronic ignition system circuit (Sec 10)

1 *Control unit module*   4 *Battery*
2 *Ignition coil*   5 *Ignition switch*
3 *Distributor*

Lightning symbols denote high voltage

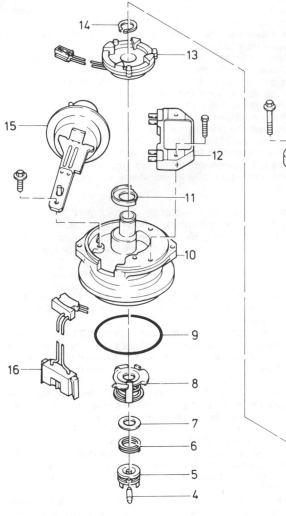

Fig. 13.26 Exploded view of AC Delco type breakerless distributor (Sec 10)

1   Distributor cap
2   Rotor
3   Shaft
4   Pin
5   Drive dog
6   Spring
7   Washer
8   Spring
9   O-ring
10 Body
11 Seal
12 Module
13 Induction sensor
14 Circlip
15 Vacuum unit
16 Plug

Breakerless distributor – removal and refitting
14 The procedure is as described in Chapter 4, Section 6, except that the distributor is secured by two nuts on 1.6 and 1.8 models.

Breakerless distributor – dismantling and reassembly
15 Extract the retaining screws with an Allen key and lift off the distributor cap.
16 Extract the retaining screws and remove the rotor.
17 Pull the wiring plug from the module.
18 Unscrew the two retaining screws and remove the vacuum unit.
19 Unscrew the two retaining screws and remove the module.
20 Renew any defective components.
21 If a new module is being fitted, apply the silicone grease supplied with it between the module mounting base and the distributor body.

Spark plug heat shields
22 On some overhead camshaft engined models, heat shields are fitted over the spark plugs (photo).
23 To remove the shields, pull off the HT leads and then withdraw the shields. These are tight and will require a sharp pull to release them.

Fault diagnosis – breakerless ignition system
24 Total ignition failure or misfiring may be due to loose or disconnected wires or plugs, or to component malfunction. Misfiring may also be due to the same faults on the HT side as those described in Chapter 4, Section 11.
25 **Do not** remove plug caps whilst the engine is running in an attempt to locate a misfire. Personal electric shock and/or damage to the coil insulation may result.
26 Testing of the ignition system units should be left to a GM dealer or automobile electrician. Beware of haphazard testing by substitution – a fault in one component may damage other units.

27 If sealing compound is observed to have spilled from the coil cap, displacing the sealing plug, both the coil and the control unit should be renewed.
28 It is possible for the ignition system to malfunction when in close proximity to certain types of VHF radio transmitters. Consult your GM dealer if this is a problem.

10.22 Typical spark plug heat shields

Retarding the ignition timing (for unleaded fuel)

29 When using unleaded high octane fuel, the ignition timing may be retarded in the following way.

30 Turn the engine by means of the crankshaft pulley bolt, or by engaging top gear and pulling the car forward, until No 1 piston is at TDC on the firing stroke. This can be felt by removing No 1 spark plug and feeling for compression with your fingers as the engine is turned.

31 Make a mark on the crankshaft pulley in alignment with the timing mark, or pointer, on the engine. This mark indicates TDC, the original pulley mark indicates 5° or 10° BTDC (see Specifications).

32 For models with ignition timing at 5° BTDC, a retardation of 5° puts the ignition timing at TDC. For models with ignition timing at 10° BTDC, a retardation of 5° puts the timing at 5° BTDC (ie halfway between the 10° and TDC marks on the pulley).

33 GM recommend the ignition timing on fuel injection engines be retarded by exactly 5° when using unleaded high octane petrol. For carburettor engines, the recommendation is up to 5° if detonation occurs; some experimentation may be worthwhile to achieve satisfactory running.

34 Make a new timing mark on the crankshaft pulley, and adjust the ignition timing as described in Chapter 4, Section 8 (see also paragraphs 11 and 12 in this Section).

Delco-Remy distributor – later models

35 Later models may be fitted with a Delco-Remy contact breaker type distributor. No further information was available at the time of writing.

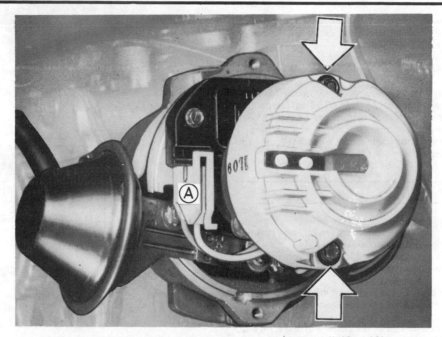

Fig. 13.27 Distributor rotor fixing screws (arrowed) (Sec 10)

A   Module connecting plug

Fig. 13.28 Distributor vacuum unit fixing screws (arrowed) (Sec 10)

11 Clutch

Vibration when engaging clutch – 1196 cc

1   If vibration is experienced when engaging the clutch on models with the 1196 cc engine, check that the flexible joint in the exhaust system is allowing sufficient free movement.

2   Dismantle the joint and apply a little graphite paste or copper-based anti-seize compound if necessary.

3   Make sure that all the exhaust mountings are in good condition and that the exhaust system cannot contact the underside of the vehicle.

Clutch unit removal and refitting – all models

4   The procedure in Chapter 5, Section 5, still applies, but note the following points:

   (a) *Mark the relationship of the clutch driveshaft to its gear cluster, using a dab of paint, before withdrawing it. Match up the paint marks on reassembly*

   (b) *The clutch driveshaft may be very tight on 5-speed models. A proper puller or even a slide hammer may be needed to withdraw it*

   (c) *The retaining clips used in conjunction with the F16/4 and F16/5 transmissions measure 15 mm (0.59 in) across the arms of the 'U' (photo). Their official part number is KM 526*

   (d) *The tightening torque for the end cover sealing plug is different for 5-speed transmissions – see Specifications – and no sealant is needed on the plug threads*

12 Manual transmission

Lubrication

1   Routine maintenance is restricted to checking the oil level; draining and refilling with fresh lubricant is not specified.

2   However, if the lubricant must be drained for any reason, most of it can be removed if the pressed steel cover plate is unbolted and pulled away from the differential.

3   The level plug is located close to the driveshaft inboard joint on the right-hand side of the car on F16 transmissions and on the left-hand side of the car on F10 transmissions.

4   The oil level should be maintained at the bottom of the level plug opening. If topping up is required, remove the breather from the transmission casing and pour it into the breather plug hole. *On no account attempt to top up by pouring oil into the level plug hole.*

F10/5 transmission – description

5   The F10/5 transmission is available as an option on later models with 1.2 or 1.3 engines.

6   The transmission design is the same as that of the F10/4 described in Chapter 6, with the addition of a 5th gear housed in the end cover.

7   Additional operations involved in dismantling and reassembling this type of transmission are described below.

11.4 Clutch compressing clip

Fig. 13.29 Manual transmission oil level plug (arrowed) on 1.6/1.8 F16 (Sec 12)

F10/5 transmission – dismantling and reassembly

8   With the transmission removed from the vehicle, remove the end cover and separate the transmission casing from the intermediate plate.

9   Move 5th gear synchro unit by hand to its engaged position, then use an Allen key to unbolt 5th gear selector fork.

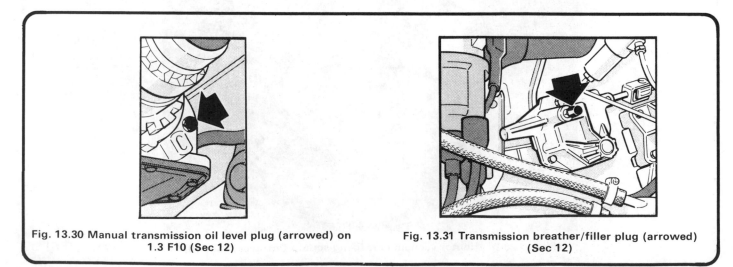

Fig. 13.30 Manual transmission oil level plug (arrowed) on 1.3 F10 (Sec 12)

Fig. 13.31 Transmission breather/filler plug (arrowed) (Sec 12)

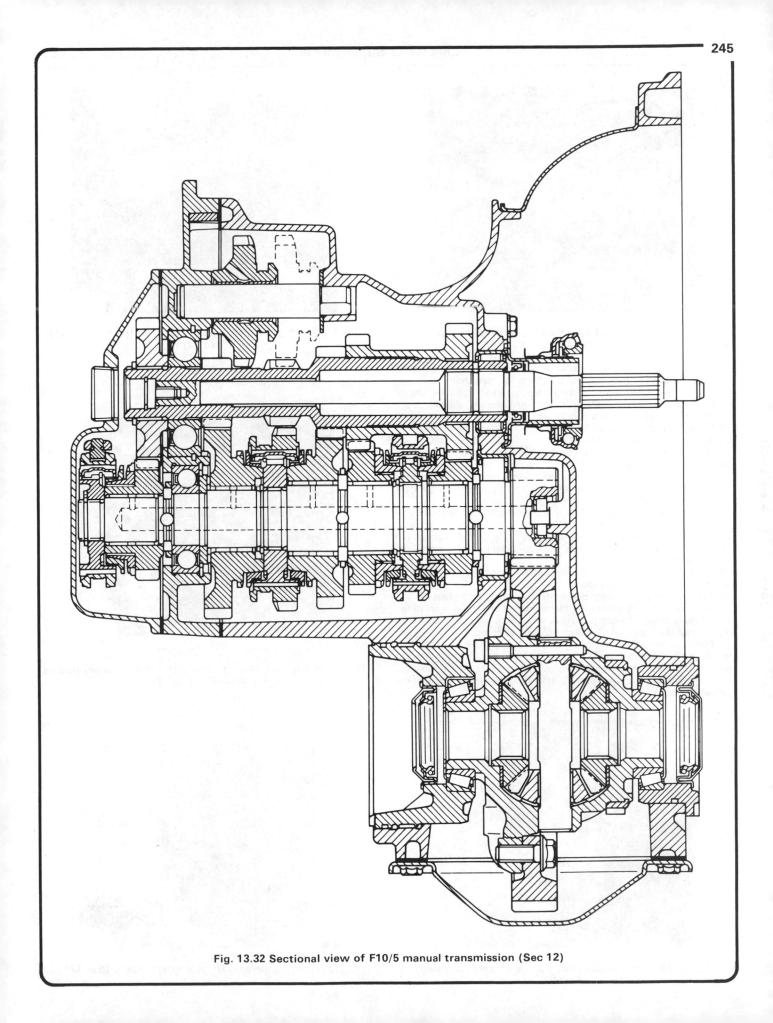

Fig. 13.32 Sectional view of F10/5 manual transmission (Sec 12)

Fig. 13.33 5th speed gear selector fork Allen screws
(arrowed) (Sec 12)

Fig. 13.34 5th gear components removed from mainshaft
(Sec 12)

10 Extract the circlip from the end of the mainshaft and then use a puller to remove 5th gear synchro unit from the mainshaft.

11 5th gear can now be removed from the mainshaft, together with its bearing, the split thrust washer and the thrust washer retaining ring.

12 Remove the circlip from the end of the input shaft, then lever or pull off 5th gear. If using a puller, take care not to damage the input shaft – use a thrust piece to spread the load.

13 Use an Allen key to undo the screws which hold the 5th gear selector interlock pawl to the intermediate plate.

14 Prise out the detent plugs from the intermediate plate and remove the detent springs and plungers. Make a note to obtain new plugs if you damage the old ones during removal.

15 Move 5th gear selector rod to its engaged position, and push 2nd gear selector fork to engage 2nd gear.

16 Use an Allen key to remove the screws securing the interlock pin bridge piece. Remove the bridge piece and return the gears to the neutral position.

17 Drive out the roll pins securing 3rd/4th and reverse shift forks. Remove the forks and their rods.

18 Pull the 5th gear selector dog from the intermediate plate.

19 Remove the circlips retaining the mainshaft and input shaft to the intermediate plate. The geartrains can now be removed, together with the reverse idler gear, 1st/2nd shift fork and shift rod.

20 Further dismantling and overhaul can now proceed as described for the F10/4 transmission in Chapter 6. Note that both 1st and 5th gears on the F10/5 transmission mainshaft have split needle bearings.

21 Reassembly is a reversal of the dismantling procedure, but note the following points:

Fig. 13.35 5th gear selector interlock pawl securing screws
(arrowed) (Sec 12)

Fig. 13.36 Interlock pin bridge piece screws (arrowed)
(Sec 12)

Fig. 13.37 Removing 5th gear selector dog (Sec 12)

(a) Use new screws to secure the interlock pin bridge piece and the 5th gear selector interlock pawl. The proper screws are pre-coated with thread locking compound and must be renewed whenever they have been loosened

(b) Note that the longer detent plug serves 3rd/4th gears (Fig. 13.38)

(c) Heat 5th gear synchro unit to 100°C (212°F) before fitting it to the mainshaft

(d) There is no need to use sealant on the end cover plug threads

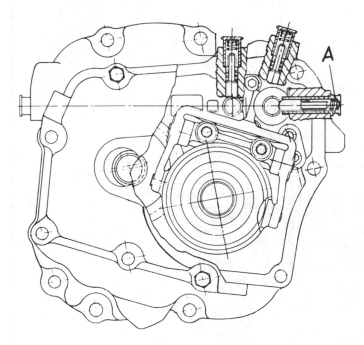

Fig. 13.38 Longer 3rd/4th detent plug A (Sec 12)

F16 transmission – description

22 The F16/4 and the F16/5 transmissions are fitted to the larger-engined models in the range. They are essentially heavy duty versions of the F10/4 and F10/5 transmissions.

23 A special lubricant is specified for the F16/5 transmission in the 1.8 model. This lubricant is obtainable from your GM dealer; no other should be used as noisy operation may result.

F16/4 transmission – dismantling and reassembly

24 The operations are very similar to those described in Chapter 6 for the Type F10 transmission, but if the mainshaft is being overhauled then the modified design of the mainshaft must be noted, together with the additional components. These include:

(a) Axial needle bearing against 1st gear

(b) Needle roller bearings for 1st, 2nd, 3rd and 4th gears

(c) Semi-circular thrust washers between 2nd and 3rd gears, complete with washer retaining ring

(d) 3rd/4th synchro retaining circlip

(e) Composite mainshaft with pinion gear

(f) Roller bearing, semi-circular thrust washers and washer retaining ring next to pinion gear

25 If either the crownwheel or pinion (part of mainshaft) is being renewed then the pair must be renewed as a matching set.

26 All synchromesh sleeves are interchangeable. Do not interchange part-worn sleeves though, since wear patterns are unlikely to be identical.

27 When reassembling the mainshaft, oil each component liberally when fitting and observe the following points. First slide the roller bearing onto the shaft so that the smaller diameter of the inner track is against the pinion gear.

28 Fit the semi-circular thrust washers and slip the retaining ring over them.

29 Follow with the needle bearing and 4th gear.

30 Continue with 4th gear baulk ring, 3rd/4th synchro (heated in boiling water) and the synchro circlip.

31 Fit the dual row needle bearing, 3rd speed baulk ring and gear and the semi-circular thrust washers with their retaining ring.

32 Fit the needle bearing and 2nd gear with baulk ring.

33 Heat 1st/2nd synchro in boiling water and fit it to the mainshaft so that the groove in its sleeve is towards the rear cover of the transmission. Secure the synchro with a new circlip.

34 Fit the next needle bearing and 1st gear with its synchro baulk ring.

35 Place the axial needle bearing up against the face of 1st gear.

36 Fit the spacer. This should be heated in boiling water before fitting and the larger diameter of the spacer will be next to the axial needle bearing.

37 Fit the ball-bearing so that the ball positioning cage is towards the end of the shaft. Fit a new circlip.

F16/5 transmission – dismantling and overhaul

38 With the transmission removed from the vehicle, clean away external dirt using paraffin or a water soluble solvent and a stiff brush.

39 Unbolt the cover plate from the final drive housing and allow the lubricant to drain.

40 Unbolt and remove the cover plate from the flywheel housing.

41 Unbolt and remove the selector housing and peel off the flange gaket.

42 Unbolt and remove the end cover with gasket.

43 Extract the circlip from the end of the input shaft now exposed. This circlip is located deep in the shaft recess and a pair of long-nosed pliers will be needed to extract it.

44 Unscrew and remove the Torx type screw from the shaft recess. It is possible to use a close-fitting Allen key to do the job.

45 Unbolt and remove the transmission main casing from the intermediate plate.

46 Using an Allen key, unbolt the 5th gear selector fork. It will facilitate removal of the socket-headed screws if 5th gear synchro unit is first moved by hand to its engaged position.

47 Extract the circlip from the end of the mainshaft and then, using a two-legged puller, draw 5th gear and 5th gear synchro unit from the mainshaft. Locate the puller claws under 5th gear.

48 Extract the circlip from the end of the input shaft and withdraw 5th gear from the shaft. Two tyre levers placed under the gear will remove it quite easily (photos).

12.48A Extracting input shaft circlip

49 Using an Allen key, unscrew the socket-headed screws which hold the 5th gear selector interlock pawl to the intermediate plate.

50 Using a forked lever or slide hammer with suitable attachment withdraw the detent plugs from the edge of the intermediate plate. Be prepared to catch the coil springs which will be ejected. Pull out the detent plungers (photos).

51 If you have damaged the detent caps during removal, they should be renewed.

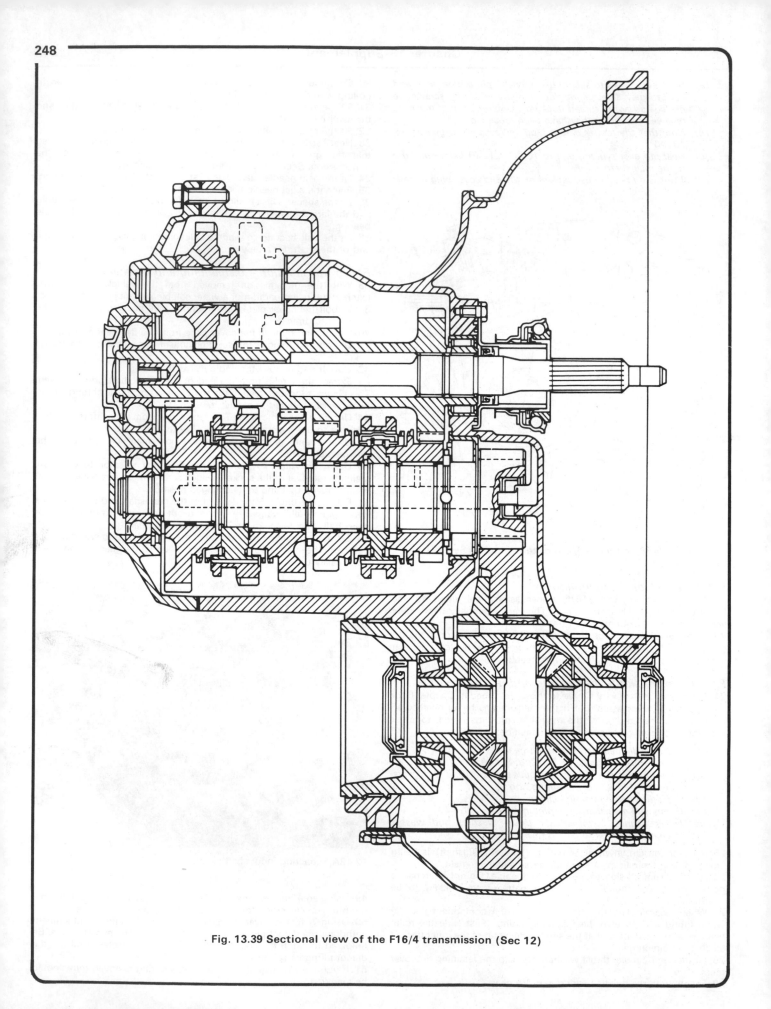

Fig. 13.39 Sectional view of the F16/4 transmission (Sec 12)

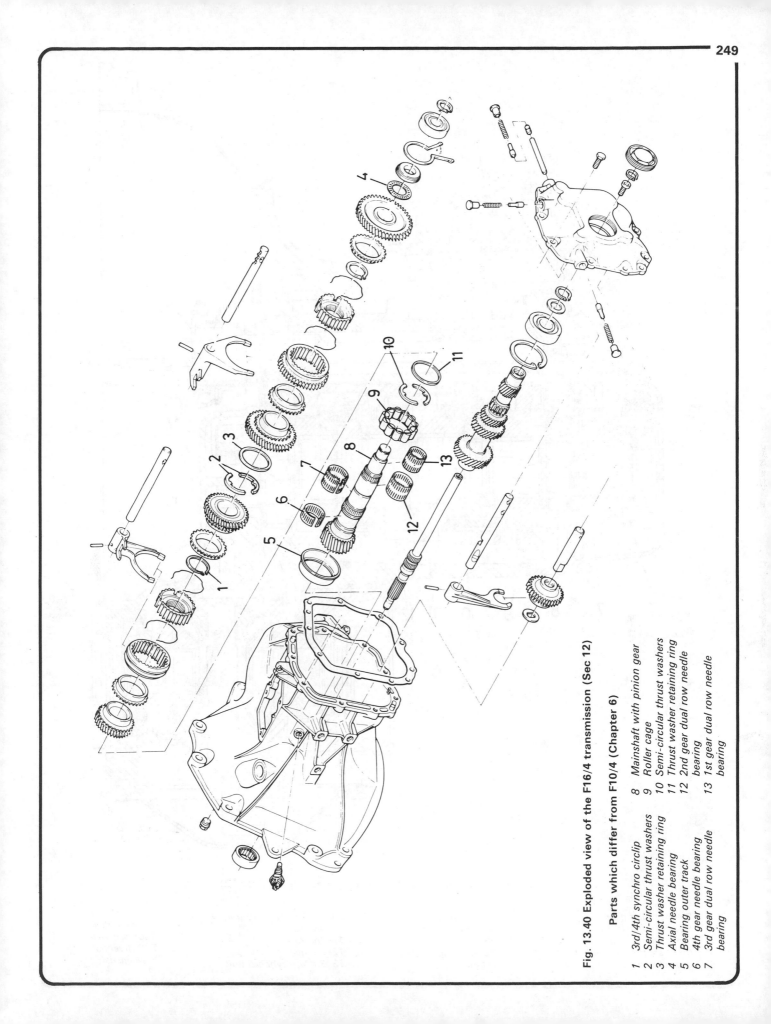

Fig. 13.40 Exploded view of the F16/4 transmission (Sec 12)

Parts which differ from F10/4 (Chapter 6)

1 3rd/4th synchro circlip
2 Semi-circular thrust washers
3 Thrust washer retaining ring
4 Axial needle bearing
5 Bearing outer track
6 4th gear needle bearing
7 3rd gear dual row needle bearing

8 Mainshaft with pinion gear
9 Roller cage
10 Semi-circular thrust washers
11 Thrust washer retaining ring
12 2nd gear dual row needle bearing
13 1st gear dual row needle bearing

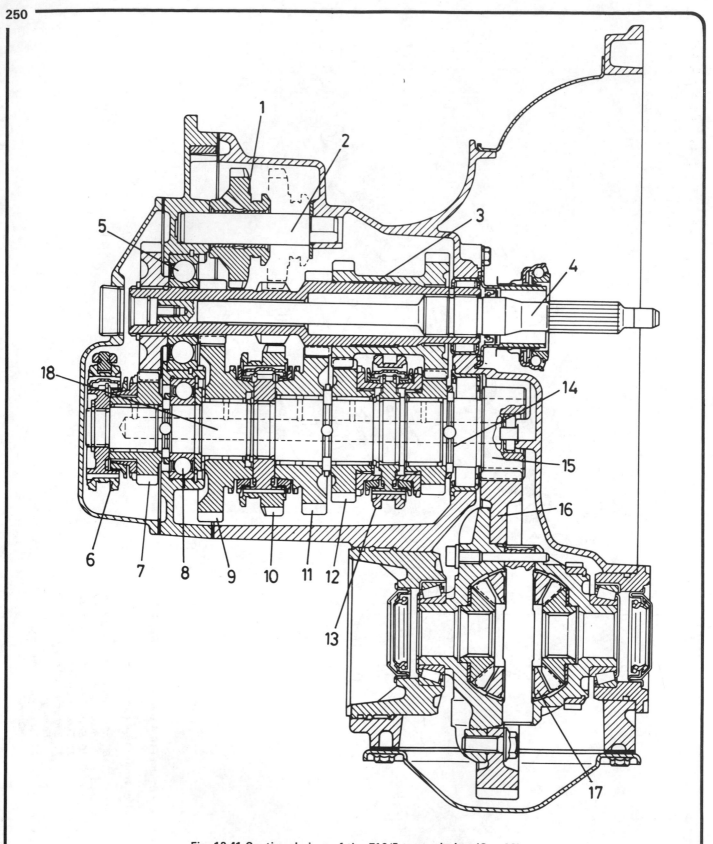

Fig. 13.41 Sectional view of the F16/5 transmission (Sec 12)

1 Reverse idler gear	5 Ball-bearing	10 1st/2nd synchro unit with reverse	14 Pinion gear
2 Reverse idler shaft	6 5th gear synchro unit	11 2nd gear	15 Pinion gear
3 Input gear cluster	7 5th gear	12 3rd gear	16 Crownwheel
4 Input shaft (removable from gear cluster)	8 Ball-bearing	13 3rd/4th synchro unit	17 Differential
	9 1st gear		18 Mainshaft

52 Move 5th gear selector rod to its engaged position.

53 Push 2nd gear selector fork to engage the gear.

54 Again using the Allen key unscrew the socket-headed screws and remove the interlock pin bridge piece.

55 Return all gears to neutral.

56 Drive out the securing roll pin and remove the selector shaft and fork for 3rd/4th gears. Remove reverse selector in a similar way.

57 Withdraw the interlock rod from the intermediate plate.

58 Pull the 5th gear selector driver from the intermediate plate.

59 Drive out the roll pin and remove the 1st/2nd selector rod and fork.

60 Squeeze together the ends of the large circlip which hold the mainshaft bearing into the intermediate plate. A piece of thin rod should be made up to form a retaining clip to keep the circlip contracted (photo).

61 Now expand the legs of the circlip which holds the input shaft bearing in the intermediate plate.

62 With the help of an assistant, withdraw the geartrains complete with reverse idler gear. The shafts and bearings may require a little gentle tapping with a plastic faced hammer to eject them from the intermediate plate. Note the thrust washer on the reverse idler.

Input shaft and gear cluster

63 Examine the gear teeth for wear. If evident then the cluster must be renewed (photo).

64 The bearings may be removed using a suitable puller.

12.48B Levering off 5th gear

12.50A Levering out a detent plug

12.50B Typical detent plug extractor tool

12.60 Circlip retaining clip

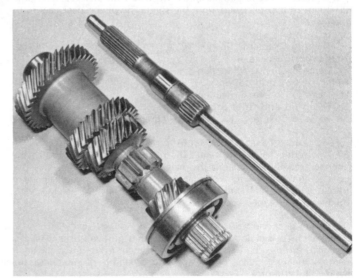

12.63 Input shaft and gear cluster

65 The shaft may be tapped from the gear cluster using a plastic-faced hammer.

Mainshaft

66 Place the claws of a two-legged puller under the 1st gear and draw the gear and shaft ball-bearing from the mainshaft (photo).

12.66 Removing 1st gear and bearing from mainshaft

67 Extract the circlip, remove the plain thrust washer and then the needle type thrust washer.
68 Remove 1st gear baulk ring.
69 Remove the split type needle roller bearing.
70 Extract the circlip.
71 Take off the plain thrust washer.
72 Place the claws of a puller under 2nd gear and withdraw 1st/2nd synchro unit (with reverse), the baulk ring and 2nd gear all together from the mainshaft. Note that the reverse gear teeth on the synchro sleeve are towards the pinion gear on the end of the shaft.
73 Remove the semi-circular thrust washers and their retaining ring.
74 Remove the 3rd gear.
75 Remove 3rd gear baulk ring.
76 Take off the split type needle roller bearing.
77 Extract the circlip which retains the 3rd/4th synchro unit.
78 Take off the thrust washer.
79 Place the claws of a puller behind 4th gear and draw off 3rd/4th synchro unit, 4th gear baulk ring and 4th gear all together from the mainshaft.
80 Take off the split type needle roller bearing.
81 Remove the semi-circular thrust washers with their retaining ring.
82 Remove the roller race from the shaft. The pinion gear cannot be removed.

Synchromesh units

83 Refer to Chapter 6, Section 12.

Transmission case

84 Refer to Chapter 6, Section 9.

Selector housing cover

85 Refer to Chapter 6, Section 8.

Differential and final drive

86 Refer to Chapter 6, Section 7, paragraph 15 onwards.

F16/5 transmission – reassembly

87 Apply thick grease to retain the rollers to their cage and fit the bearing assembly up against the mainshaft pinion gear.
88 Locate the semi-circular thrust washers so that their keys engage in the holes in the shaft and then fit the retaining ring.
89 Fit the split type needle roller bearing.
90 Fit 4th gear.
91 Fit 4th gear baulk ring (photo).
92 Fit 3rd/4th synchro unit so that the thin groove in the sleeve is furthest from the shaft pinion. Drive the synchro-hub down the shaft using a bearing puller or by applying a length of tubing to the synchrohub (photo).
93 Fit the thrust washer (photo).

12.91 4th gear baulk ring

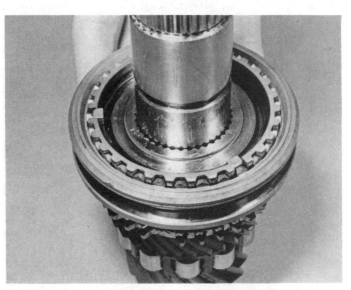

12.92 3rd/4th synchro unit with narrower groove upwards

12.93 3rd/4th synchro thrust washer

94 Fit the circlip (photo).
95 Fit 3rd gear baulk ring (photo).
96 Fit the split type needle roller bearing (photo).
97 Fit 3rd gear (photo).
98 Fit the semi-circular thrust washers and their retaining ring. Fit the needle roller bearing (photos).
99 Fit 2nd gear (photo).
100 Fit 2nd gear baulk ring (photo).
101 Fit 1st/2nd synchro unit so that the reverse gear teeth on its sleeve are towards the shaft pinion gear. Draw or tap the assembly down the shaft (photo).
102 Fit the plain thrust washer (photo).
103 Fit the circlip (photo).
104 Fit the split type needle roller bearing.
105 Fit the 1st gear baulk ring and then 1st gear (photo).
106 Fit the needle roller type thrust washer (photo).
107 Fit the plain thrust washer so that the step is positioned as shown.

This is essential to allow for clearance when the mainshaft bearing circlip is contracted ready for geartrain installation into the intermediate plate. Drop the large mainshaft bearing circlip onto the shaft (photos).
108 Fit the ball-bearing to the mainshaft so that the sealed side is visible when fitted (photo).
109 Locate the mainshaft bearing circlip in the step of the thrust washer, squeeze the legs of the circlip together and fit a retainer as previously described.
110 Expand the input shaft bearing circlip (photo).
111 With the help of an assistant, mesh the input and mainshaft geartrains together, with the reverse idler gear held in position with the fingers (selector fork groove towards mainshaft pinion gear).
112 Install the geartrains with reverse gear into the intermediate plate (photo). Release the input shaft bearing circlip and remove the mainshaft bearing circlip retaining clip.

12.94 Fitting circlip

12.95 Fitting 3rd gear baulk ring

12.96 3rd gear split type needle roller bearing

12.97 Fitting 3rd gear

12.98A Semi-circular thrust washers

12.98B Thrust washer retaining ring

12.98C 2nd gear needle roller bearing

12.99 Fitting 2nd gear

12.100 2nd gear baulk ring

12.101 Fitting 1st/2nd synchro unit with reverse gear teeth towards shaft pinion

12.102 Thrust washer fitted

12.103 Circlip fitted

12.105A 1st gear baulk ring and split needle roller bearing in position

12.105B Fitting 1st gear

12.106 Thrust type needle roller bearing

12.107A Thrust washer with step towards end of shaft

12.107B Mainshaft bearing large circlip

12.108 Mainshaft bearing

12.110 Expanding the input shaft bearing circlip

12.112 Fitting geartrains to intermediate plate. Note circlip retainer (arrowed)

12.113A 1st/2nd selector rod and fork

113 Refit the 1st/2nd selector rod and fork. Drive in the roll pin which retains the fork to the rod (photos).

114 Fit reverse selector rod and fork and drive in a new roll pin (photo).

115 Fit 5th speed selector driver into the intermediate plate.

116 Locate 5th speed selector dog and 3rd/4th selector fork and insert the selector rod through them (photo).

117 Fix 3rd/4th selector fork to its rod with a new roll pin.

118 Insert the interlock rod into the hole in the intermediate plate (photo).

119 Fit the interlock pin bridge piece. The screws will only be able to be screwed up if 2nd gear and then 5th gear driver are moved to the engaged position (photos). Use new screws (see paragraph 21).

120 Engage the 5th gear interlock pawl in the cut-out of the driver and then bolt the pawl to the intermediate plate (photos). Use new screws.

121 Insert the detent plungers and their coil springs in their holes in the intermediate plate (photos).

122 Tap in the plugs, noting that the one for 3/4th selector is longer than the other three.

123 Locate the thrust washer (which has the centre hole with flat sides) on the reverse idler shaft. Retain it with thick grease (photo).

124 Fit the magnet (clean) into its slot in the intermediate plate (photo).

125 Place a new gasket on the transmission casing flange and lower the geartrains with intermediate plate into the casing (photo).

126 Mesh the pinion and crownwheel teeth as the geartrains are lowered.

127 Screw in the securing bolts.

128 If the input shaft was removed, now is the time to refit it into the input shaft gear cluster.

12.113B Selector fork roll pin

12.114 Reverse selector fork and rod

12.116 5th gear selector dog and 3rd/4th selector fork and rod

12.118 Interlock rod in intermediate plate

12.119A Interlock pin bridge piece

12.119B Bridge piece socket-headed screws

12.120A 5th gear interlock pawl

12.120B Tightening a pawl securing screw

12.121A Fitting detent components to intermediate plate

12.121B Detent plug and selector fork identification

12.121C Reverse detent plug

12.123 Reverse gear thrust washer

12.124 Swarf collecting magnet

129 Fit the 5th gear to the end of the input shaft. Secure it with the circlip (photo).
130 To the end of the mainshaft fit the semi-circular thrust washers and retaining ring (photos).
131 Fit the split type needle roller bearing to the mainshaft (photo).
132 Fit 5th gear to the mainshaft (photo).
133 Fit 5th gear baulk ring (photo).
134 Fit 5th gear synchro unit so that the side where the movable keys are visible is towards 5th gear (photo).
135 Fit the retaining circlip (photo).
136 Move 5th gear to its engaged position and fit the selector fork/pivot assembly. Tighten the socket-headed screws (photo).
137 Fit the screw and the circlip to the end of the input shaft. The circlip is located in a groove deep in the recess in the end of the shaft and a pair of long-nosed pliers will be required to reach it (photos).
138 Using a new gasket bolt on the end cover (photo).
139 Screw the threaded plug (if removed) into the end cover (photo).
140 Using a new gasket locate the selector cover so that the selector fingers engage in the dogs (gears in neutral). Insert and tighten the fixing bolts (photo).
141 Bolt on the final drive cover plate
142 Bolt on the flywheel housing cover plate (photo).
143 Check the selector of all gears is smooth and positive.
144 Fill the transmission with lubricant after it has been refitted to the vehicle.

12.125 Lowering geartrains into transmission casing

12.128 Fitting the input shaft

12.129 Fitting 5th gear to input shaft

12.130A Semi-circular thrust washers

12.130B Thrust washer retaining ring

12.131 5th gear split type needle roller bearing

12.132 Fitting 5th gear to mainshaft

12.133 5th gear baulk ring

12.134 5th gear synchro unit

12.135 Fitting circlip to mainshaft

12.136 Tightening a 5th gear selector fork pivot screw

12.137A Torx screw in input shaft recess

12.137B Fitting circlip to input shaft recess

12.138 Fitting the end cover

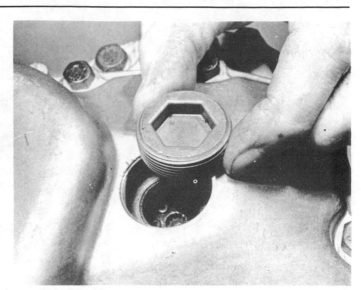

12.139 Screwing in the end plug

12.140 Fitting the selector cover

12.142 Flywheel housing cover plate

Gearchange vibration damper

145 Fuel injection models are equipped with a vibration damper to prevent the transmission jumping out of gear on rough roads.

146 When removing the damper, first engage 5th gear. Disconnect the damper from the selector housing cover before pulling it off the ball-stud.

147 Refitting the damper is the reverse of the removal procedure. Make sure that 5th gear is selected before refitting commences, and coat the ball-stud with silicone grease.

148 If it is wished to fit a damper to other models, note that it is only possible when an F16/4 or F16/5 transmission having a threaded hole in the selector housing cover is fitted. A shift rod with a ball-stud bracket must then be installed. It is not possible to fit the damper to the F10/4 or F10/5 transmission.

13 Automatic transmission

General description and precautions

1 The automatic transmission is of General Motors design and manufacture and is optionally available on certain models. The unit provides three forward speeds and reverse with a 'kickdown' facility.

As with manual transmission, the differential and final drive are built into the transmission casing.

2 The main components are a torque converter (fluid coupling), which transmits power to the geartrains through a chain drive, and a hydraulic circuit which regulates the selection of gears, clutches and brakes according to speed and engine load.

3 Due to the close tolerances to which the unit operates, cleanliness is absolutely essential whenever fluid is being added or any component removed. Entry of grit or dirt into the transmission will cause a malfunction of the valves and possible damage to the internal components.

4 The automatic transmission is a complex piece of equipment and the home mechanic should limit himself to undertaking the operations described in the following paragraphs. More extensive operations should be left to your dealer or automatic transmission specialist.

Fluid level checking

5 The importance of maintaining the correct fluid level in the automatic transmission cannot be over-emphasised.

6 The level may be checked cold or hot.

7 To check cold, have the vehicle standing on a level floor with the engine running and P selected. Withdraw the dipstick, wipe it clean with a fluff-free cloth, replace it and withdraw it for the second time.

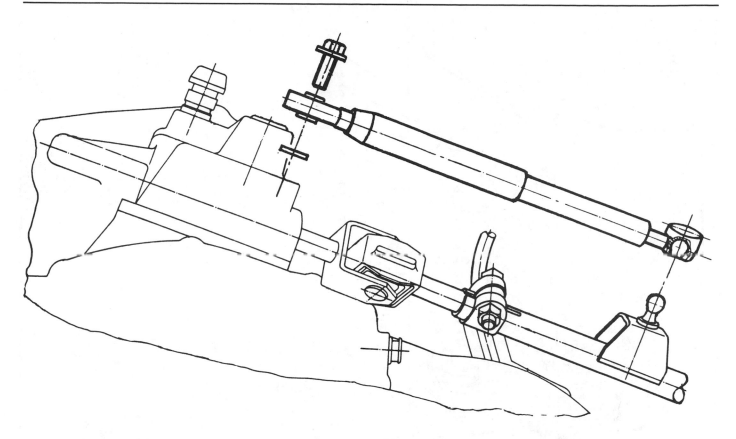

Fig. 13.42 Gearchange vibration damper fitted to fuel injection models (Sec 12)

Read the fluid level on the side of the dipstick marked with +20°C, it should be up to the MAX mark.

8   To check the fluid level hot, the vehicle must have just covered a road operating distance of at least 10 miles (15 km). Check the fluid level in a similar way to that just described, but read off the level on the side marked +94°C, it should be between the MIN and MAX marks.

9   Carry out the foregoing checks when the engine has been idling for one minute but not more than three minutes, otherwise an incorrect reading will be obtained.

10 Top up as necessary through the dipstick guide tube. Make sure that the fluid is absolutely clean and of the specified type. Do not fill above the MAX mark.

11 With the transmission cold, a fluid level 5.0 mm below the MAX mark will indicate the need for the addition of 0.25 litre of fluid. With the transmission hot, 0.5 litre of fluid is needed to raise the level from MIN to MAX.

Fluid changing

12 At the intervals specified in Section 3, the transmission fluid must be renewed. Do this more frequently if the vehicle is used under particularly arduous operating conditions or for towing a trailer.

13 Allow the transmission to cool down before draining as the fluid can be very hot indeed.

14 Remove all the fluid pan screws except one which should be unscrewed through several turns.

15 Release the fluid pan from its gasket and as the end of the pan tilts downward, catch the fluid in a suitable container.

16 Remove the remaining screw and the pan. Peel off the joint gasket or sealant bead.

17 Pull the filter mesh from its securing clips then clean it in fuel and allow it to dry.

18 Renew the O-ring seal exposed by removal of the filter and then refit the filter securely.

19 Bolt on the fluid pan using a new gasket. On some transmissions, a gasket is not used. Instead, a bead of silicone rubber (instant gasket) is used. In this case, apply a bead of sealant about 5 mm (0.2 in) thick to clean surfaces. The fluid pad which is fitted with a gasket can be identified by the strengthening ribs on the pan flanges. The pan for use with silicone sealant has plain flanges.

20 Fill the transmission with the specified quantity of fluid and then check the level as described for the COLD process earlier in this Section.

21 Discoloration of the fluid noticed when changing the fluid will probably be due to overheating.

Kickdown cable – renewal and adjustment

22 Remove the air cleaner from the carburettor.

23 Disconnect the kickdown cable from the carburettor by pulling the clip from the support bracket and then prising the cupped end fitting from the ball stud on the lever.

24 Working at the transmission casing, remove the locking bolt from the sleeve. Pull the sleeve upwards and disconnect the inner cable.

25 Release the cable adjusting mechanism from its support bracket by depressing the lug.

26 Fit the new cable by reversing the removal operations. Note that it runs between (not under) the brake pipes.

27 Adjust the cable with the help of an assistant in the following way. Depress the accelerator pedal fully, but slowly, until it contacts the kickdown switch. Check that the throttle valve plate in the carburettor is wide open. If not, adjust the throttle cable at the carburettor base to achieve this. Adjust the throttle cable at the accelerator pedal to remove any slackness from the cable when the carburettor valve plate is in the idle position.

28 Now depress the accelerator pedal further past the kickdown switch detent. The ratchet of the self-adjusting mechanism should be heard to operate, confirming that adjustment is correct.

29 Release the accelerator pedal and refit the air cleaner.

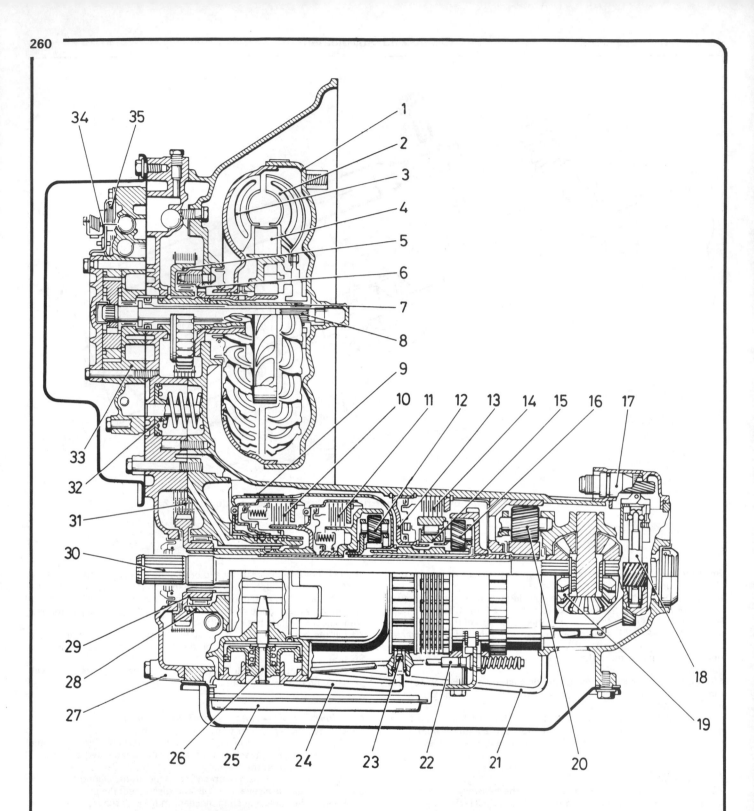

Fig. 13.43 Sectional view of the 125 THM automatic transmission (Sec 13)

1 Torque converter	10 Direct clutch	19 Differential	28 Driven sprocket carrier
2 Turbine wheel	11 Forward clutch	20 Axle drive	29 Driven sprocket
3 Pump wheel	12 Input planet carrier	21 Governor fluid line	30 Axleshaft
4 Guide wheel	13 Clutch housing	22 Parking lock actuator	31 Chain drive
5 Drive sprocket	14 Low and reverse clutch	23 Seal	32 Accumulator
6 Drive sprocket carrier	15 Freewheel	24 Fluid line	33 Valve and pump assembly
7 Turbine shaft	16 Reaction planetary set	25 Fluid filter	34 Throttle valve kickdown
8 Oil pump shaft	17 Tachometer drive pinion	26 Brake band servo unit	actuator
9 Brake band	18 Governor	27 Casing	35 Line boost valve

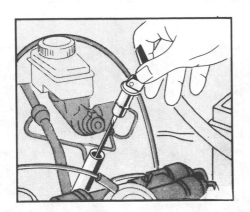

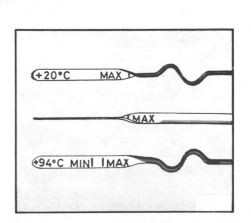

Fig. 13.44 Automatic transmission fluid dipstick (Sec 13)

Fig. 13.45 Dipstick markings (Sec 13)

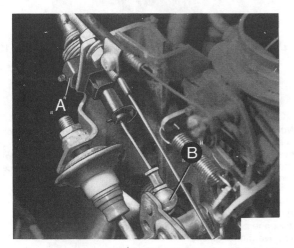

Fig. 13.46 Kickdown cable connection at carburettor
(Sec 13)

A   Adjuster mechanism – retract pin to release
B   Ball and socket end fitting

Fig. 13.47 Kickdown cable connection at transmission
(Sec 13)

Retaining bolt arrowed

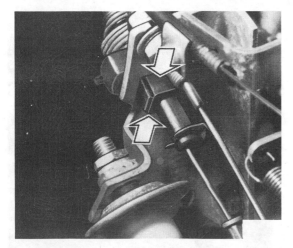

Fig. 13.48 Kickdown cable adjusting mechanism release
lug. Press in direction of arrows to release (Sec 13)

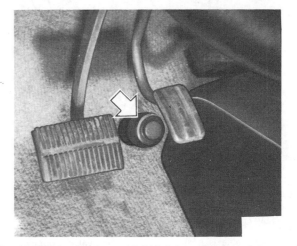

Fig. 13.49 Accelerator pedal kickdown switch (arrowed)
(Sec 13)

Speed selector control cable – removal, refitting and adjustment

30 From the centre console, extract the four securing screws, lift the selector lever cover, turn it and remove it, disconnecting the lamp electrical lead as it is withdrawn.

31 Extract the two console securing screws, set the selector lever in P and remove the console.

32 Working at the transmission, release the selector cable by pulling off the retaining clip and then unscrewing the cable from the support.

33 Working inside the vehicle, disconnect the cable from the selector hand control lever.

Fig. 13.51 Speed selector cable at control lever (Sec 13)

A   Clamp   B   Sleeve

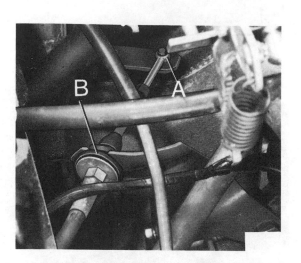

Fig. 13.50 Speed selector cable retaining clip (A) and support bracket (B) at transmission (Sec 13)

37 With the help of an assistant check that with the hand control lever in each position, the lever on the transmission can be felt to be positively positioned in its correct detent and not under any tension. Where this is not the case, adjust the cable at the adjuster adjacent to the hand control lever.

38 Refit the centre console and selector lever cover.

Transmission – removal and refitting

39 Disconnect and remove the battery.

40 Remove the air cleaner.

41 Disconnect the earth strap from the transmission.

42 Disconnect the kickdown cable from the carburettor and from the transmission.

43 Disconnect the speed selector control cable at the transmission.

44 Unscrew the selector cable support bracket. There is no need to disconnect the cable from the bracket.

45 Unscrew the top three bolts which connect the transmission to the engine. Note that the centre bolt of the three also secures a coolant pipe bracket.

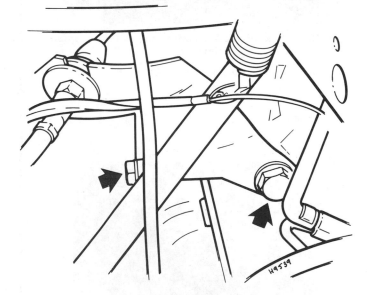

Fig. 13.52 Speed selector cable bracket bolts (arrowed) (Sec 13)

34 Release the cable from the clamp and loosen and remove the sleeve.

35 Withdraw the cable assembly by pulling it into the engine compartment.

36 Fitting a new cable is a reversal of the removal operations, but observe the following points. Check that the cable grommet at the bulkhead makes a good seal. Set the cable in the sleeve so that it is not under tension. When connecting the cable make sure that the hand control lever is in P.

Fig. 13.53 Top engine-to-transmission connecting bolts (arrowed) (Sec 13)

46 Disconnect the speedometer cable at the transmission.

47 Remove the transmission oil dipstick from the filler tube.

48 The engine must now be supported, preferably with a bar across the wings and an adjustable hook (Fig. 13.55). In the absence of such a support it may be possible to improvise using a jack (with a block of wood to spread the load) or a hoist. In that case it may be as well to raise the vehicle to the required height before supporting the engine.

49 Remove the front roadwheels and raise the front of the vehicle high enough that the transmission can be withdrawn from underneath.

50 Disconnect the suspension control arm balljoints from the steering knuckles.

51 Release the driveshafts from the transmission. Rest the shafts on the control arm or exhaust pipe, or support them in some other fashion, in order to avoid straining the rubber gaiters or inadvertent separation of the joints.

52 Disconnect and remove the horn. Disconnect the fluid cooler lines at the transmission and plug the holes. On 13N and 13S engined models after 1984, a fluid cooler is not fitted as experience has dictated that this is no longer required.

53 Remove the cover from the bottom of the torque converter housing.

54 Remove the screws which secure the torque converter to the driveplate. These screws are accessible through the aperture revealed by removal of the cover. Jam the starter ring gear with a large screwdriver to prevent the driveplate rotating as the screws are undone. Rotate the engine to bring each screw into an accessible position. The screws are pre-coated with locking compound and **must** be renewed once they have been slackened.

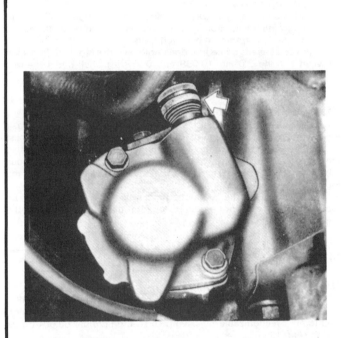

Fig. 13.54 Speedometer cable connection at transmission. Knurled nut arrowed (Sec 13)

Fig. 13.55 Typical cross-bar type engine support (Sec 13)

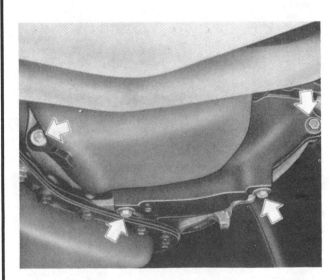

Fig. 13.56 Torque converter housing cover bolts (arrowed) (Sec 13)

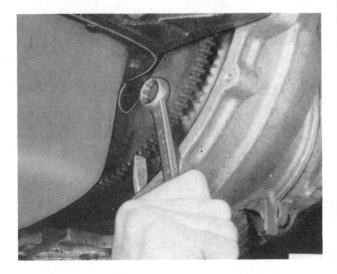

Fig. 13.57 Unscrewing a driveplate-to-torque converter bolt (Sec 13)

55 Remove the remaining screws which hold the transmission to the engine.
56 Unbolt the rear engine/transmission mounting from the body. Also unscrew the adjacent exhaust bracket.
57 Support the transmission securely on a jack, preferably of the trolley type.
58 Unbolt the left-hand engine/transmission mounting from the left-hand side-member.
59 Remove the two bolts which hold the transmission to the engine mounting bracket.
60 Pull the fluid filler tube out of the transmission. Have ready a plug for the hole that will be left, otherwise most of the transmission fluid will run out.
61 Carefully move the transmission away from the engine and withdraw it from below the vehicle.
62 If the transmission is to be renewed, do not forget to salvage the mounting brackets and the fluid cooler unions.
63 Refitting is a reversal of removal, but observe the following points.
64 Before offering the transmission to the engine, check that the torque converter is fully meshed with the oil pump. To do this, measure (A) as shown in Fig. 13.59. This should be between 9.00 and 10.00 mm (0.35 and 0.39 in). If it is not, turn the converter at the same time applying hand pressure.

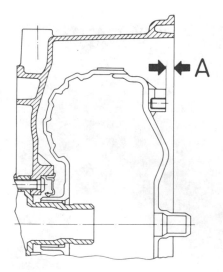

Fig. 13.58 Transmission to engine mounting bracket bolts (arrowed) (Sec 13)

65 Apply a smear of molybdenum disulphide grease to the torque converter pilot spigot.
66 When bolting the torque converter to the driveplate, align the white spot on the plate with the coloured spot on the torque converter, and use new bolts of the correct type.
67 When connecting the kickdown cable, first attach it to the transmission. Adjust as described earlier in this Section.
68 Fill the transmission as described earlier in this section.
69 Check all nuts and bolts have been tightened to the specified torque and that thread locking compound has been applied to the threads (clean) of the suspension control arm support bolts.

Starter inhibitor switch – adjustment
70 Failure of the starter motor to operate when the speed selector lever is in N or P may be due to incorrect setting of the inhibitor switch.
71 To set the switch, first move the selector lever to P.
72 Release the two switch mounting bolts.
73 Turn the switch very slowly in a clockwise direction until, with an assistant turning the ignition key, the point is reached when the starter motor is actuated. Tighten the switch bolts.
74 If the adjustment procedure does not solve the problem, fit a shim between 1.0 and 2.0 mm (0.039 and 0.078 in) thick under the rear mounting bracket of the switch.
75 If the switch still does not operate, renew it.

Fault diagnosis – automatic transmission
76 As has been mentioned elsewhere in this Section, no service repair work should be considered by anyone without the specialist knowledge and equipment required to undertake this work. This is also relevant to fault diagnosis. If a fault is evident, carry out the various adjustments previously described, and if the fault still exists consult the local garage or specialist.
77 Before removing the automatic transmission for repair, make sure that the repairer does not require to perform diagnostic tests with the transmission installed.

14 Driveshafts

Driveshaft joints – automatic transmission models
1 On automatic transmission models produced after October 1982, either or both driveshafts may incorporate a modified inboard joint. This joint is recognizable by having three longitudinal bulges on its casing (Fig. 13.60).
2 The new type of joint does not have an internal stop to limit the sliding travel within the joint. *Great care must be taken when removing or handling this type of driveshaft not to pull on the shaft itself.*
3 If the joint is inadvertently separated, the complete driveshaft must be renewed.

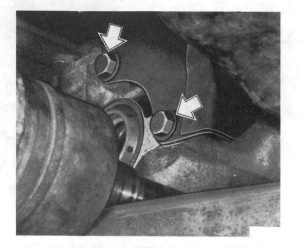

Fig. 13.59 Torque converter engagement diagram (Sec 13)

A = 9.0 to 10.0 mm (0.35 to 0.39 in)

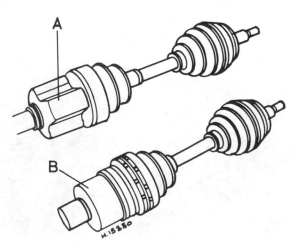

Fig. 13.60 Automatic transmission driveshafts (Sec 14)

A   Later type   *B   Earlier type*

Driveshafts – refitting (manual transmission)

4   In order to eliminate any possibility of damage to the transmission when refitting the driveshafts, a special pressure tool (KM 564) is now available from GM dealers. The tool is connected to the clutch shaft and applies pressure to the driveshaft inboard joint.

5   It has been found from experience that firm pressure or, at most, one or two reasonable blows with a plastic-faced mallet are usually enough to install the driveshaft and seat its retaining circlip without using the special tool.

6   Test the engagement of the inboard joint circlip after fitting the driveshaft by pulling the joint outwards with the hands.

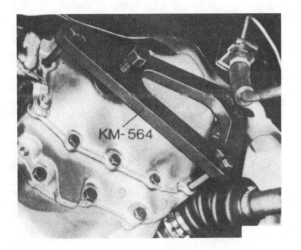

Fig. 13.61 Special driveshaft fitting tool (KM 564) (Sec 14)

15 Braking system

General description

1   The principles of operation of the braking system remain unchanged. Larger discs, drums and linings are used on larger-engined models.

2   Detail changes affecting later and/or larger models are given here.

Caliper mounting bolts (all models)

3   From 1982 model year, thread locking compound (Locktite 262) is applied to brake caliper mounting bolts in production.

4   Whenever a brake caliper is removed, therefore, the mounting bolt threads should be cleaned and thread locking compound applied on reassembly. This is a sensible precaution regardless of whether or not it was done on original assembly.

Brake disc removal and refitting – ventilated disc

5   To provide adequate clearance for removing the thicker ventilated disc, the brake caliper must first be removed.

6   If the caliper mountings are unscrewed, the caliper can be suspended from the steering knuckle using a piece of wire or string. There is no need to disconnect the hydraulic hose, but do not allow the caliper to hang by the hose.

Master cylinder removal and refitting (1982 and later models)

7   When the brake pressure proportioning valves are screwed into the master cylinder (see below), master cylinder removal is carried out as follows.

8   Disconnect the two direct brake pipes from the master cylinder (ie those not connected via the valves).

9   Loosen, but do not remove, the brake pipes which are screwed into the proportioning valves.

10   Unscrew both proportioning valves from the master cylinder.

11   Unbolt the master cylinder from the servo and remove it.

12   Refitting is a reversal of removal. Tighten the proportioning valves to their correct torque – see Specifications at the beginning of this Chapter. Bleed the hydraulic system on completion.

Brake pressure proportioning valves (1982 and later models)

13   The remote pressure-dependent proportioning valve described in Chapter 9 has been superseded by a pair of valves screwed into the master cylinder outlets feeding the rear brakes.

14   It is not possible to check the functioning of the valves without special test equipment. Consult your GM dealer if malfunction is suspected.

15   When removing the valves, disconnect the brake lines before unscrewing them from the master cylinder. Refit in the reverse order and bleed the hydraulic system on completion.

16   If the valves are to be renewed, check that the markings on each valve (denoting the operating pressure) are identical.

Brake servo removal and refitting (all models)

17   If care is taken not to strain the hydraulic pipes, the master cylinder can be moved forwards (after unbolting it from the servo) far enough to allow removal of the servo.

18   Note the connecting point for the servo vacuum hose on fuel injection models (Fig. 13.64)

19   If it becomes necessary to renew the non-return valve in the servo vacuum line, the vacuum line itself should also be renewed.

Self-adjusting rear brakes – description

20   As from 1984, self-adjusting rear brakes are fitted, the shoe linings being kept at optimum proximity to the drum by the action of the footbrake pedal.

21   The brake components are handed and marked L or R, and black (left) or silver (right) to avoid confusion.

22   The fixed strut which is fitted between the shoes on manually-adjusted brakes is replaced by a threaded rod, star wheel and a sleeve. When the shoe-to-drum clearance exceeds a certain value, a spring-loaded lever rotates the star wheel as the brake pedal is depressed, so increasing the effective length of the sleeve/rod.

23   In order to eliminate over-adjustment when the brake drums expand due to the heat generated by friction, a thermoclip is fitted between the star wheel and sleeve of the adjuster. The thermoclip expands at a pre-determined temperature level to prevent rotation of the star wheel.

Self-adjusting rear brakes – lining renewal

24   Chock the front wheels and engage a gear. Slacken the rear wheel nuts on the side being worked on, then jack up the rear of the car and remove the wheel. Release the handbrake.

25   Remove the brake drum securing screw and pull off the drum. If it is tight, collapse the brake shoes by removing the plug in the brake backplate and pushing the handbrake operating lever outwards with a screwdriver.

26   Remove the steady pins and clips or springs and washers. Renew them if they are damaged (photo).

27   Disconnect the handbrake cable from the operating lever (photo). If there is insufficient slack in the cable, disconnect it at the equaliser.

28   The return springs may be unhooked now and the shoes removed separately, or the assembly of shoes, strut and springs may be removed together. The second course is particularly easy if the rear hub is removed, as has been done for photographic purposes here. Be careful not to damage the wheel cylinder rubber boots.

29   Clean the brake backplate, being careful not to inhale the dust or disperse it into the air. (Original equipment linings are now asbestos free, but the same will not necessarily be true of aftermarket linings.)

30   Apply a smear of copper-based anti-seize compound, or other suitable product, to the shoe rubbing areas on the brake backplate.

31   Investigate and rectify any source of contamination of the linings before fitting the new shoes.

32   Dismantle the shoes, strut and springs. Note how the springs are fitted, and which way round the strut goes. Be careful not to interchange left-hand and right-hand adjuster components.

33   Dismantle and clean the adjusting strut. Apply a smear of silicone-based lubricant to the adjuster threads.

34   If a new handbrake lever was not supplied with the new shoes, transfer the old lever. It may be secured with a pin and circlip (photo), or by a rivet which will have to be drilled out.

35   Assemble the new shoes, springs and adjuster components. Expand the adjuster strut to ease fitting (photos).

36   Offer the shoes to the brake backplate. Be careful not to damage the wheel cylinder boots or to displace the pistons. When the shoes are

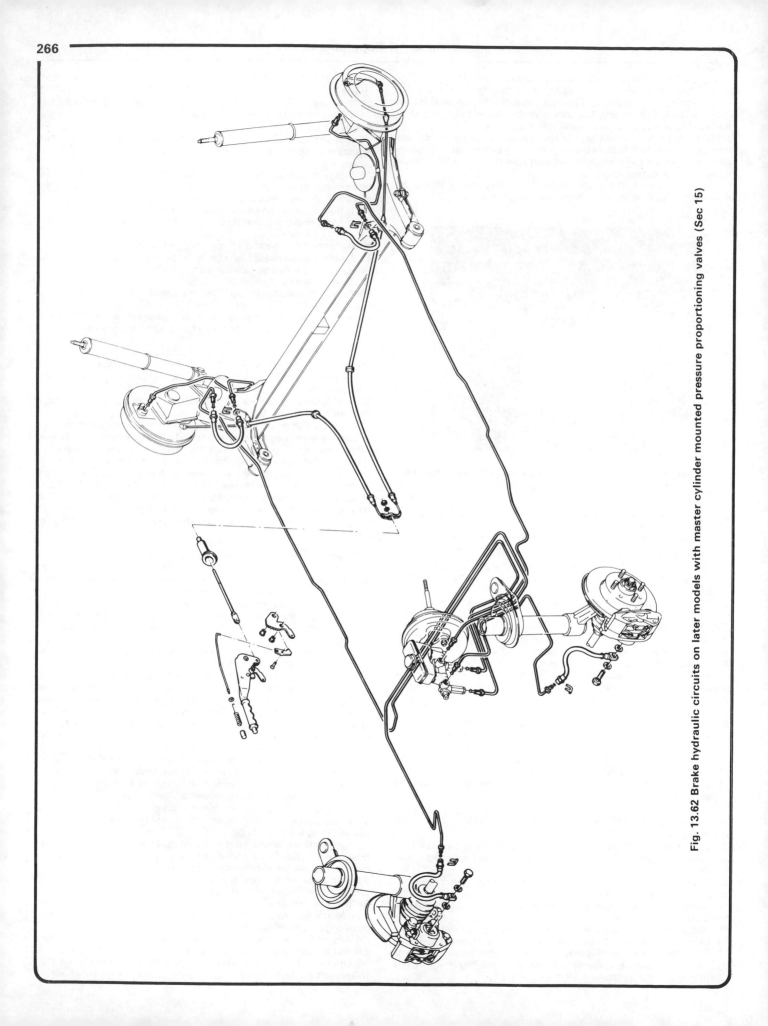

Fig. 13.62 Brake hydraulic circuits on later models with master cylinder mounted pressure proportioning valves (Sec 15)

15.26 Brake shoe steady clip

15.27 Disconnecting the handbrake cable

15.34 Shoe lever secured by circlip

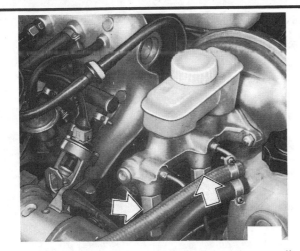

Fig. 13.63 Pressure proportioning valves (arrowed) screwed into brake master cylinder (Sec 15)

Fig. 13.64 Servo vacuum hose connection (arrowed) on fuel injection models (Sec 15)

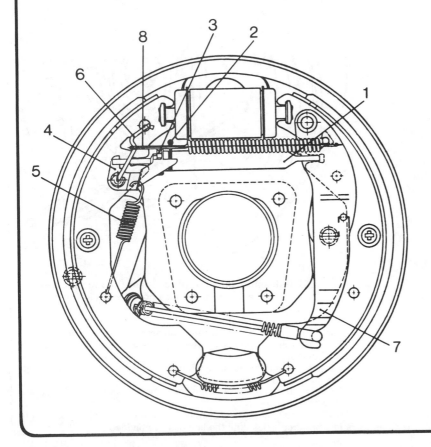

Fig. 13.65 Left-hand self-adjusting brake assembly (Sec 15)

1 Strut
2 Thermoclip
3 Star wheel
4 Adjuster lever
5 Lever return spring
6 Return spring ratchet
7 Handbrake lever
8 Shoe upper return spring

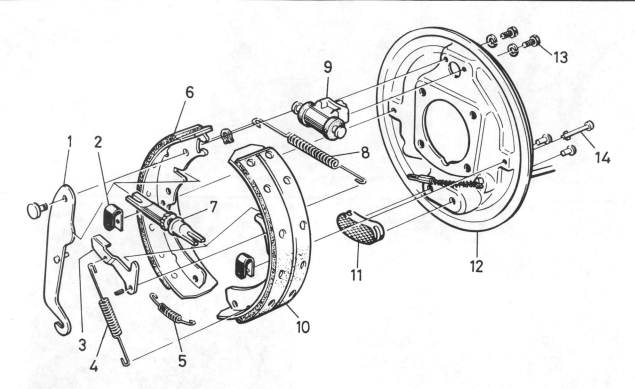

Fig. 13.66 Self-adjusting rear brake components (RH) (Sec 15)

1	Handbrake lever on shoe	5	Shoe lower return spring
2	Shoe holddown clip	6	Trailing shoe
3	Adjuster lever	7	Adjuster strut
4	Adjuster lever return spring	8	Shoe upper return spring

9	Wheel cylinder	12	Backplate
10	Leading shoe	13	Wheel cylinder fixing bolts
11	Backplate plug	14	Shoe steady pin

15.35A Fitting the adjuster lever

Fig. 13.67 Releasing shoe handbrake lever using screwdriver inserted into backplate hole (Sec 15)

in position, insert and secure the steady pins. Reconnect the handbrake cable, and refit and adjust the hub if it was removed (photo).

37 If fitting the shoes and springs together is found too difficult, it is possible to fit the shoes and secure them with the steady pins, then to introduce the adjuster strut and fit the springs and adjuster lever.

38 Back off the adjuster pinion to reduce the length of the strut until the brake drum will pass over the new linings. Make sure that the handbrake lever is correctly positioned (pin on the edge of the shoe

web, not riding on top of it). Refit and secure the brake drum.

39 Repeat the operations on the other rear brake, then adjust the brakes by operating the footbrake. A clicking noise will be heard at the drums as the automatic adjusters operate; when the clicking stops, adjustment is complete.

40 Check the handbrake adjustment and correct it if necessary (Chapter 9, Section 19).

41 When new linings have been fitted, exercise restraint in braking for a few hundred miles until the linings have bedded in.

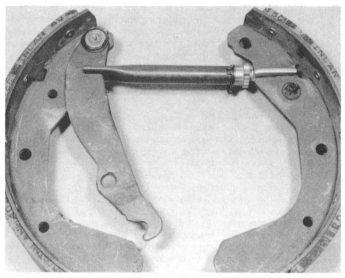

15.35B Fitting the shoe lower return spring

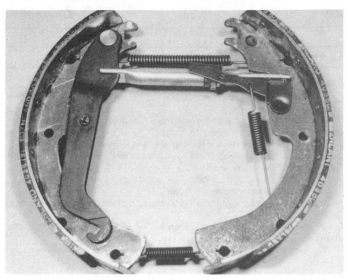

15.35C Brake shoes ready for fitting

15.35D Adjuster strut and shoe lever – alternative type shown

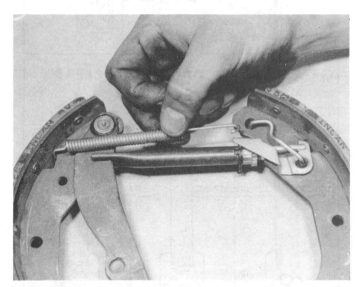

15.35E Shoe upper return spring – alternative type shown

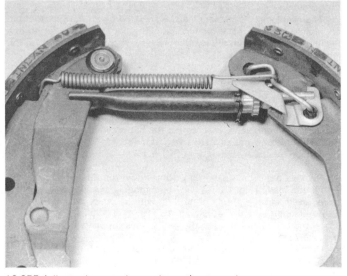

13.35F Adjuster lever spring – alternative type shown

15.36 Rear brake assembly (right-hand) – alternative type shown

16 Electrical system

Maintenance-free (freedom) battery

1 Later models are equipped with a maintenance-free battery which requires no topping-up.

2 The battery is fitted with an integral hydrometer which indicates the state of charge of the battery by colour.

3 If the 'eye' shows green, the battery is in a good state of charge. If the colour is dark or even black, the battery is discharged and should be charged from a mains charger.

4 Should the 'eye' appear clear/yellow in colour, this may be due to low electrolyte level or overcharging.

5 If the battery does not respond to charging from an external source, renew it.

6 If the battery becomes discharged or is overcharged, have the alternator performance checked by your dealer.

7 **Do not** attempt to jump start a car if the 'eye' is clear/yellow.

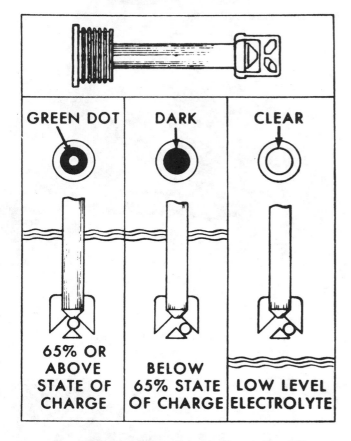

Fig. 13.68 Battery condition indicator (Sec 16)

Speedometer cable – renewal

8 Disconnect the speedometer drive cable from the speedometer head by reaching up behind the instrument panel, depressing the retaining spring and pulling the drive cable out of the instrument panel.

9 Working at the transmission, unscrew the knurled ring and pull the cable from the transmission casing.

10 Withdraw the cable through the bulkhead grommet.

11 Fit the new cable by reversing the removal operations. Make sure that the cable bends are no sharper than those in the original routing.

Starter motor wiring harness

12 From mid-1982, the routing and attachment of the starter motor wiring has been changed in order to prevent chafing.

13 Where the harness was previously strapped to the starter motor itself, now it is strapped to the adjacent heater pipe.

14 This modification is easily carried out on earlier models in cases where chafing of the starter motor harness is noticed.

Wiper motor starts spontaneously

15 On models with a wash/wipe delay facility, it is not unknown for the wiper motor to start spontaneously. This is caused by a voltage 'spike' accidentally triggering the wiper motor control relay.

16 Various items of electrical equipment may produce these spikes. Some known causes are:

    (a) Coil secondary (HT) winding defective (open-circuit)
    (b) Alternator voltage regulator defective
    (c) Washer pump wires too close to HT leads
    (d) Carburettor solenoid cut-off valve loose or defective
    (e) Poor earth connections

17 Consult your GM dealer before embarking on an expensive and haphazard course of component substitution. The coil secondary winding may be checked with an ohmmeter; a small break in the winding will show up as infinite resistance on an ohmmeter, even though the ignition system may function normally as the HT voltage can jump the break.

18 Fitting a suppression capacitor to the alternator is the first line of attack if this is the source of the problem. Failing this, it may be necessary to renew the voltage regulator.

Instrument voltage stabiliser malfunction

19 Refer to Section 7 of this Chapter for details of instrument voltage stabiliser malfunction affecting the temperature gauge readings.

20 If it is necessary to renew the old (bi-metallic strip) type instrument voltage stabiliser with a new (electronic) one, it is also necessary to renew the instrument panel itself (although the old instruments can be transferred), the printed circuit board, the heat shield and the securing screw.

21 Persistently low gauge readings may be due to the (electronic) type stabiliser input and output terminals being reversed.

Headlamp washer system

22 A headlamp washer system is fitted as standard equipment on some models and is available as an optional extra on others. When the system is fitted, a larger reservoir, serving both the headlamp and the windscreen washers, is installed.

23 A separate pump serves the headlight washer jets. The pump operates when the windscreen washer is operated and the lights are switched on. The pressure of the water emerging from the headlight washer jets is very high, thus eliminating the need for separate wipers.

24 If the high pressure pump malfunctions it must be renewed. Check first (by applying battery voltage directly to the pump terminals) that the fault is indeed in the pump and not in the wiring or control circuitry.

25 Disconnect the pump electrical connector and remove the pump by pulling it forwards and upwards. Be prepared for some fluid spillage unless the reservoir is empty.

26 Cut the hose off the old pump as close to the spigot as possible.

27 Fit the new pump in the reverse order. Lubricate the spigots with washing-up liquid to ease assembly. The hose is a simple push fit over the spigot.

28 The headlamp washer jets may be adjusted by inserting a stout pin or similar pointed instrument. A straight line from the jet to the headlight should touch the headlight glass on the square mark on the lens.

Radio/cassette – installation of vehicle manufacturer's equipment

29 The following procedure should be followed to install standard GM radio/cassette player, speakers and aerial.

30 Before starting work, disconnect the battery negative lead.

Radio receiver – preparation for fitting

31 Extract the two screws (Fig. 13.70) and withdraw the ashtray plate.

32 Remove the switch plate by prising down the three retaining tabs with a thin blade (Fig. 13.71). On some models, two screws must first be removed and the switch plate then withdrawn by prising the three lower retaining tabs upwards (Fig. 13.72).

33 Fit the radio bracket using the two screws supplied in the fitting kit (Fig. 13.73).

34 Connect the radio earth cable to the central earth bolt.

35 Connect the radio supply cable to the hazard warning switch spare terminal (Fig. 13.75).

36 The radio should not be connected or fitted until the speakers and aerial have been fitted.

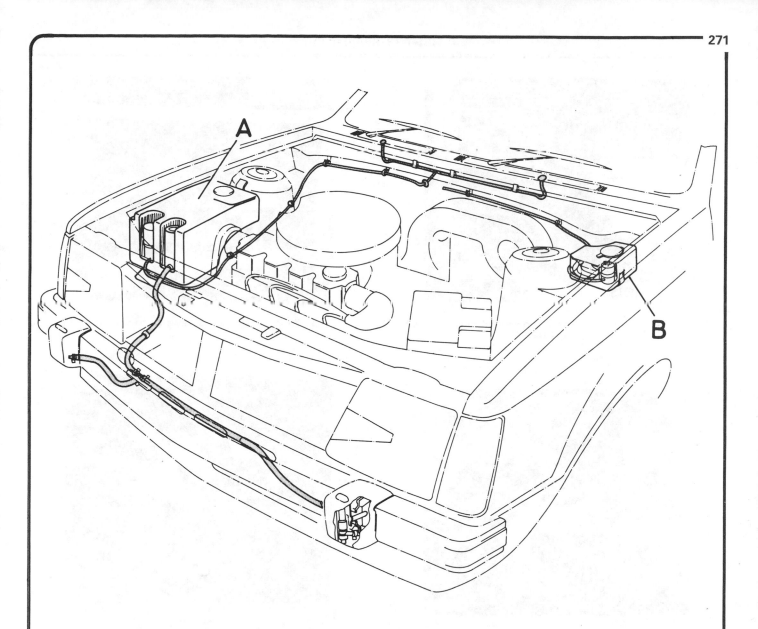

Fig. 13.69 Washer system (Sec 16)

A Combined windscreen/headlamp fluid reservoir
B Windscreen only reservoir

Fig. 13.70 Ashtray plate screws (arrowed) (Sec 16)

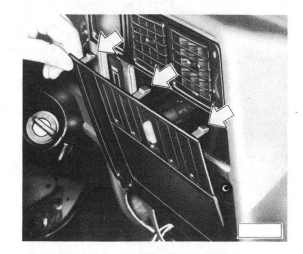

Fig. 13.71 Switch plate tabs (arrowed) (Sec 16)

Fig. 13.72 Switch plate screws on special models (black arrows) (Sec 16)

White arrows indicate retaining tabs

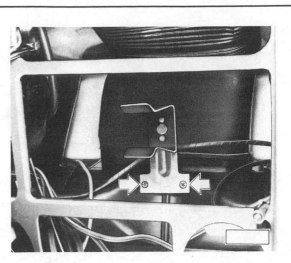

Fig. 13.73 Radio bracket screws (arrowed) (Sec 16)

Fig. 13.74 Central earth bolt (arrowed) (Sec 16)

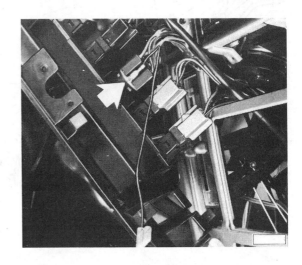

Fig. 13.75 Hazard warning switch spare terminal (arrowed) (Sec 16)

Loudspeakers (Saloon models)

37 The speaker in the centre of the facia panel can be fitted after the clock or blanking plate have been removed, the centre air duct detached from the nozzle and the heater control lever unit released.

38 Locate the speaker mounting stud, fit the speaker and secure it with washer and nut.

39 Connect the speaker leads and refit the clock or plate and reconnect the air duct.

40 If two speakers are being fitted in the front then they should be located under their respective perforated areas.

41 Installation will require removal of the glove compartment and the instrument panel, as described in Chapters 12 and 10 respectively. The fuse block must also be detached by depressing the retaining lug at its base.

42 Connect the speaker leads and route them towards the rear of the radio position.

43 The two front speakers are retained by springs locating in square holes.

44 To fit two rear speakers, locate the pre-punched holes in the rear shelf and then remove the left-hand side panel and door sill moulding. Remove the rear seat cushion and backrest.

45 Remove the rear shelf. If a rear wiper is fitted, release the spindle bezel nut.

46 Clear the pre-punched holes, opening the speaker mounting screw

Fig. 13.76 Speaker mounting stud (A) and heater control lever unit screws (arrowed) (Sec 16)

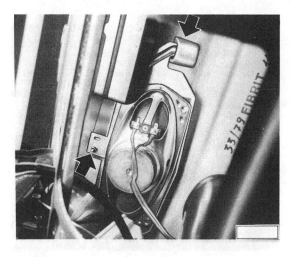

Fig. 13.77 Speaker secured with washer and nut (arrowed) (Sec 16)

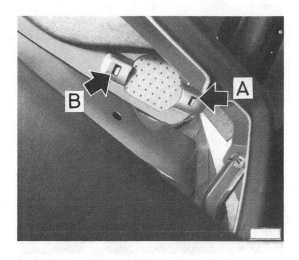

Fig. 13.78 Front speaker retaining spring holes (A and B) on glovebox side (Sec 16)

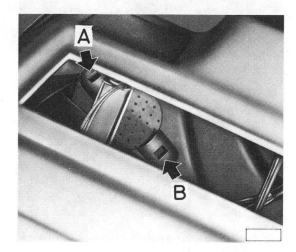

Fig. 13.79 Front speaker retaining spring holes (A and B) on fuse block side (Sec 16)

Fig. 13.80 Rear shelf speaker mounting holes (arrowed) (Sec 16)

holes if necessary to 10.0 mm (0.39 in) diameter with a drill. Fit the spire nuts.

47 Fit the speakers and grilles, run the speaker leads to the radio position, locating them in the wiring channel and taping them securely in position.

Loudspeakers (Hatchback models)

48 The installation procedure is similar to that described for Saloon models except that the rear speakers should be located in the luggage cover side panels, as shown in Fig. 13.81.

Loudspeakers (Estate models)

49 The rear speakers in these models are installed behind the luggage area side panels.

Speaker balance control

50 This should be fitted to the facia panel after drilling a 10.5 mm (0.41 in) hole.

Aerial

51 The recommended position for the aerial is on the right-hand front wing. Mark the position for the hole by referring to the diagram – Fig. 13.84.

52 Drill a second hole on the inner wing for feeding the aerial lead through into the car and fit a grommet.

Fig. 13.81 Location of rear speaker – Hatchback models (arrowed) (Sec 16)

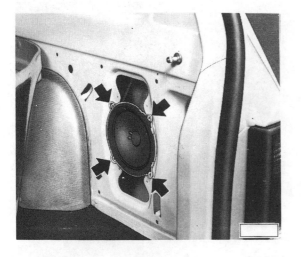

Fig. 13.82 Rear speaker securing screws – Estate models (arrowed) (Sec 16)

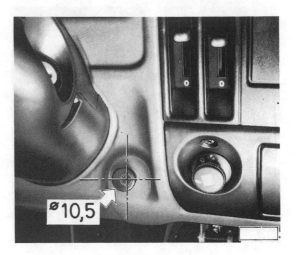

Fig. 13.83 Speaker balance control (arrowed) (Sec 16)

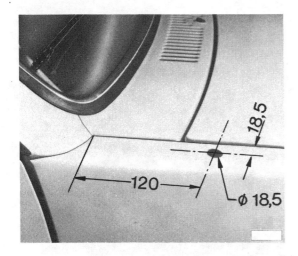

Fig. 13.84 Aerial fitting diagram (Sec 16)

Dimensions in mm

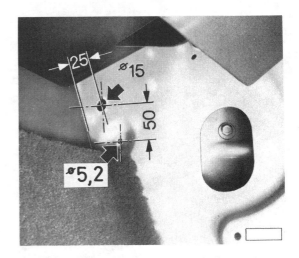

Fig. 13.85 Aerial lead hole in inner wing (Sec 16)

Dimensions in mm

53 Bend the bracket supplied in the fitting kit in accordance with the diagram (Fig. 13.86), and install it and the aerial mast. The aerial mounting flange must make good earth contact with the wing, so scrape some paint away to provide a clean contact area. Smear petroleum jelly around it under the wing to prevent corrosion.

Radio receiver – fitting and connection

54 To the rear of the receiver connect the earth, power feed and aerial leads.

55 Connect the speaker leads according to the number installed and by reference to Fig. 13.89.

56 Fit the receiver fixing springs and push the radio into position.

57 Refit all items removed for installation and reconnect the battery.

58 Trim the radio aerial in the following way. Tune into a weak station on the medium wave band. Insert a thin screwdriver in the small trim screw hole provided on the face of the receiver and turn the screw until the loudest volume is obtained. Remove the screwdriver and switch off.

59 Removal of the in-car entertainment components is a reversal of removal, but to withdraw the receiver insert two U-shaped pieces of stiff wire (welding rod) into the four holes provided. Pinch the wires together to close the U and compress the radio securing clips. The radio can now be withdrawn employing the wires as handles.

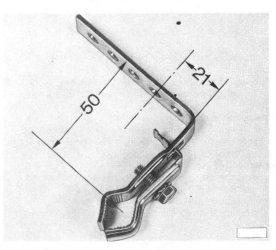

Fig. 13.86 Aerial lower bracket (Sec 16)

Dimensions in mm

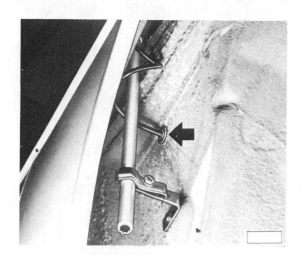

Fig. 13.87 Aerial lower mounting and grommet
(arrowed) (Sec 16)

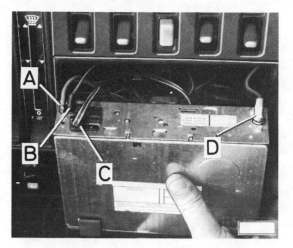

Fig. 13.88 Radio connections (Sec 16)

A Earth   C Speaker leads
B Power feed (+)   D Aerial lead

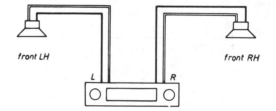

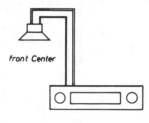

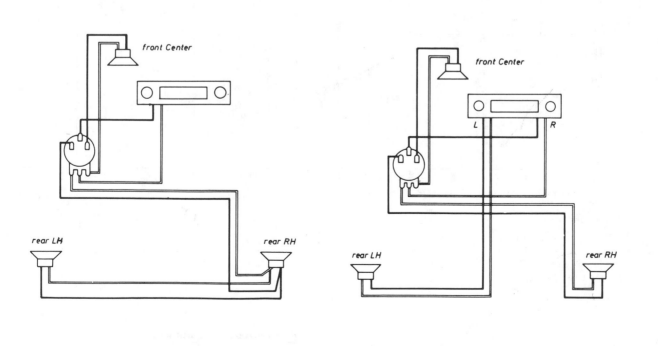

Fig. 13.89 Various speaker arrangements (Sec 16)

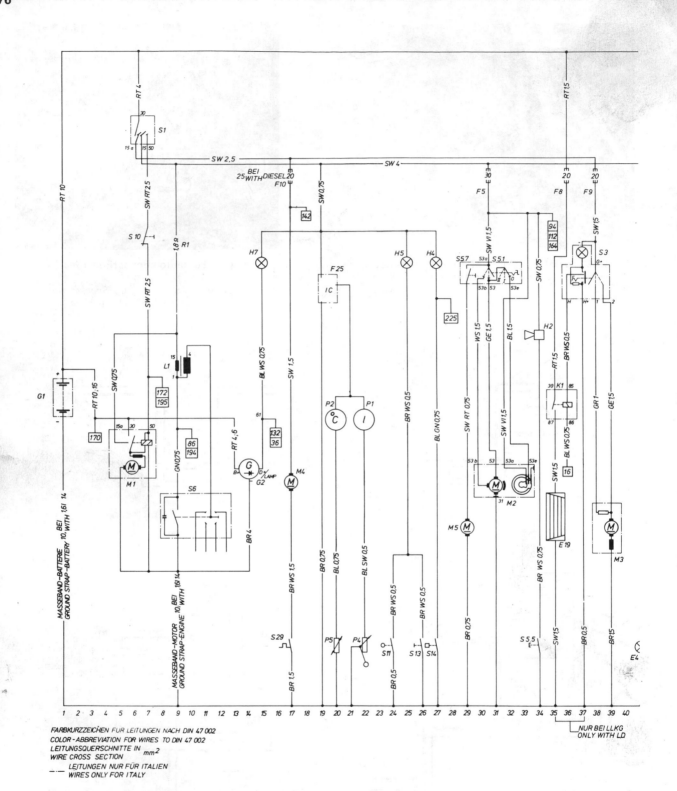

Fig. 13.90 Wiring diagram – 1982 models with basic equipment

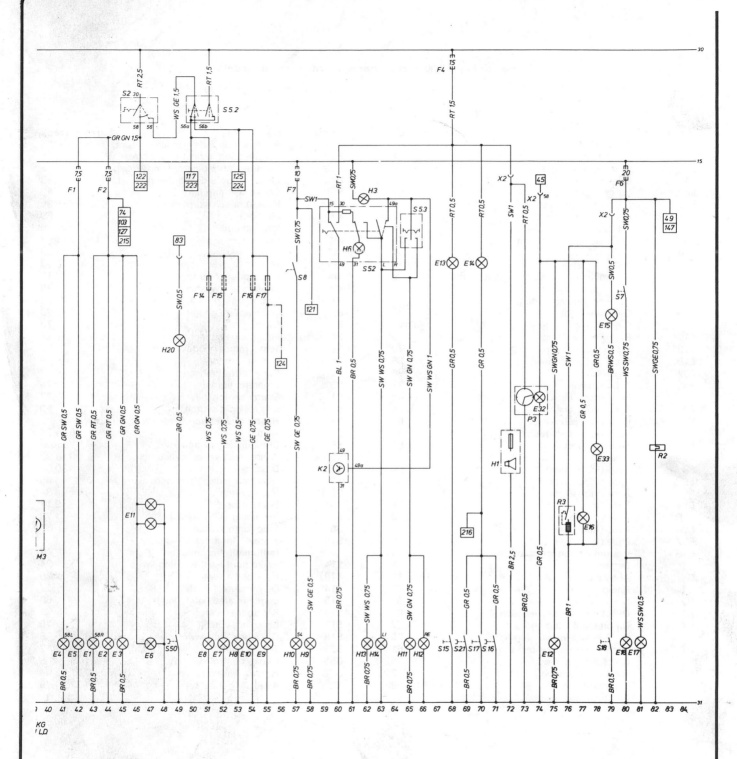

Fig. 13.90 Wiring diagram – 1982 models with basic equipment (continued)

Key to Fig. 13.90. Not all items are fitted to all models

Number	Item	Current track
E1	RH sidelight	43
E2	RH tail light	44
E3	Number plate light	45
E4	LH sidelight	51
E5	LH tail light	42
E6	Engine compartment light	46,48
E7	RH high beam headlight	52
E8	LH high beam headlight	51
E9	RH low beam headlight	55
E10	LH low beam headlight	54
E11	Instrument lights	46,48
E12	Automatic transmission selector light	75
E13	Luggage area light	68
E14	Passenger compartment light	70
E15	Glovebox light	78
E16	Cigarette lighter light	77
E17	RH reversing lamp	80
E18	LH reversing lamp	79
E19	Heated rear window	35
E32	Clock lamp	74
E33	Ashtray lamp	78
F1	Fuse (in fusebox)	42
F2	Fuse (in fusebox)	44
F4	Fuse (in fusebox)	68
F5	Fuse (in fusebox)	31
F6	Fuse (in fusebox)	80
F7	Fuse (in fusebox)	57
F8	Fuse (in fusebox)	36
F9	Fuse (in fusebox)	38
F10	Fuse (in fusebox)	17
F14	Fuse (Italy only)	51
F15	Fuse (Italy only)	52
F16	Fuse (Italy only)	54
F17	Fuse (Italy only)	55
F25	Instrument voltage stabilizer	19
G1	Battery	1
G2	Alternator	13 to 15
H1	Radio	72
H2	Horn	34
H3	Direction indicator repeater	61
H4	Oil pressure warning light	27
H5	Braking system warning light	25
H6	Hazard warning system repeater	61
H7	No charge warning light	15
H8	High beam warning light	53
H9	RH stop-lamp	58
H10	LH stop-lamp	57

Number	Item	Current track
H11	RH direction indicator lamp (front)	65
H12	RH direction indicator lamp (rear)	66
H13	LH direction indicator lamp (front)	62
H14	LH direction indicator lamp (rear)	63
H20	Choke warning light	49
K1	Heated rear window relay	35,36
K2	Flasher unit	60
L1	Ignition coil	9
M1	Starter motor	5 to 7
M2	Windscreen wiper motor	30 to 33
M3	Heated blower motor	38,39
M4	Radiator cooling fan	17
M5	Windscreen washer pump	29
P1	Fuel gauge	22
P2	Temperature gauge	20
P3	Clock	73
P4	Fuel gauge sender	21
P5	Temperature gauge sender	20
R1	Ballast resistor	9
R2	Carburettor preheater	82
R3	Cigarette lighter	76
S1	Starter switch	46,47
S2.1	Interior light switch	69
S3	Heater blower and heated rear window switch	36 to 39
S5	Combination switch	Various
S5.1	Windscreen wiper switch	30 to 32
S5.2	Dipstick	30,51
S5.3	Direction indicator switch	65
S5.5	Horn switch	34
S6	Distributor	9,11
S7	Reversing lamp switch	79
S8	Stop-lamp switch	57
S10	Starter inhibitor switch (automatic transmission)	7
S11	Brake fluid level warning switch	24
S13	Handbrake switch	26
S14	Oil pressure switch	27
S15	Luggage area light switch	68
S16	RH door switch	71
S17	LH door switch	70
S18	Glovebox light switch	78
S29	Thermoswitch (for radiator fan)	17
S50	Choke control switch	49
S52	Hazard warning switch	59,60,61,63,64
X2	Auxiliary connector	49,72,74,79

Colour code

BL	Blue	LI	Lilac
BR	Brown	RT	Red
GE	Yellow	SW	Black
GN	Green	VI	Violet
GR	Grey	WS	White
HBL	Light blue		

Key to Fig. 13.91. Not all items are fitted to all models

Number	Item	Current track
E20	LH foglamp (front)	121
E20	RH foglamp (front)	122
E22	LH spotlamp	118
E23	RH spotlamp	119
E24	Rear foglamp	125
E25	Seat heating pad	147
E31	Switch illumination	127
E34	Heater control illumination	128
F3	Fuse (in fusebox)	125
F12	Fuse (in fusebox)	122
F13	Fuse (in fusebox)	118
F18	Fuse (air conditioning)	133
F19	Fuse (trailer wiring)	157
F20	Fuse (headlamp washer)	104
H17	Trailer direction indicator repeater	149
K4	Spotlamp relay	117,118
K5	Front foglamp relay	121,122
K6	Air conditioning relay	132,133
K7	Air conditioning blower relay	133,134
K8	Windsceen washer delay relay	94 to 97
K9	Headlamp washer delay relay	102 to 104
K10	Trailer flasher unit	149 to 151
K24	Radiator fan relay	141,142
M2	Windscreen wiper motor	93 to 97
M4	Radiator fan relay	142
M5	Windscreen washer pump	94,95
M8	Tailgate washer motor	109 to 112
M9	Tailgate washer pump	113,165
M10	Air conditioning blower motor	133
M24	Headlamp washer pump	104
M25	Rear wiper motor (Estate)	161 to 166
P7	Tachometer	86,87
P8	Oil pressure gauge	89
P9	Voltmeter	88
P10	Oil pressure gauge sender	89
R6	Resistor (air conditioning blower)	137
S5.6	Windscreen wiper delay switch	93 to 97
S5.7	Wiper unit switch	92
S20	Tailgate wiper switch	112 to 114
S21	Foglamp switch (front)	119 to 121
S22	Foglamp switch (rear)	125,126
S24	Air conditioning blower switch	134 to 136
S25	Air conditioning control	138 to 140
S27	Air conditioning pressure switch	139
S28	Air conditioning compressor cut-off switch	139
S29	Radiator fan thermoswitch	143
S30	Heated seat switch	147
X1	Trailer socket	152 to 159
X2	Auxiliary connector	147,157
Y1	Air conditioning compressor	139

Colour code

BL	Blue	LI	Lilac
BR	Brown	RT	Red
GE	Yellow	SW	Black
GN	Green	VI	Violet
GR	Grey	WS	White
HBL	Light blue		

280

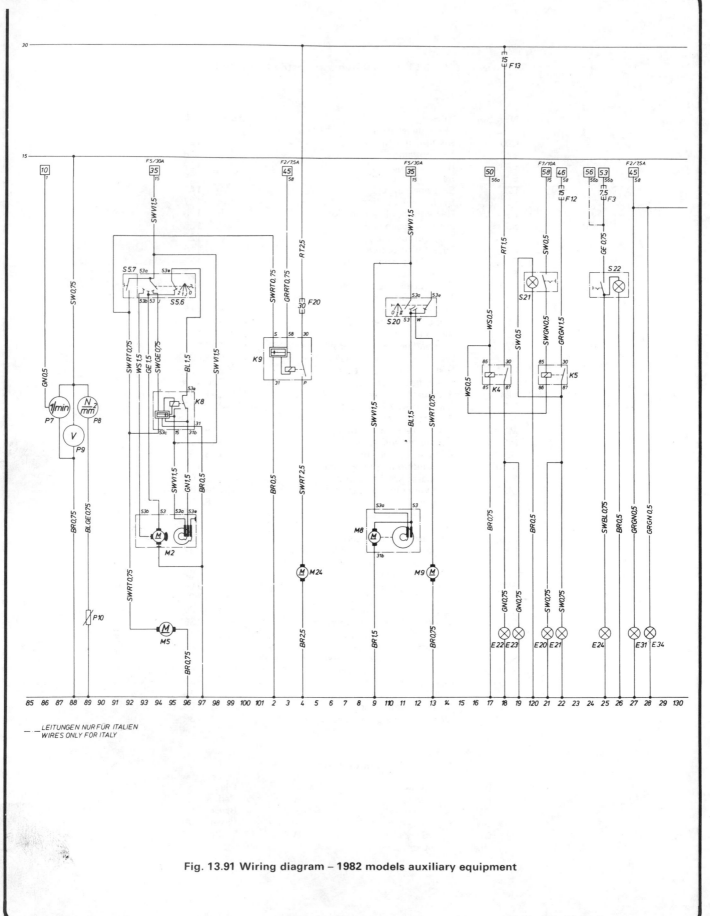

Fig. 13.91 Wiring diagram – 1982 models auxiliary equipment

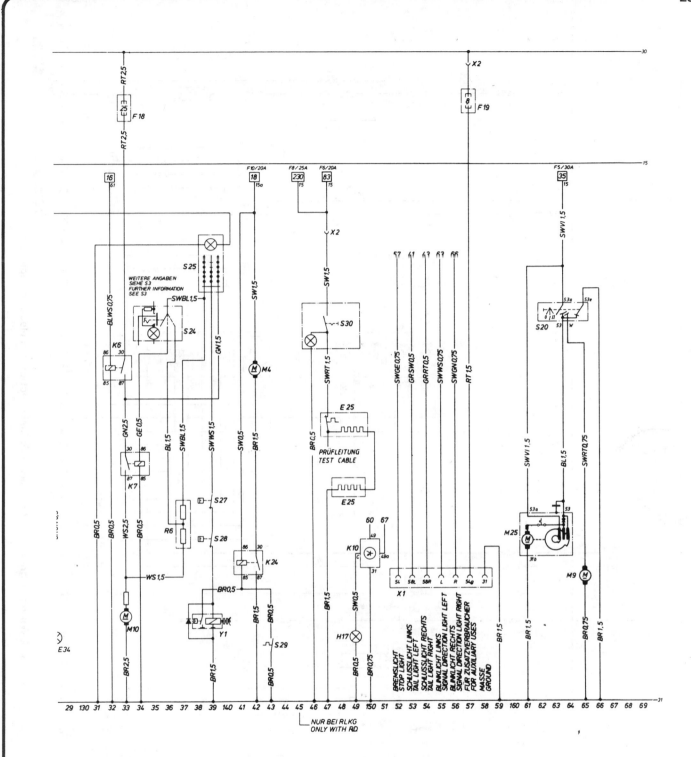

Fig. 13.91 Wiring diagram – 1982 models auxiliary equipment (continued)

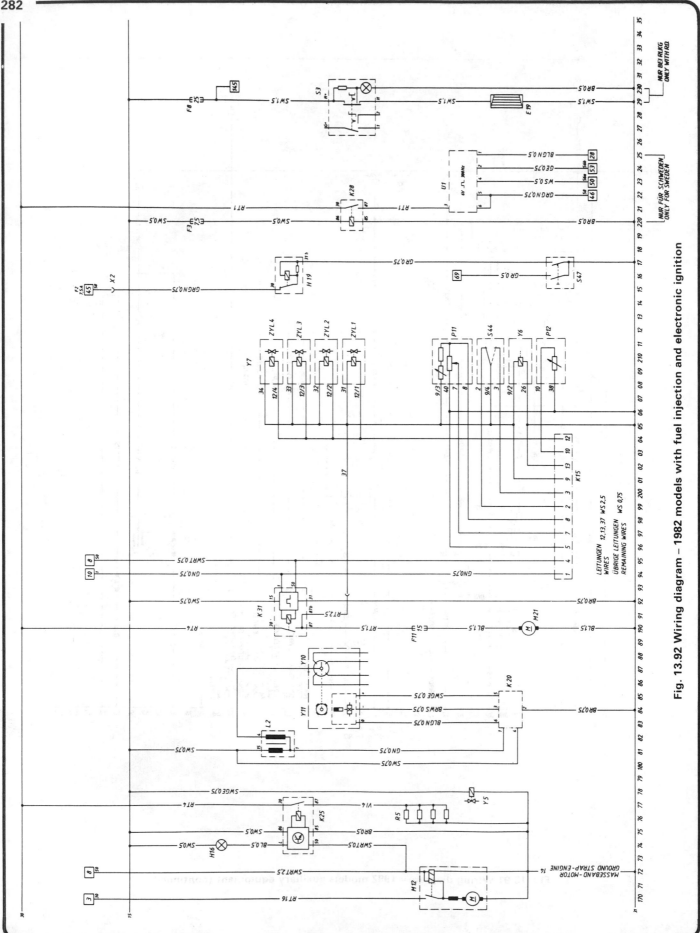

Fig. 13.92 Wiring diagram – 1982 models with fuel injection and electronic ignition

Key to Fig. 13.92. Not all items are fitted to all models

Number	Item	Current track
E19	Heated rear window (RHD)	
F3	Fuse (in fusebox)	220
F8	Fuse (in fusebox)	229
F11	Fuse (in fusebox)	190
H16	Preheat indicator (diesel only)	174
H19	Headlamps on warning buzzer	215 to 217
K15	Fuel injection control unit	194 to 204
K20	Electronic ignition module	183 to 185
K25	Preheat relay (Diesel only)	174 to 177
K28	Day running lights relay (Sweden only)	220,221
K31	Fuel pump relay (fuel injection	190 to 192
L2	Ignition coil (electronic ignition)	181,182
M12	Starter motor (Diesel only)	170 to 172
M21	Fuel pump (fuel injection	190
P11	Airflow sensor (fuel injection)	210
P12	Temperature sensor (fuel injection)	210
R5	Glow plugs (Diesel only)	176
S3	Heater blower/heated rear window switch (RHD)	227 to 230
S44	Throttle valve switch (fuel injection)	210
S47	Door switch (headlamps on warning system)	216,217
U1	Voltage transformer for day running lights (Sweden only)	221 to 225
Y5	Solenoid valve (Diesel only)	178
Y6	Auxiliary air valve (fuel injection)	210
Y7	Fuel injectors	210
Y10	Distributor (electronic ignition)	187
Y11	Hall sensor (electronic ignition)	183 to 185

Colour code

BL	Blue	HBL	Light blue
BR	Brown	LI	Lilac
GE	Yellow	RT	Red
GN	Green	SW	Black
GR	Grey	VI	Violet

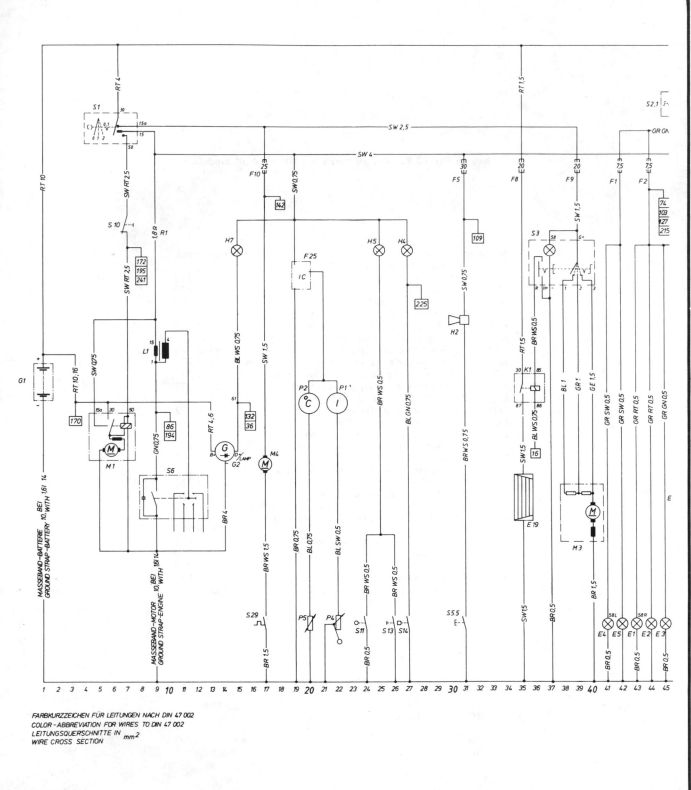

Fig. 13.93 Wiring diagram – 1983 models with basic equipment

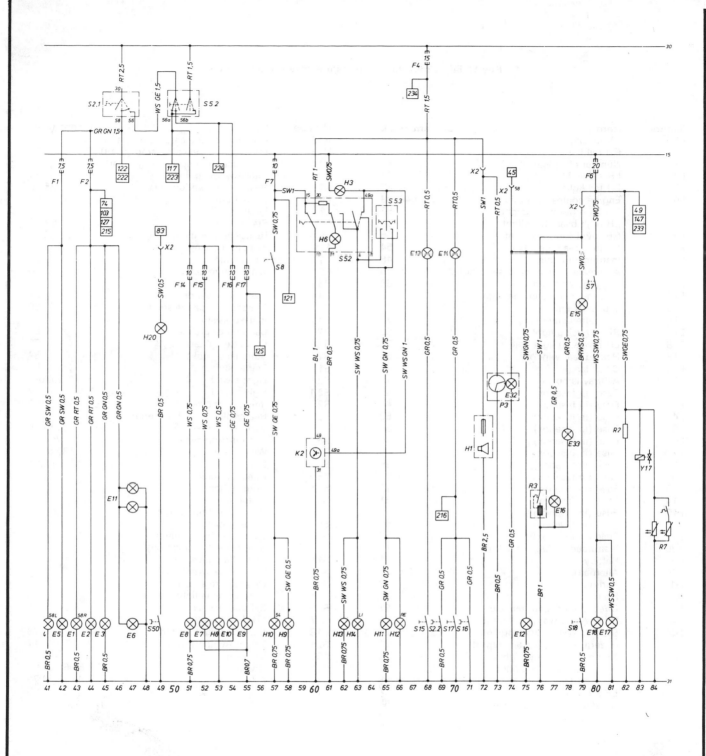

Fig. 13.93 Wiring diagram – 1983 models with basic equipment (continued)

Key to Fig. 13.93 Not all items are fitted to all models

Number	Item	Current track
E1	RH sidelight	43
E2	RH tail light	44
E3	Number plate light	45
E4	LH sidelight	41
E5	LH tail light	42
E6	Engine compartment light	46, 48
E7	RH high beam headlight	52
E8	LH high beam headlight	51
E9	RH low beam headlight	55
E10	LH low beam headlight	54
E11	Instrument lights	46,48
E12	Automatic transmission selector light	75
E13	Luggage area light	68
E14	Passenger compartment light	70
E15	Glovebox light	78
E16	Cigarette lighter lamp	77
E17	RH reversing light	80
E18	LH reversing light	79
E19	Heated rear window	35
E32	Clock lamp	74
E33	Ashtray lamp	78
F1	Fuse (in fusebox)	42
F2	Fuse (in fusebox)	44
F4	Fuse (in fusebox)	68
F5	Fuse (in fusebox)	31
F6	Fuse (in fusebox)	80
F7	Fuse (in fusebox)	57
F8	Fuse (in fusebox)	35
F9	Fuse (in fusebox)	39
F10	Fuse (in fusebox)	17
F14	Fuse (in fusebox)	51
F15	Fuse (in fusebox)	52
F16	Fuse (in fusebox)	54
F17	Fuse (in fusebox)	55
F25	Instrument voltage stabiliser	19
G1	Battery	1
G2	Alternator	3 to 15
H1	Radio	72
H2	Horn	34
H3	Direction indicator repeater	61
H4	Oil pressure warning light	27
H5	Braking system warning light	25
H6	Hazard warning system repeater	61
H7	No charge warning light	15
H8	High beam warning light	53
H9	RH stop-lamp	58
H10	LH stop-lamp	57
H11	RH direction indicator lamp (front)	65

Number	Item	Current track
H12	RH direction indicator lamp (rear)	66
H13	LH direction indicator lamp (front)	62
H14	LH direction indicator lamp (rear)	63
H20	Choke warning light	49
K1	Heated rear window relay	35,36
K2	Flasher unit	60
L1	Ignition coil	9
M1	Starter motor	5 to 7
M3	Heater blower motor	38,39
M4	Radiator cooling fan	17
P1	Fuel gauge	22
P2	Temperature gauge	20
P3	Clock	73
P4	Fuel gauge sender	21
P5	Temperature gauge sender	20
R1	Ballast resistor	9
R2	Carburettor preheater	82
R3	Cigarette lighter	76
R7	Automatic choke	84
S1	Starter switch	6,7
S2	Light switch	Various
S2.1	Light switch	46,47
S2.2	Interior light switch	69
S3	Heater blower and heated rear window switch	36 to 39
S5	Combination switch	Various
S5.1	Windscreen wiper switch	30 to 32
S5.2	Dipswitch	50,51
S5.3	Direction indicator switch	65
S5.5	Horn switch	31
S6	Distributor	9,11
S7	Reversing lamp switch	79
S8	Stop-lamp switch	57
S10	Starter inhibitor switch (automatic transmission)	7
S11	Brake fluid level warning switch	24
S13	Handbrake switch	26
S14	Oil pressure switch	27
S15	Luggage area light switch	68
S16	RH door switch	71
S17	LH door switch	70
S18	Glovebox light switch	78
S29	Thermoswitch (for radiator fan)	17
S50	Choke control switch	49
S52	Hazard warning switch	59,60,61,63
X2	Auxiliary connector	49,72,74,79
Y17	Idle cut-off solenoid	83

Colour code

BL	Blue	LI	Lilac
BR	Brown	RT	Red
GE	Yellow	SW	Black
GN	Green	VI	Violet
GR	Grey	WS	White
HBL	Light blue		

Key to Fig. 13.94. Not all items are fitted to all models

Number	Item	Current track
E20	LH foglamp (front)	121
E21	RH foglamp (front)	122
E22	LH spotlamp	118
E23	RH spotlamp	119
E24	Rear foglamp	125
E25	Seat heating pad	147
E31	Switch illumination	127
E34	Heater control illumination	128
E39	Rear foglamp	124
F3	Fuse (in fusebox)	157
F12	Fues (in fusebox)	122
F13	Fuse (in fusebox)	118
F18	Fuse (air condition)	133
F19	Fuse (trailer wiring)	157
F20	Fuse (headlamp washer)	104
H17	Trailer direction indicator repeater	149
K4	Spotlamp relay	117,118
K5	Front foglamp relay	121,122
K6	Air conditioning relay	132,133
K7	Air conditioning blower relay	133,134
K8	Windscreen washer delay relay	94 to 96,98
K9	Headlamp washer delay relay	102 to 104
K10	Trailer flasher unit	149 to 151
K24	Radiator fan relay	141,142
K30	Tailgate wiper relay	108 to 110
K41	Tailgate wiper delay relay (Estate)	112 to 115
M2	Windscreen wiper motor	93 to 96
M4	Radiator fan relay	142
M5	Windscreen washer pump	92,164
M8	Tailgate washer motor	106 to 108 167 to 169
M9	Tailgate washer pump	111,164
M10	Air conditioning blower motor	133
M24	Headlamp washer pump	104
M25	Rear wiper motor (Estate)	113 to 116, 160 to 163
P7	Tachometer	86,87
P8	Oil pressure gauge	89
P9	Voltmeter	88
P10	Oil pressure gauge sender	89
R6	Resistor (air conditioning blower)	137
S9	Windscreen wiper switch	Various
S9.2	Windscreen wiper delay switch	92 to 98
S9.3	Tailgate wiper delay switch	109,110,163,164
S21	Foglamp switch (front)	119 to 121
S22	Foglamp switch (rear)	125,126
S24	Air conditioning blower switch	134 to 136
S25	Air conditioning control	138 to 140
S27	Air conditioning pressure switch	139
S28	Air conditioning compressor cut-off switch	139
S29	Radiator fan thermoswitch	143
S30	Heated seat switch	147
X1	Trailer socket	152 to 159
X2	Auxiliary connector	147
Y1	Air conditioning compressor	139

Colour code

BL	Blue	Li	Lilac
BR	Brown	RT	Red
GE	Yellow	SW	Black
GN	Green	VI	Violet
GR	Grey	WS	White
HBL	Light blue		

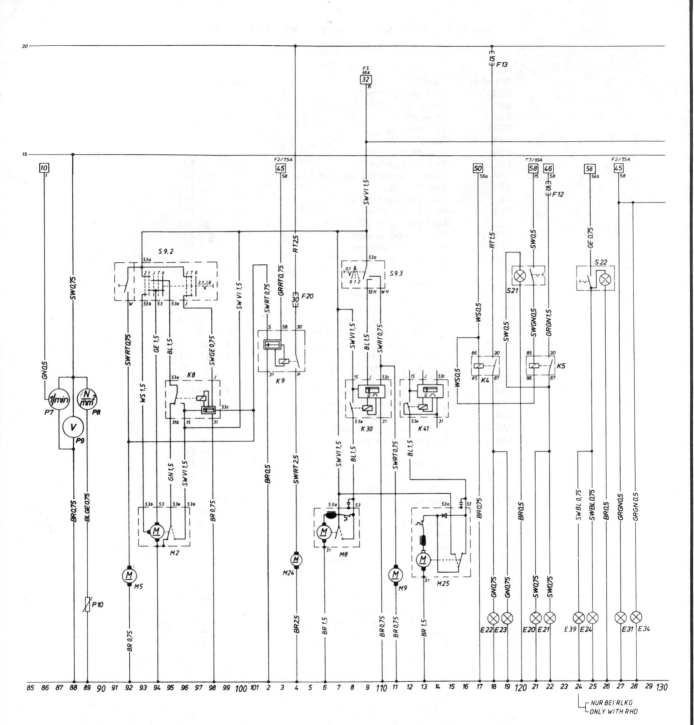

Fig. 13.94 Wiring diagram – 1983 models auxiliary equipment

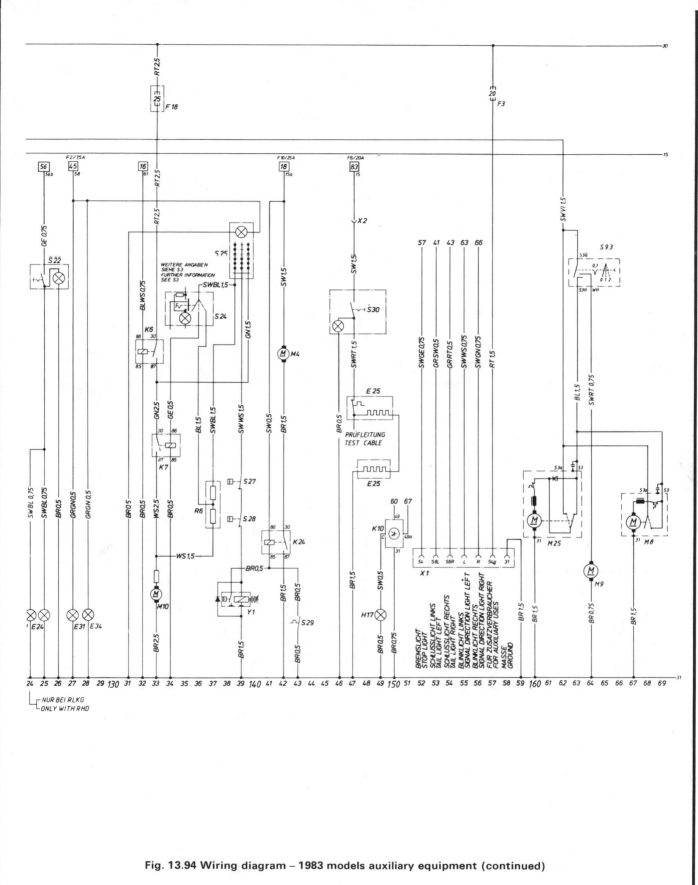

Fig. 13.94 Wiring diagram – 1983 models auxiliary equipment (continued)

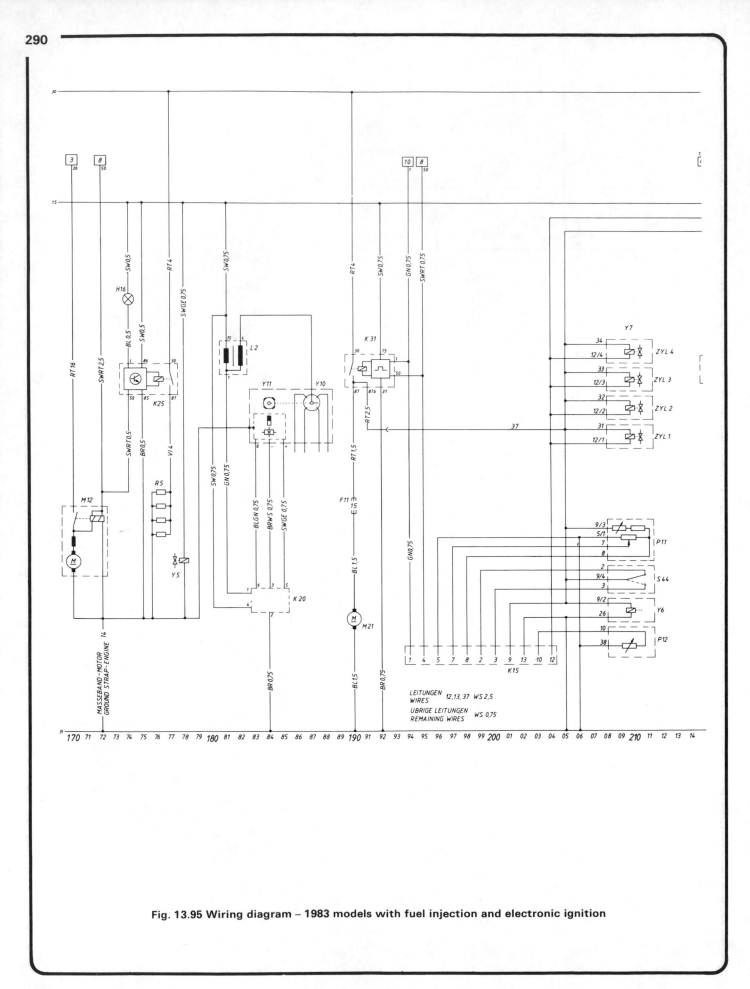

Fig. 13.95 Wiring diagram – 1983 models with fuel injection and electronic ignition

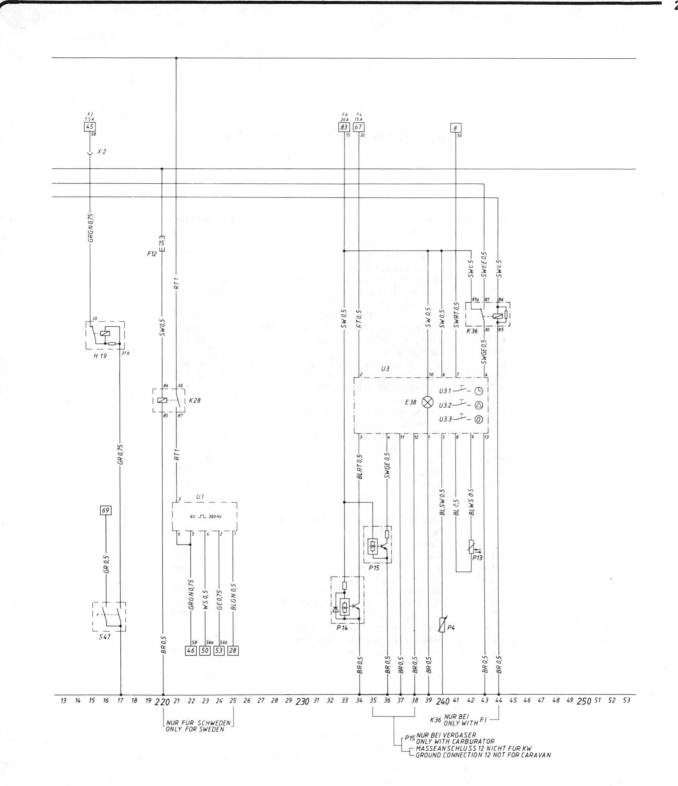

Fig. 13.95 Wiring diagram – 1983 models with fuel injection and electronic ignition (continued)

Key to Fig. 13.95. Not all items are fitted to all models

Number	Item	Current track
E38	Computer board	239
F11	Fuse (in fusebox)	190
F12	Fuse (in fusebox)	220
H16	Preheat indicator (Diesel only)	174
H19	Headlamps on warning buzzer	215 to 217
K15	Fuel injection control unit	194 to 204
K20	Electronic ignition module	183 to 185
K25	Preheat relay (Diesel only)	174 to 177
K28	Day running lights relay (Sweden only)	220,221
K31	Fuel pump relay (fuel injection)	190 to 192
K36	Computer relay	242 to 244
L2	Ignition coil (electronic ignition)	181,182
M12	Starter motor (Diesel only)	170 to 172
M21	Fuel pump (fuel injection)	190
P4	Fuel sensor	240
P11	Airflow sensor (fuel injection)	
P12	Temperature sensor (fuel injection)	210
P13	Temperature sensor (outside)	242
P14	Distance sensor	233,234
P15	Fuel flow sensor	235,236
R5	Glow plugs (Diesel only)	176
S44	Throttle valve switch (fuel injection)	210
S47	Door switch (headlamps on warning system)	216,217
U1	Voltage transformer for day running lights (Sweden only)	221 to 225
U3	Computer board	Various
U3.1	Clock switch	241
U3.2	Function select switch	241
U3.3	Function control switch	241
Y5	Solenoid valve (Diesel only)	178
Y6	Auxiliary air valve (fuel injection)	210
Y7	Fuel injectors	210
Y10	Distributor (electronic ignition)	187
Y11	Hall sensor (electronic ignition)	183 to 185
X2	Auxiliary connector	215

Colour code

BI	Blue	HBL	Light blue
BR	Brown	LI	Lilac
GE	Yellow	RT	Red
GN	Green	SW	Black
GR	Grey	VI	Violet

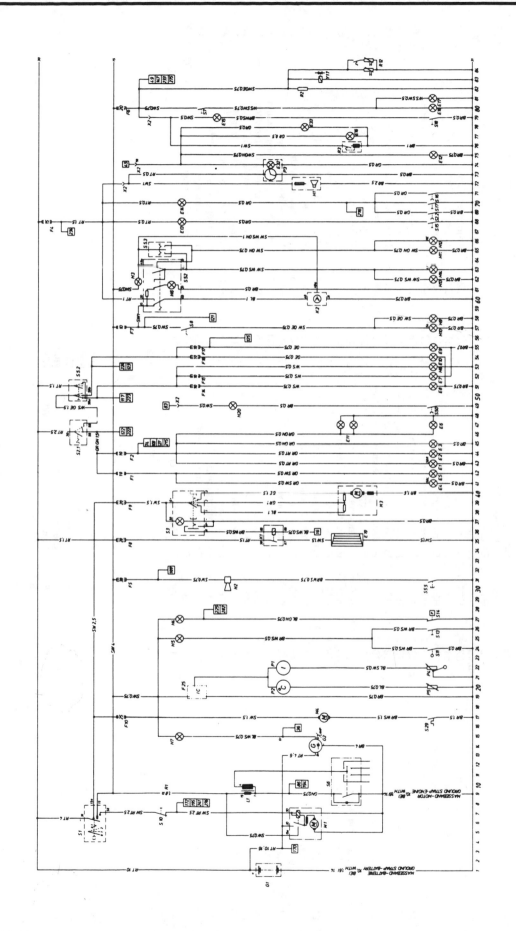

Fig. 13.96 Wiring diagram – 1984 models lighting, switches and auxiliary equipment

Key to Fig. 13.96 Not all items fitted to all models

Number	Item	Current track
E1	RH parking lamp	43
E2	RH tail lamp	44
E3	Rear number plate lamp	45
E4	LH parking lamp	41
E5	LH tail lamp	42
E6	Engine compartment lamp	46,48
E7	RH headlamp (main beam)	52
E8	LH headlamp (main beam)	51
E9	RH headlamp (dipped beam)	56
E10	LH headlamp (dipped beam)	56
E11	Instrument panel lamps	46,48
E12	Selector lever (auto)	75
E13	Boot lamp	68
E14	Interior lamp	70
E15	Glovebox lamp	78
E16	Cigar lighter lamp	77
E17	RH reversing lamp	80
E18	LH reversing lamp	79
E19	Heated rear window	35
E32	Clock lamp	74
E33	Ashtray lamp	76
F1	Fuse	42
F2	Fuse	44
F4	Fuse	68
F5	Fuse	31
F6	Fuse	80
F7	Fuse	57
F8	Fuse	35
F9	Fuse	39
F10	Fuse	17
F14	Fuse	51

Number	Item	Current track
F15	Fuse	52
F16	Fuse	54
F17	Fuse	55
F25	Voltage stabiliser	19
G1	Battery	1
G2	Alternator	13,14,15
H1	Radio	72
H2	Horn	31
H3	Direction indicator lamp	61
H4	Oil pressure warning lamp	27
H5	Handbrake warning lamp	25
H6	Hazard warning indicator lamp	61
H7	Ignition (charge) warning lamp	15
H8	Headlamp main beam warning lamp	53
H9	RH stoplamp	58
H10	LH stoplamp	57
H11	RH front direction indicator	65
H12	RH rear direction indicator	66
H13	LH front direction indicator	62
H14	LH rear direction indicator	63
H20	Choke warning lamp	49
K1	Heated rear window relay	35,36
K2	Flasher unit	60
L1	Ignition coil	9
M1	Starter	5,6,7
M3	Heater blower	38,39
M6	Heater matrix fan	17
P1	Fuel contents gauge	22
P2	Coolant temperature gauge	20
P3	Clock	73
P4	Fuel level transmitter	21

Number	Item	Current track
P5	Coolant temperature transmitter	20
R1	Resistor cable	9
R2	Carburettor preheater	82
R3	Cigar lighter	76
R12	Automatic choke	84
S1	Starter motor switch	6,7
S2	Lighting switch	46
S2.1	Lighting switch	47
S2.2	Courtesy lamp switch	69
S3	Switch – blower and heated rear window	36,39
S5.2	Headlamp dipper switch	50,51
S5.3	Direction indicator switch	65
S5.5	Horn switch	31
S6	Distributor	9,11
S7	Reversing lamp switch	79
S8	Stop lamp switch	57
S10	Inhibitor switch (auto)	7
S11	Brake fluid level switch	74
S13	Handbrake 'on' switch	26
S14	Oil pressure switch	27
S15	Luggage boot lamp switch	68
S16	RH door courtesy lamp switch	71
S17	LH door courtesy lamp switch	70
S18	Glove box lamp switch	78
S29	Thermo switch (radiator fan)	17
S50	Manual choke switch	49
S52	Headlamp flasher switch	59,63
Y17	Idle cut-off solenoid	83
X2	Auxiliary connector	49,72,74,79

Colour code

BL	Blue	LI	Lilac
BR	Brown	RT	Red
GE	Yellow	SW	Black
GN	Green	VI	Violet
GR	Grey	WS	White
HBL	Light blue		

Key to Fig. 13.97 Not all items are fitted to all models

Number	Item	Current track
E20	LH front foglamp	121
E21	RH front foglamp	122
E22	LH spot lamp	118
E23	RH spot lamp	119
E26, E39	Rear foglamps	125,124
E25	Front seat heater	147
E31	Switch illumination	127
E34	Heater control lamp	128
F3	Fuse	157
F12	Fuse	122
F13	Fuse	118
F20	Time delay relay fuse	104
H17	Direction indicator warning lamp (trailer)	149
K4	Front spotlamp relay	117,118
K5	Front foglamp relay	121,122
K8	Wiper delay relay	95 to 98
K9	Headlamp washer delay relay	102 to 104
K10	Flasher relay (trailer)	149 to 151

Number	Item	Current track
K30	Wiper delay relay, rear window	106 to 110
M1	Wiper motor windscreen	93 to 96
M5	Windscreen washer pump	92, 164
M8	Wiper motor – rear window	106,108,167,169
M9	Washer pump – rear window	111,164
M24	Headlamp washer pump	104
P7	Tachometer	86,86
P8	Oil pressure gauge	89
P9	Battery condition indicator	88
P10	Oil pressure switch	89
S92	Windscreen wiper delay switch	92 to 98
S93	Rear window wiper delay switch	109,110,163,164
S21	Front foglamp switch	119,121
S22	Rear foglamp switch	125,126
S30	Front seat heater switch	147
X1	Trailer socket	152,159
X2	Auxiliary socket	147

Cable colour code as for wiring diagram Fig. 13.96

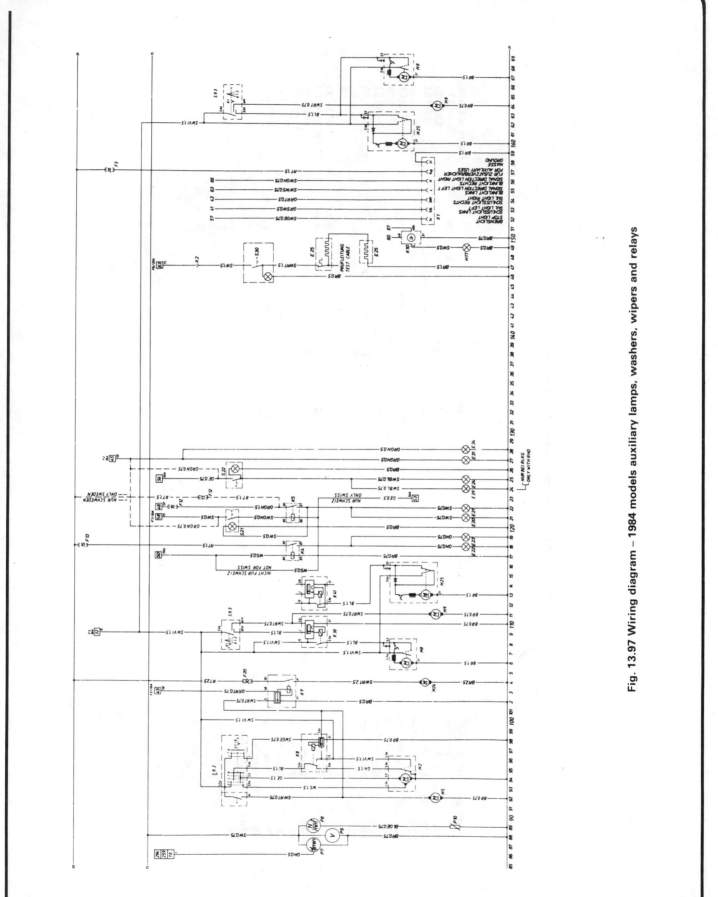

Fig. 13.97 Wiring diagram – 1984 models auxiliary lamps, washers, wipers and relays

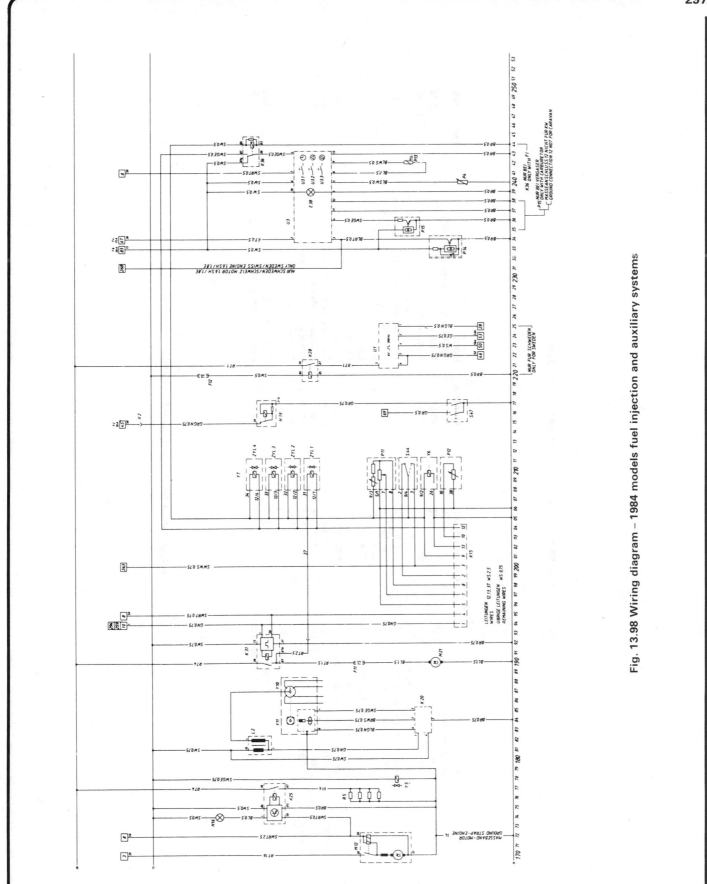

Fig. 13.98 Wiring diagram – 1984 models fuel injection and auxiliary systems

Key to Fig. 13.98 Not all items are fitted to all models

Number	Item	Current track
E38	Computer lamp	239
F11	Fuse	190
F12	Fuse	220
M16	Preheater indicator lamp	176
M19	Headlamp 'on' buzzer	215 to 217
K15	Fuel injection timer	194 to 204
K20	Ignition module	183 to 185
K25	Preheater relay (Diesel)	174 to 177
K28	Running lamps relay	220,221
K31	Fuel injection pump relay	190 to 192
K36	Computer relay	242 to 244
L2	Ignition coil	181,182
M12	Starter (diesel)	170 to 172
M21	Fuel injection pump	190
P4	Fuel level transmitter	240
P11	Airflow meter (fuel injection)	210
P12	Temperature probe (fuel injection)	210
P13	Temperature sensor (ambient)	242
P14	Distance sensor	233,234
P15	Flowmeter	235,236
R5	Glow plugs (diesel)	176
S44	Throttle valve switch (fuel injection)	210
S47	Warning system – doors and headlamps	216,217
U1	Running lamps transformer	221 to 225
U3	Computer board	234 to 243
U31	Clock	241
U32	Function switch (select)	241
U33	Function switch (reset)	241
Y5	Solenoid valve (diesel)	178
Y6	Auxiliary air slide valve	210
Y7	Solenoid valves	210
Y10	Ignition distributor	187
Y11	Distributor (Hall) sensor	183 to 185
X2	Auxiliary connector	215

Cable colour code as for wiring diagram Fig. 13.96

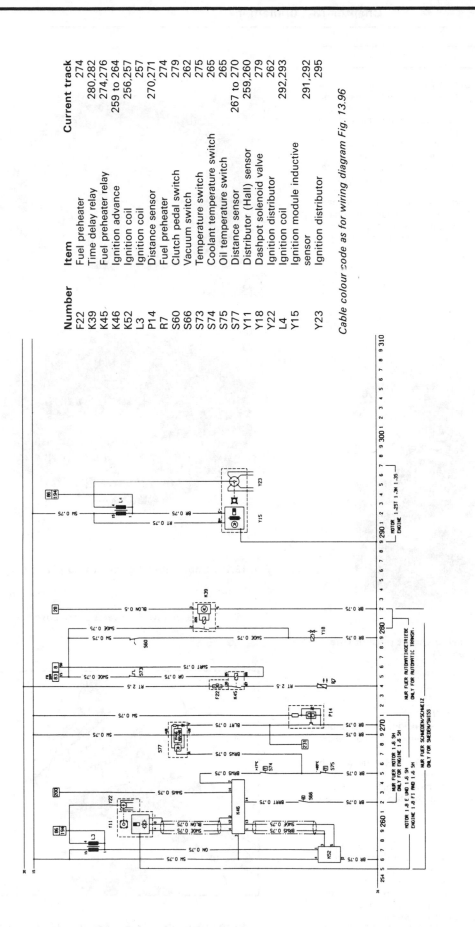

Number	Item	Current track
F22	Fuel preheater	274
K39	Time delay relay	280,282
K45	Fuel preheater relay	274,276
K46	Ignition advance	259 to 264
K52	Ignition coil	256,257
L3	Ignition coil	257
P14	Distance sensor	270,271
R7	Fuel preheater	274
S60	Clutch pedal switch	279
S66	Vacuum switch	262
S73	Temperature switch	275
S74	Coolant temperature switch	265
S75	Oil temperature switch	265
S77	Distance sensor	267 to 270
Y11	Distributor (Hall) sensor	259,260
Y18	Dashpot solenoid valve	279
Y22	Ignition distributor	262
L4	Ignition coil	292,293
Y15	Ignition module inductive sensor	291,292
Y23	Ignition distributor	295

Cable colour code as for wiring diagram Fig. 13.96

Fig. 13.99 Wiring diagram – 1984 models fuel injection and ignition

17 Suspension

Rear wheel bearing adjustment procedure

1   On cars with light alloy wheels, it will be necessary to remove the wheel to gain access to the hub.

2   An alternative means of determining the correct tightness of the rear wheel bearing adjusting nut is given here.

3   After tightening the nut to the specified initial torque (see Chapter 11), slacken the nut until the thrust washer can *just* be moved. Determine this by trying to rotate the washer with a screwdriver blade. Do not lever against the hub, simply apply the blade directly to the washer.

4   If the split pin holes are not aligned with the nut castellations, tighten the nut until the first available alignment occurs and check whether the thrust washer can still be moved. If it can, fit the split pin; if not, back off the nut to the next available position and then fit the split pin.

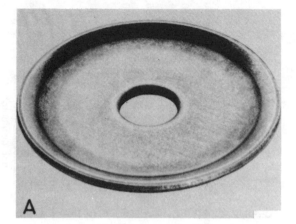

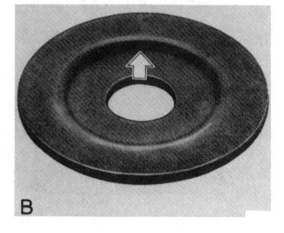

Fig. 13.101 Shock absorber mounting plates (Sec 17)

A   Old type   B   Later type

Raised side (arrowed) towards shock absorber

Fig. 13.100 Checking rear hub bearing thrust washer free movement (Sec 17)

Rear shock absorber removal and refitting

5   Note that due to the design of the rear suspension, the rear shock absorbers should only be removed and refitted from one side of the car at a time.

6   When refitting a rear shock absorber, observe the torque wrench setting given in the Specifications at the beginning of this Chapter. This torque wrench setting applies to the fixed mounting, ie the bottom mounting on Saloon/Hatchback models and the top mounting on Estates.

Rear shock absorber retainer plate

7   If squeaking noises are noticed from the rear shock absorbers on Saloon/Hatchback models, it may be possible to cure these by fitting the latest style retainer plates at the top of the shock absorbers.

8   There is no need to remove the shock absorbers completely to renew the retainer plates. If the top mounting is disconnected and the vehicle raised slightly at the rear, taking care that the springs do not come out of their seats, the retainer plate can be removed.

9   With the new type plates fitted, dimension X in Fig. 11.19 (Chapter 11) should be 9 mm (0.354 in).

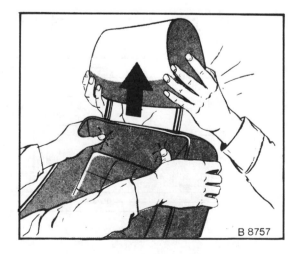

Fig. 13.102 Removing a front seat headrest (Sec 18)

18 Bodywork

Door glass lift mechanism

1   As from January 1983, the scissors type window lift mechanism is riveted to the door.
2   To remove the assembly, drill out the rivet heads using an 8.5 mm (0.335 in) diameter drill.
3   Pop rivet the assembly into place.

Head restraints – sport type front seats

4   To remove the head restraint from this type of seat requires two people.
5   While one person exerts pressure downwards on the head restraint, the other person should depress the springs within the backrest using the thumbs as shown in Fig. 13.102.

6   Maintaining pressure on the springs, pull the headrest upwards out of the backrest.
7   Refit the headrest simply by pushing it into the seat backrest.

Vehicle identity codes

8   The following codes indicate the body type of a particular vehicle.

Code	Description
33	3 door Hatchback – base
33/XJ4	3 door Hatchback SR
33/W3Q	3 door Hatchback GTE
34	5 door Hatchback
35	3 door Estate
43	3 door Hatchback L
44	5 door Hatchback L
45	3 door Estate L
45/XQ1	5 door Estate GL
46	5 door Estate L
46/XM0	5 door Estate GL

General repair procedures

Whenever servicing, repair or overhaul work is carried out on the car or its components, it is necessary to observe the following procedures and instructions. This will assist in carrying out the operation efficiently and to a professional standard of workmanship.

Joint mating faces and gaskets

Where a gasket is used between the mating faces of two components, ensure that it is renewed on reassembly, and fit it dry unless otherwise stated in the repair procedure. Make sure that the mating faces are clean and dry with all traces of old gasket removed. When cleaning a joint face, use a tool which is not likely to score or damage the face, and remove any burrs or nicks with an oilstone or fine file.

Make sure that tapped holes are cleaned with a pipe cleaner, and keep them free of jointing compound if this is being used unless specifically instructed otherwise.

Ensure that all orifices, channels or pipes are clear and blow through them, preferably using compressed air.

Oil seals

Whenever an oil seal is removed from its working location, either individually or as part of an assembly, it should be renewed.

The very fine sealing lip of the seal is easily damaged and will not seal if the surface it contacts is not completely clean and free from scratches, nicks or grooves. If the original sealing surface of the component cannot be restored, the component should be renewed.

Protect the lips of the seal from any surface which may damage them in the course of fitting. Use tape or a conical sleeve where possible. Lubricate the seal lips with oil before fitting and, on dual lipped seals, fill the space between the lips with grease.

Unless otherwise stated, oil seals must be fitted with their sealing lips toward the lubricant to be sealed.

Use a tubular drift or block of wood of the appropriate size to install the seal and, if the seal housing is shouldered, drive the seal down to the shoulder. If the seal housing is unshouldered, the seal should be fitted with its face flush with the housing top face.

Screw threads and fastenings

Always ensure that a blind tapped hole is completely free from oil, grease, water or other fluid before installing the bolt or stud. Failure to do this could cause the housing to crack due to the hydraulic action of the bolt or stud as it is screwed in.

When tightening a castellated nut to accept a split pin, tighten the nut to the specified torque, where applicable, and then tighten further to the next split pin hole. Never slacken the nut to align a split pin hole unless stated in the repair procedure.

When checking or retightening a nut or bolt to a specified torque setting, slacken the nut or bolt by a quarter of a turn, and then retighten to the specified setting.

Locknuts, locktabs and washers

Any fastening which will rotate against a component or housing in the course of tightening should always have a washer between it and the relevant component or housing.

Spring or split washers should always be renewed when they are used to lock a critical component such as a big-end bearing retaining nut or bolt.

Locktabs which are folded over to retain a nut or bolt should always be renewed.

Self-locking nuts can be reused in non-critical areas, providing resistance can be felt when the locking portion passes over the bolt or stud thread.

Split pins must always be replaced with new ones of the correct size for the hole.

Special tools

Some repair procedures in this manual entail the use of special tools such as a press, two or three-legged pullers, spring compressors etc. Wherever possible, suitable readily available alternatives to the manufacturer's special tools are described, and are shown in use. In some instances, where no alternative is possible, it has been necessary to resort to the use of a manufacturer's tool and this has been done for reasons of safety as well as the efficient completion of the repair operation. Unless you are highly skilled and have a thorough understanding of the procedure described, never attempt to bypass the use of any special tool when the procedure described specifies its use. Not only is there a very great risk of personal injury, but expensive damage could be caused to the components involved.

Conversion factors

Length (distance)

Inches (in)	X 25.4	= Millimetres (mm)	X 0.0394	= Inches (in)
Feet (ft)	X 0.305	= Metres (m)	X 3.281	= Feet (ft)
Miles	X 1.609	= Kilometres (km)	X 0.621	= Miles

Volume (capacity)

Cubic inches (cu in; in³)	X 16.387	= Cubic centimetres (cc; cm³)	X 0.061	= Cubic inches (cu in; in³)
Imperial pints (Imp pt)	X 0.568	= Litres (l)	X 1.76	= Imperial pints (Imp pt)
Imperial quarts (Imp qt)	X 1.137	= Litres (l)	X 0.88	= Imperial quarts (Imp qt)
Imperial quarts (Imp qt)	X 1.201	= US quarts (US qt)	X 0.833	= Imperial quarts (Imp qt)
US quarts (US qt)	X 0.946	= Litres (l)	X 1.057	= US quarts (US qt)
Imperial gallons (Imp gal)	X 4.546	= Litres (l)	X 0.22	= Imperial gallons (Imp gal)
Imperial gallons (Imp gal)	X 1.201	= US gallons (US gal)	X 0.833	= Imperial gallons (Imp gal)
US gallons (US gal)	X 3.785	= Litres (l)	X 0.264	= US gallons (US gal)

Mass (weight)

Ounces (oz)	X 28.35	= Grams (g)	X 0.035	= Ounces (oz)
Pounds (lb)	X 0.454	= Kilograms (kg)	X 2.205	= Pounds (lb)

Force

Ounces-force (ozf; oz)	X 0.278	= Newtons (N)	X 3.6	= Ounces-force (ozf; oz)
Pounds-force (lbf; lb)	X 4.448	= Newtons (N)	X 0.225	= Pounds-force (lbf; lb)
Newtons (N)	X 0.1	= Kilograms-force (kgf; kg)	X 9.81	= Newtons (N)

Pressure

Pounds-force per square inch (psi; lbf/in²; lb/in²)	X 0.070	= Kilograms-force per square centimetre (kgf/cm²; kg/cm²)	X 14.223	= Pounds-force per square inch (psi; lbf/in²; lb/in²)
Pounds-force per square inch (psi; lbf/in²; lb/in²)	X 0.068	= Atmospheres (atm)	X 14.696	= Pounds-force per square inch (psi; lbf/in²; lb/in²)
Pounds-force per square inch (psi; lbf/in²; lb/in²)	X 0.069	= Bars	X 14.5	= Pounds-force per square inch (psi; lbf/in²; lb/in²)
Pounds-force per square inch (psi; lbf/in²; lb/in²)	X 6.895	= Kilopascals (kPa)	X 0.145	= Pounds-force per square inch (psi; lbf/in²; lb/in²)
Kilopascals (kPa)	X 0.01	= Kilograms-force per square centimetre (kgf/cm²; kg/cm²)	X 98.1	= Kilopascals (kPa)

Torque (moment of force)

Pounds-force inches (lbf in; lb in)	X 1.152	= Kilograms-force centimetre (kgf cm; kg cm)	X 0.868	= Pounds-force inches (lbf in; lb in)
Pounds-force inches (lbf in; lb in)	X 0.113	= Newton metres (Nm)	X 8.85	= Pounds-force inches (lbf in; lb in)
Pounds-force inches (lbf in; lb in)	X 0.083	= Pounds-force feet (lbf ft; lb ft)	X 12	= Pounds-force inches (lbf in; lb in)
Pounds-force feet (lbf ft; lb ft)	X 0.138	= Kilograms-force metres (kgf m; kg m)	X 7.233	= Pounds-force feet (lbf ft; lb ft)
Pounds-force feet (lbf ft; lb ft)	X 1.356	= Newton metres (Nm)	X 0.738	= Pounds-force feet (lbf ft; lb ft)
Newton metres (Nm)	X 0.102	= Kilograms-force metres (kgf m; kg m)	X 9.804	= Newton metres (Nm)

Power

Horsepower (hp)	X 745.7	= Watts (W)	X 0.0013	= Horsepower (hp)

Velocity (speed)

Miles per hour (miles/hr; mph)	X 1.609	= Kilometres per hour (km/hr; kph)	X 0.621	= Miles per hour (miles/hr; mph)

Fuel consumption*

Miles per gallon, Imperial (mpg)	X 0.354	= Kilometres per litre (km/l)	X 2.825	= Miles per gallon, Imperial (mpg)
Miles per gallon, US (mpg)	X 0.425	= Kilometres per litre (km/l)	X 2.352	= Miles per gallon, US (mpg)

Temperature

Degrees Fahrenheit = (°C x 1.8) + 32

Degrees Celsius (Degrees Centigrade; °C) = (°F - 32) x 0.56

*It is common practice to convert from miles per gallon (mpg) to litres/100 kilometres (l/100km), where mpg (Imperial) x l/100 km = 282 and mpg (US) x l/100 km = 235

Index